PRIMARY MATHEMATICS 6B

HOME INSTRUCTOR GUIDE

Authored by: Jennifer Hoerst

Avyx

Primary Mathematics 6B

Published by Avyx, Inc.
Reprinted 2009

Avyx, Inc.
8032 South Grant Way
Littleton, CO 80122-2705
USA

www.avyx.com
info@avyx.com
303-483-0140

ISBN 978-1-887840-99-6
Printed in the United States of America

Avyx, in an effort to help purchasers of the Singapore Primary Mathematics 6B Textbook and Workbook, is providing this Home Instructor's Guide. We welcome your feedback and input. If you find errors, we also welcome your pointing these out to us. To give us feedback or to note corrections, please send an email to info@avyx.com, or to the author at jenny@singmath.com, or you may send via the postal system to Avyx, Inc., 8032 South Grant Way, Littleton, CO, 80122-2705.

As errors are detected and corrected, you may find the error corrections posted online at the author's web site, http://www.singmath.com. Additional help may be obtained at the forum linked there. **Note**: This site is the sole property of Jennifer Hoerst and is not a site maintained by Avyx. This site is offered solely as a courtesy to help purchasers see corrections as Jennifer Hoerst posts them. All corrections captured will be included in updates to the manuals prior to their reprinting.

Contents

Using this Guide

This guide is meant to help instructors using *Primary Mathematics 6A* when teaching one student or a small group of students. It should be used as a guide and adapted as needed.

The textbook is divided into units and parts. Within each part, there is a page for discussion, followed by *learning tasks*.

This guide further subdivides each textbook part into ***sessions*** (designated with A, B, C,...) for a specific set of learning tasks. A session can take 1-2 days to teach. For each session, the guide provides

 objectives

 and background notes to the instructor. Following the notes, there are some

 instructional ideas and suggested activities to introduce the material in the textbook. These are not scripted. They are for your information, so that you can read them, understand them, and then teach them using your own words. Even if you don't use all of them, reading them can help you gain more understanding of the concepts being applied in the learning tasks. Each student is different, and some will need these activities more than others.

After the introductory activities, the guide indicates

 corresponding textbook pages and learning tasks, along with answers and sometimes solutions, and sometimes with some additional notes to you and suggestions for discussion as you do the textbook pages with your student. Before doing the lesson with your student, you should read this material and study the textbook pages yourself. This will make the lesson go more smoothly.

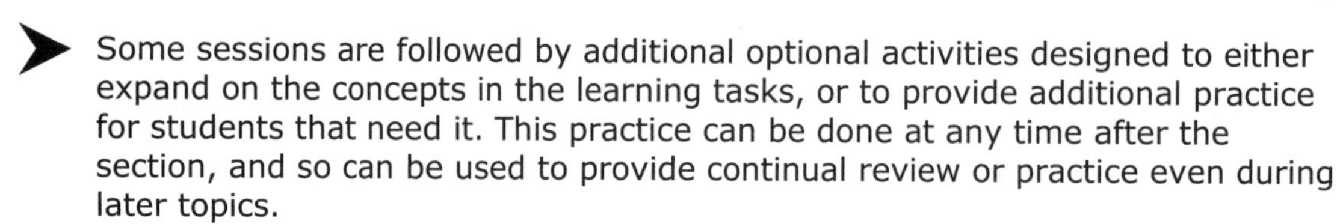 Some sessions are followed by additional optional activities designed to either expand on the concepts in the learning tasks, or to provide additional practice for students that need it. This practice can be done at any time after the section, and so can be used to provide continual review or practice even during later topics.

 At the end of the session, the corresponding workbook exercise is indicated.

The textbook contains periodic **practices**. They can be done as encountered, or used for additional problems during a lesson. Generally they cover the material taught in the previous few pages, but can also bring in concepts from other previous units. They contain occasional challenging problems that can be used for discussion. In this guide, the practices are treated as separate lessons

The textbook also has periodic **reviews**. These reviews cover all previous material and can be lengthy. They are meant to be used as reviews; that is, a way to see if your student remembers previous material, and to re-teach if necessary. If your student has trouble with some of the problems, it may mean than you need to go back and review the concepts, provide additional practice from a supplementary book, or simply "remind" the student of a concept. The reviews not only provide more practice, but also include problems which combine earlier concepts with new concepts, or ask the student to apply a concept in a new way. So it is not always possible to go back to one place in the textbook and find a problem just like the one in the review. The review problems can therefore deepen a student's understanding, particularly through discussion. Textbook reviews are an important part of this curriculum.

There are answers and solutions to workbook problems at the back of the guide. You can use workbook reviews as assessments (after using the textbook review as review).

On the next page is a *suggested* weekly schedule.

This guide can be used with both the third edition and the U.S. edition of *Primary Mathematics 5A*.

3d› indicates portions pertaining only to the third edition, and
US› indicates portions pertaining only to the US edition (except for number words).

The U.S. edition has an extra unit at the beginning on fractions. About 3 weeks are spent on this unit. If you are using the third edition, you will start at week 4.

In writing out numbers, the US edition uses the word "and" only for the decimal place, not for whole numbers (e.g. four hundred one thousand, sixty-two). The 3rd edition uses "and" in more places (e.g. four hundred and one thousand and sixty-two). Answers in this guide for number words will only be given for the US edition — you can allow your student to use "and" as you wish according to the conventions in your country if you are using the 3d edition.

I wish to thank Suzanne Arganbright for her invaluable help in proofing this guide.

Suggested Weekly Schedule

Week	Unit	Part	Textbook	Workbook	Materials
1	**US›** 1 Fractions	1 Division	p. 6 p. 7, tasks 1-3	Ex. 1	
			pp. 7-8, tasks 4-6	Ex. 2	
			p. 8, tasks 8-9		
			p. 9, tasks 10-12	Ex. 3	
		Practice	p. 10, Practice 1A		
2		2 Order of Operations	p. 11 pp. 12-13, tasks 1-7	Ex. 4	
			pp. 13-14, tasks 8-13	Ex. 5	
			p. 14, tasks 14-15	Ex. 6	
		Practice	p. 15, Practice 1B		
3		3 Word Problems	p. 16 p. 17, tasks 1-2	Ex. 7	
			pp. 18019, tasks 3-6	Ex. 8	
		Practice	p. 20, Practice 1C		
			p. 21, Practice 1D		
4	**US›** 2 **3d›** 1 Circles	1 Radius and Diameter	US› p. 22 pp. 23-25, tasks 1-7	US› Ex. 9	cardboard tack string compasses
			3d› p. 6 pp. 7-9, tasks 1-7	3d› Ex. 1	
		2 Circumference	US› p. 26 pp. 27-29, tasks 1-8	US› Ex. 10	Wiggle Woods CD-ROM Circles: Learn and Explore I
			3d› p. 10 pp. 11-13, tasks 1-8	3d› Ex. 2	
			US› p. 29, tasks 9-11	US› Ex. 11	
			3d› p. 13, tasks 9-11	3d› Ex. 3	
		Practice	US› p. 30, Practice 2A		
			3d› p. 14, Practice 1A		
5		3 Area	US› p. 31 pp. 32-34, tasks 1-7	US› Ex. 12	
			3d› p. 15 pp. 16-18, tasks 1-7	3d› Ex. 4	
			US› pp. 34-35, tasks 8-10	US› Ex. 13-14	Wiggle Woods CD-ROM Circles: Learn and Explore 2, Activity, Challenge
			3d› pp. 18-19. tasks 8-10	3d› Ex. 5-6	
			US› p. 35, tasks 11-12	US› Ex. 15-16	
			3d› p. 9, tasks 11-12	3d› Ex. 7-8	
		Practice	US› p. 36, Practice 2B p. 37, Practice 2C		
			3d› p. 20, Practice 1B p. 21, Practice 1C		
6	**US›** 3 **3d›** 2 Graphs	1 Pie Charts	US› p. 38 p. 39, tasks 1-2	US› Ex. 17	
			3d› p. 22 p. 23, tasks 1-2	3d› Ex. 9	
			US› p. 40, tasks 3-4	US› Ex. 18	Fraction Circle Fraction Graph
			3d› p. 24, tasks 3-4	3d› Ex. 10	
			US› p. 41, tasks 5-6	US› Ex. 19	Percentage Circle Percentage Graph
			3d› p. 25, tasks 5-6	3d› Ex. 11	
7	Review		US› pp. 42-47, Review A pp. 48-53, Review B		
			3d› pp. 26-31. Review A pp. 31-37, Review B		

Week	Unit	Part	Textbook	Workbook	Materials
8	**US›** 4 **3d›** 3 Volume	1 Solving Problems	US› p. 54-55 p. 55, tasks 1-3 3d› p. 38-39 p. 39, tasks 1-3	US› Ex. 20 3d› Ex. 12	
			US› p. 56, tasks 4-5 3d› p. 40, tasks 4-5	US› Ex. 21 3d› Ex. 13	liter jar 1000-cube
			US› p. 57, tasks 6-7 3d› p. 41, tasks 6-7	US› Ex. 22 3d› Ex. 14	
9			US› p. 58, tasks 8-9 3d› p. 42, tasks 8-9	US› Ex. 23 3d› Ex. 15	
		Practice	US› pp. 59-60, Practice 4A-4C 3d› pp. 43-45, Practices 3A-3C		Wiggle Woods CD-ROM Game 2
10	Review			Review 3 Review 4	
11	**US›** 5 **3d›** 4 Triangles and 4-Sided Figures	1 Finding Unknown Angles	US› p. 62 p. 63, tasks 1-3 3d› p. 46 p. 47, tasks 1-3	US› Ex. 24 3d› Ex. 16	
			US› pp. 64-65, tasks 4-7 3d› pp. 48-49, tasks 4-7	US› Ex. 25 3d› Ex. 17	
		Practice	US› p. 66, Practice 5A p. 67, Practice 5B 3d› p. 50, Practice 4A p. 51, Practice 4B		
12 13	Review		US› pp. 68-72, Review C pp. 73-77, Review D pp. 78-82, Review E 3d› pp. 52-56, Reviews C pp. 57-61, Reviews D pp. 62-66, Reviews E	Review 5 Review 6 Review 7	
14	**US›** 6 **3d›** 5 More Challenging Word Problems	1 Whole Numbers and Decimals	US› pp. 83-86, tasks 1-4 p. 87, Practice 6A 3d› pp. 67-70, tasks 1-4 p. 71 Practice 5A		
		2 Fractions	US› pp. 88-91, tasks 1-4 pp. 92-93, Practices 6B-6C 3d› pp. 72-75, tasks 1-5 p. 76-77, Practices 5B-5C		
15		3 Ratio	US› pp. 94-96, tasks 1-3 pp. 97-98, Practices 6D-6E 3d› pp. 78-80, tasks 1-3 pp. 81-82, Practices 5D-5E		
		4 Percentage	US› pp. 99-100, tasks 1-2 p. 101, Practice 6F 3d› pp. 83-4, tasks 1-3 p. 85, Practice 5F		
		5 Speed	US› 102-104, tasks 1-3 p. 105, Practice 6G 3d› pp. 86-88, tasks 1-3 p. 89. Practice 5G		
16	Review		US› pp. 106-109, Review F pp. 111-116, Review G pp. 117-120, Review H 3d› pp. 90-93, Review F pp. 94-100, Review G		

Additional Materials

Base-10 blocks

Fraction Circle Graph and Percentage Circle Graph
There are some in the appendix that can be copied.

US› Unit 1
Fractions

Part 1 – Division (pp. 6-9)

(A) Dividing a Whole Number by a Unit Fraction

➢ Divide a whole number by a unit fraction.

In *Primary Mathematics 4A*, students learned how to multiply a fraction by a whole number. In *Primary Mathematics 5A*, they learned how to multiply a fraction by a fraction, relate division to fractions, and divide by a whole number.

In this section, students will learn to divide by a unit fraction, that is, a fraction with 1 in the numerator.

Division can be interpreted in two contexts: sharing or grouping.

In grouping, we are given the total number and the number that goes in each part, and want to find how many parts. In $8 \div 2$, we are finding how many 2's are in 8, or what number times 2 is 8.

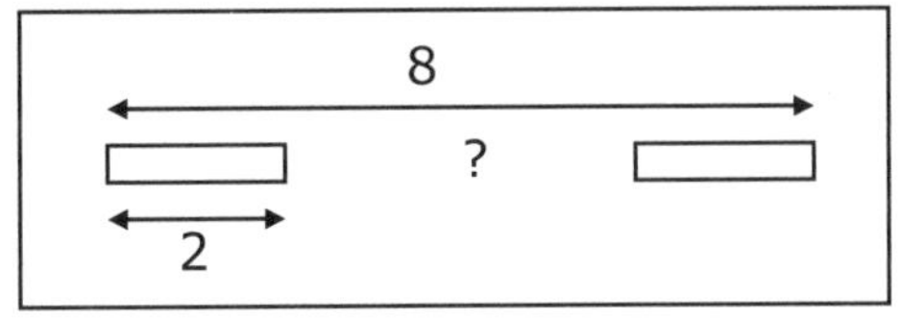

$8 \div 2 = ?$ How many 2 are in 8? 8 is how many 2's? What x 2 = 8?
$8 \div 2 = 4$ There are 4 2's in 8.

In sharing, we are given a total number and the number of parts, and need to find the value in each part. In $8 \div 2$, we are finding the "what" of "8 is 2 of what?"

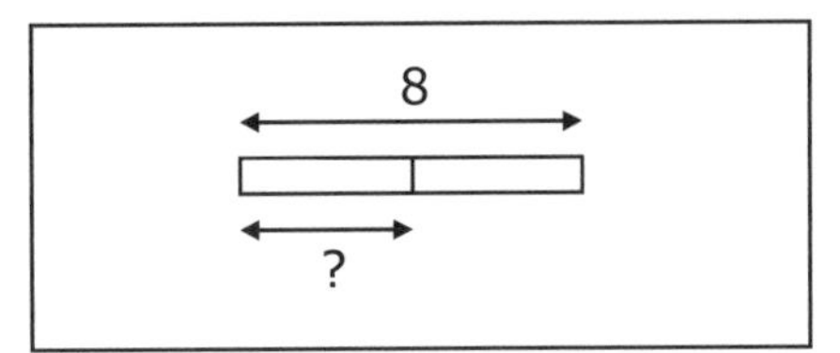

$8 \div 2 = ?$ 8 is 2 of what? Or, $2 \times ? = 8$
$8 \div 2 = 4$ 8 is 2 4's

Division of fractions can also be interpreted in two contexts:
Total ÷ _____ = ?
means
How many ____'s are there in the total? (? × ____ = total)
or
The total is ____ of what? (total = ____ of ? or, total = ____ × ?

For example, $8 \div \frac{1}{2} = ?$

Grouping: How many $\frac{1}{2}$'s are there in 8? (e.g.: There are 8 apples. Each person gets $\frac{1}{2}$ of an apple. How many people are there?)

If we divide 8 by $\frac{1}{2}$, we can think of this as putting $\frac{1}{2}$ into each part (grouping by $\frac{1}{2}$), and finding how many parts there are.
Since there are 2 halves in one whole, there would be 2×8 halves in 8 wholes.

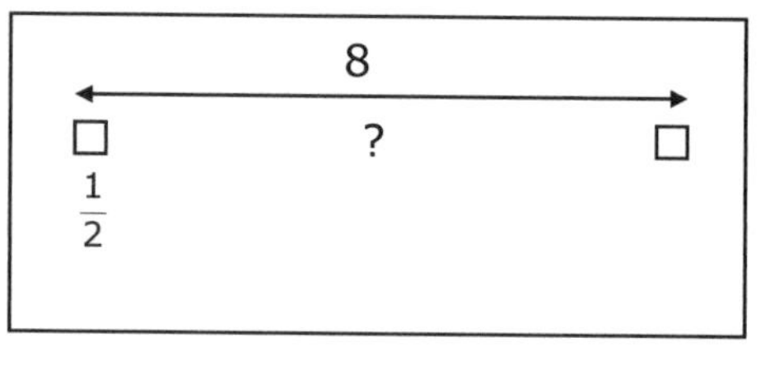

1 whole $\longrightarrow$ 2 halves
8 wholes $\longrightarrow$ 8×2 halves

So, the answer can be found by multiplying by 2:

$$8 \div \frac{1}{2} = 8 \times 2 = 16$$

There are 16 halves in 8.

Sharing: 8 is $\frac{1}{2}$ of what? (e.g.: If half of a carton of milk is 8 cups, how many cups are in the whole carton?)

If half of something is 8, then

$\frac{1}{2} \longrightarrow 8$

$1 \longrightarrow 8 \times 2$

So again, we can solve this by multiplying by 2.

$$8 \div \frac{1}{2} = 8 \times 2 = 16$$

8 is half of 16

2 is the *reciprocal* of $\frac{1}{2}$. The product of a number and its reciprocal is 1: $2 \times \frac{1}{2} = 1$

To divide by $\frac{1}{2}$, we multiply by its reciprocal, 2.

You may have learned that to divide by a fraction you "invert and multiply." It is important that your student understand what is happening in division of fractions through the use of diagrams so that he can apply the principles to word problems.

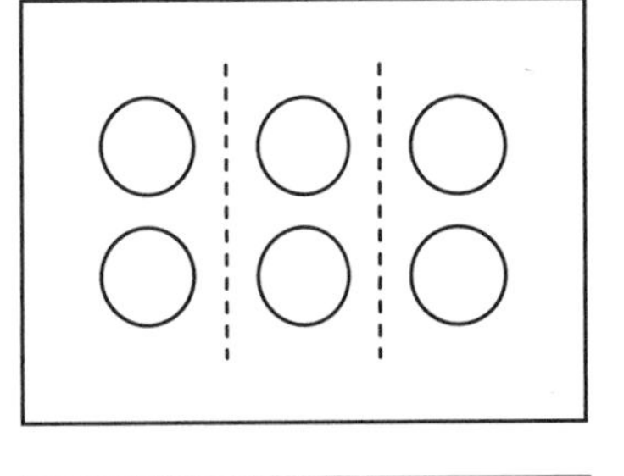

➤ Write the division problem $6 \div 2 = 3$ and illustrate it with circles as a grouping problem. Say you have 2 oranges and want to put them into groups of 2. How many groups will there be?

$6 \div 2 = ?$ How many 2's are in 6?
There are 3 groups of 2.
$6 \div 2 = 3$

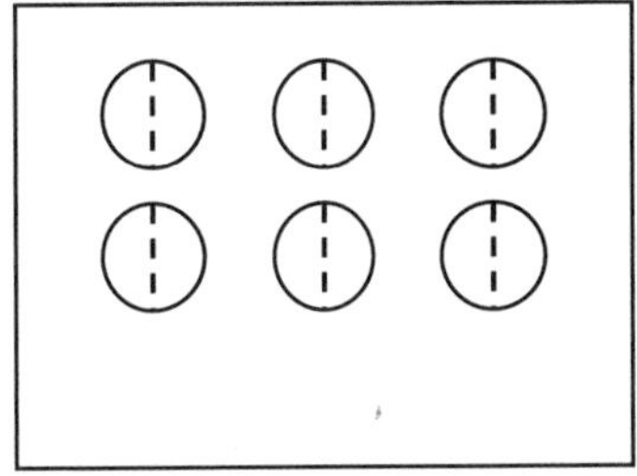

Now write $6 \div \frac{1}{2}$. Tell your student that now we want to put $\frac{1}{2}$ an orange in each group. Divide each of the 6 circles into half.

$6 \div \frac{1}{2} = ?$ How many $\frac{1}{2}$'s are in 6?

There are 12 groups of $\frac{1}{2}$ in 6.

$6 \div \frac{1}{2} = 12$

$6 \div \frac{1}{2} = 12 = 6 \times 2$

Remind your student that division is related to multiplication.
So for $6 \div 2 = 3$, we can think: _____ $\times 2 = 6$, or how many 2's in 6.
For $6 \div \frac{1}{2} =$ _____ we can think: _____ $\times \frac{1}{2} = 6$, or how many $\frac{1}{2}$'s in 6, as we have just done.

For $6 \div 2 = 3$ we can also think $2 \times$ _____ $= 6$. This could be read as 2 of *what* is 6.
Similarly, for $6 \div \frac{1}{2} =$ _____ we can think: $\frac{1}{2}$ of what is 6?

Show your student a rod divided into half with the half labeled as 6 and the whole unknown.

$6 \div \frac{1}{2} =$ _____ can mean

$\frac{1}{2} \times$ _____ $= 6$ or

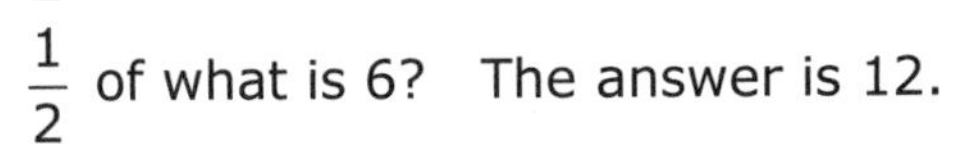

$\frac{1}{2}$ of what is 6? The answer is 12.

$6 \div \frac{1}{2} = 6 \times 2 = 12$

Page 6

Azizah is dividing each orange into one half, so we can write the problem as $3 \div \frac{1}{2}$. We can think of this as finding how many groups of $\frac{1}{2}$ of an orange make 3 oranges. Since 1 orange makes 2 $\frac{1}{2}$'s, or there are two $\frac{1}{2}$'s in 1, there will be 6 halves in 3. So dividing by $\frac{1}{2}$ gives the same answer as multiplying by 2.

Learning Tasks 1-3, p. 7

Illustrate these problems if necessary.

1. **6**
2. (a) **4; 4** (b) **5; 10**
3. (a) $4 \div \frac{1}{2} = 4 \times 2 = \mathbf{8}$ (b) $6 \div \frac{1}{6} = 6 \times 6 = \mathbf{36}$ (c) $3 \div \frac{1}{7} = 3 \times 7 = \mathbf{21}$

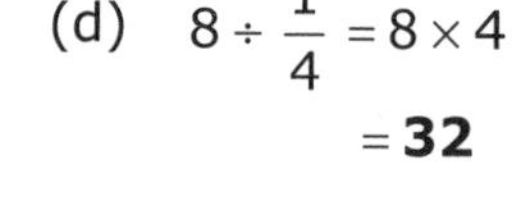

(d) $8 \div \frac{1}{4} = 8 \times 4 = \mathbf{32}$ (e) $5 \div \frac{1}{3} = 5 \times 3 = \mathbf{15}$ (f) $9 \div \frac{1}{9} = 9 \times 9 = \mathbf{81}$

Workbook Exercise 1

(B) Dividing a Fraction by a Whole Number

➤ Divide a fraction number by a whole number.

Student learned how to divide a fraction by a whole number in *Primary Mathematics 5A*. This is reviewed here.

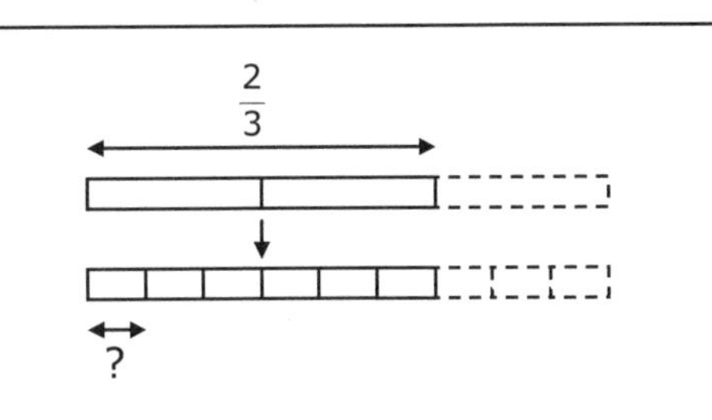

For $\frac{2}{3} \div 6$, we can interpret this as

$\frac{2}{3}$ divided into 6 equal parts.

Each part is $\frac{1}{6}$ of the $\frac{2}{3}$, or $\frac{1}{6} \times \frac{2}{3} = \frac{1}{9}$.

$$\frac{2}{3} \div 6 = \frac{2}{3} \times \frac{1}{6} = \frac{1}{9}.$$

Sometimes students can visualize these problems better if they are put in terms of a word problem. For example:

If $\frac{2}{3}$ of a cake is divided up among 6 people, how much would each person get? Each person would get $\frac{2}{3} \div 6 = \frac{1}{9}$ of a cake.

Write the division problem $6 \div 2 = 3$ and illustrate it as a sharing problem. We have 6 oranges and want to put them into two groups. We are dividing the total amount into half. So

$6 \div 2 = \frac{1}{2}$ of $6 = \frac{1}{2} \times 6 = 3$. We can also write this as

$$6 \div 2 = 6 \times \frac{1}{2} = 3$$

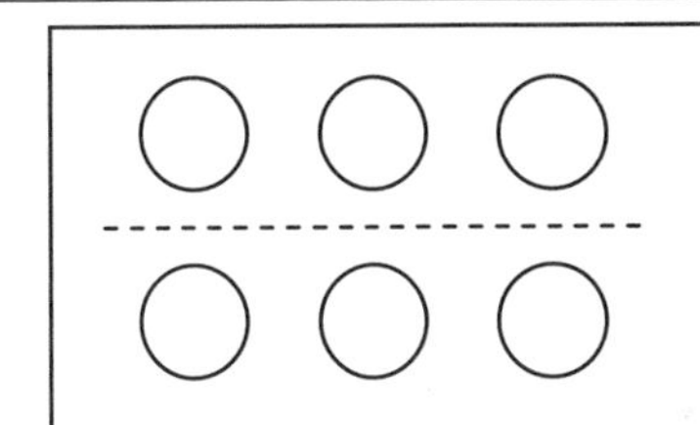

Learning Task 4, p. 7

Discuss this with your student. You can restate it as a word problem. You have half a pizza and want to share it with 4 people. How much would each person get? We need to divide the half pizza by 4. We have to find $\frac{1}{4}$ of $\frac{1}{2}$, which can be written as $\frac{1}{2} \times \frac{1}{4}$.

$$\frac{1}{2} \div 4 = \frac{1}{2} \times \frac{1}{4} = \mathbf{\frac{1}{8}}$$

Learning Tasks 5-6, p. 8

5. (a) $\mathbf{\frac{1}{2}}$; $\mathbf{\frac{1}{6}}$ (b) $\mathbf{\frac{1}{8}}$; $\mathbf{\frac{1}{10}}$

6. (a) $\frac{1}{2} \div 3 = \frac{1}{2} \times \frac{1}{3} = \mathbf{\frac{1}{6}}$

(b) $\frac{1}{4} \div 6 = \frac{1}{4} \times \frac{1}{6} = \mathbf{\frac{1}{24}}$

(c) $\frac{1}{6} \div 5 = \frac{1}{6} \times \frac{1}{5} = \mathbf{\frac{1}{30}}$

(d) $\frac{2}{3} \div 3 = \frac{2}{3} \times \frac{1}{3} = \mathbf{\frac{2}{9}}$

(e) $\frac{2}{7} \div 2 = \frac{\cancel{2}^{1}}{7} \times \frac{1}{\cancel{2}_{1}} = \mathbf{\frac{1}{7}}$

(f) $\frac{4}{9} \div 8 = \frac{\cancel{4}^{1}}{9} \times \frac{1}{\cancel{8}_{2}} = \mathbf{\frac{1}{18}}$

Workbook Exercise 2

(C) Dividing a Fraction by a Unit Fraction

➢ Divide a fraction by a unit fraction.

We can interpret $\frac{1}{2} \div \frac{1}{4}$ as starting with $\frac{1}{2}$ and, putting $\frac{1}{4}$ in each part and finding out how many parts there are, as is shown in the text. There will be two parts. So

$\frac{1}{2} \div \frac{1}{4} = \frac{1}{2} \times 4 = 2$. We can think of this as

"How many $\frac{1}{4}$'s in $\frac{1}{2}$?"

or $? \times \frac{1}{4} = \frac{1}{2}$.

We could also interpret this as "$\frac{1}{2}$ is $\frac{1}{4}$ of what?" or $\frac{1}{2} = \frac{1}{4} \times ?$. To diagram this, we could draw a bar to show the "what", divide it in fourths, mark each fourth as $\frac{1}{2}$. To find *what* we multiply by 4.

$\frac{1}{2} \div \frac{1}{4} = \frac{1}{2} \times 4 = 2$.

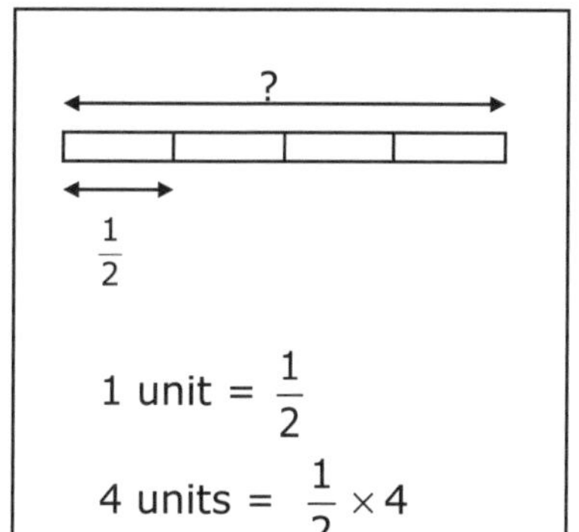

Learning Task 7, p. 8

The girl's sentence here can be confusing. Remind your student than $6 \div 3$ could mean grouping by 3, and we find how many groups there are. Here, we are putting $\frac{1}{2}$ in groups each containing $\frac{1}{4}$ and finding how many groups there are. There are 2 groups of $\frac{1}{4}$. Or, we are finding how many fourths there are in one half.

$\frac{1}{2} \div \frac{1}{4} = \frac{1}{2} \times 4 = \mathbf{2}$

Learning Tasks 8-9, p. 8

Have your student diagram a few of these so that she understands what is happening in the division. For example, for (f), how many $\frac{1}{4}$'s are there in $\frac{3}{8}$? Draw a bar showing eighths, mark three of them, and one below it showing fourths. There are $1\frac{1}{2}$ fourths in three eighths.

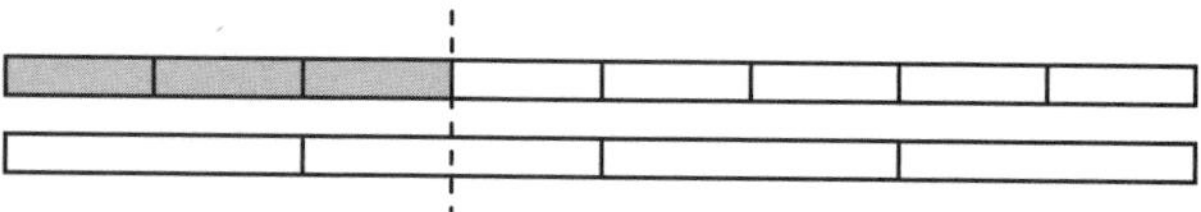

8. (a) **3; 2** (b) **6; 4**

9. (a) $\frac{1}{4} \div \frac{1}{2} = \frac{1}{\cancel{4}_2} \times \cancel{2}^1 = \mathbf{\frac{1}{2}}$

(b) $\frac{2}{5} \div \frac{1}{10} = \frac{2}{\cancel{5}_1} \times \cancel{10}^2 = \mathbf{4}$

(c) $\frac{3}{4} \div \frac{1}{8} = \frac{3}{\cancel{4}_1} \times \cancel{8}^2 = \mathbf{6}$

(d) $\frac{5}{6} \div \frac{1}{6} = \frac{5}{\cancel{6}_1} \times \cancel{6}^1 = \mathbf{5}$

(e) $\frac{2}{9} \div \frac{1}{3} = \frac{2}{\cancel{9}_3} \times \cancel{3}^1 = \mathbf{\frac{2}{3}}$

(f) $\frac{3}{8} \div \frac{1}{4} = \frac{3}{\cancel{8}_2} \times \cancel{4}^1 = \mathbf{\frac{3}{2}} = \mathbf{1\frac{1}{2}}$

(D) Dividing a Fraction by a Fraction

- Divide a whole number by a fraction.
- Divide a fraction by a fraction.

We can interpret $\frac{1}{3} \div \frac{2}{9}$ as, "How many $\frac{2}{9}$'s are there in $\frac{1}{3}$?"

One way to do this would be to diagram it. Divide a bar into thirds, mark 1 of them, draw a bar under that divided into ninths, and see how many $\frac{2}{9}$'s of them correspond to a third.

There are $1\frac{1}{2}$ $\frac{2}{9}$'s in $\frac{1}{3}$.

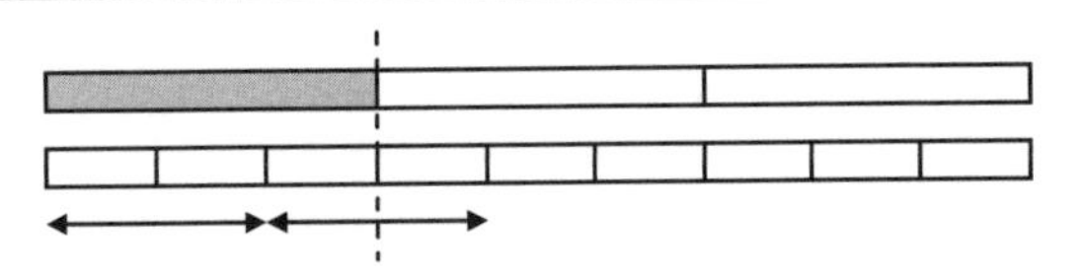

If we multiply by the reciprocal, we get the same answer:

$$\frac{1}{3} \div \frac{2}{9} = \frac{1}{3} \times \frac{9}{2} = \frac{3}{2} = 1\frac{1}{2}$$

We could also interpret $\frac{1}{3} \div \frac{2}{9}$ as, "$\frac{1}{3}$ is $\frac{2}{9}$ of what?" or $\frac{1}{3} = \frac{2}{9} \times ?$. To diagram this, we can draw a bar to show the "what", divide it in ninths, and mark two of the ninths as $\frac{1}{3}$.

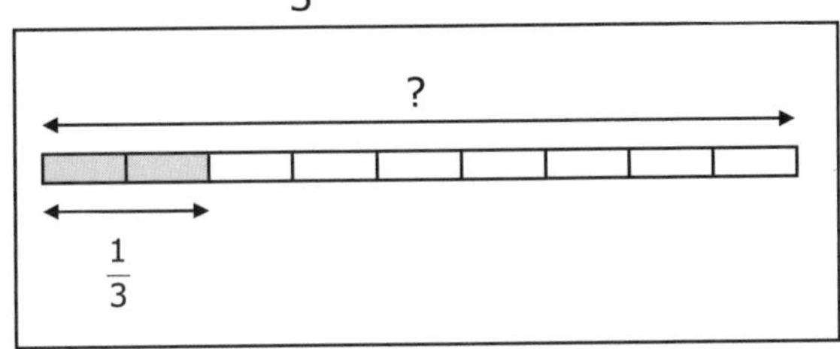

2 units = $\frac{1}{3}$

1 units = $\frac{1}{3} \div 2$

9 units = $\frac{1}{3} \div 2 \times 9$

$= \frac{1}{3} \times \frac{1}{2} \times 9$

$= \frac{1}{3} \times \frac{9}{2}$

$= \frac{3}{2}$

From this, we can also see that

$$\frac{1}{3} \div \frac{2}{9} = \frac{1}{3} \times \frac{9}{2} = \frac{3}{2} = 1\frac{1}{2}$$

Learning Tasks 10-12, p. 9

You may want to illustrate the problems in task 11 with diagrams. A diagram for 1.(c) is given in the notes on the previous page of this guide. For problems where one denominator is a simple multiple of the other, the first type of illustration will work. With problems where it is not, such as 12.(d) and 12.(f), the second type of illustration is easier to draw and interpret.

10. **4**

11. (a) $\mathbf{\frac{8}{3}; \frac{8}{3}}$ (b) $\mathbf{\frac{5}{4}; \frac{5}{2}}$

(c) $\mathbf{\frac{9}{2}; \frac{3}{2}}$ (d) $\mathbf{\frac{3}{2}; \frac{5}{4}}$

12. (a) $3 \div \frac{2}{3} = 3 \times \frac{3}{2} = \mathbf{\frac{9}{2}} = \mathbf{4\frac{1}{2}}$

(b) $6 \div \frac{3}{5} = \cancel{6}^2 \times \frac{5}{\cancel{3}_1} = \mathbf{10}$

(c) $4 \div \frac{6}{7} = \cancel{4}^2 \times \frac{7}{\cancel{6}_3} = \mathbf{\frac{14}{3}} = \mathbf{4\frac{2}{3}}$

(d) $\frac{2}{3} \div \frac{3}{5} = \frac{2}{3} \times \frac{5}{3} = \mathbf{\frac{10}{9}} = \mathbf{1\frac{1}{9}}$

(e) $\frac{3}{5} \div \frac{9}{10} = \frac{\cancel{3}^1}{\cancel{5}_1} \times \frac{\cancel{10}^2}{\cancel{9}_3} = \mathbf{\frac{2}{3}}$

(f) $\frac{5}{8} \div \frac{2}{5} = \frac{5}{8} \times \frac{5}{2} = \mathbf{\frac{25}{16}} = \mathbf{1\frac{9}{16}}$

Workbook Exercise 3

Practice (p. 10)

The word problems in this practice are not all division problems. Your student needs to read the problem carefully. If your student tries to answer the last two as division problems, have her diagram them.

Practice 1A, p. 10

1. (a) $3 \div \frac{1}{2} = 3 \times 2 = \mathbf{6}$ (b) $5 \div \frac{1}{4} = 5 \times 4 = \mathbf{20}$ (c) $6 \div \frac{2}{3} = 6 \times \frac{3}{2} = \mathbf{9}$

2. (a) $\frac{1}{5} \div 2 = \frac{1}{5} \times \frac{1}{2} = \mathbf{\frac{1}{10}}$ (b) $\frac{1}{2} \div 6 = \frac{1}{2} \times \frac{1}{6} = \mathbf{\frac{1}{12}}$ (c) $\frac{2}{7} \div 4 = \frac{\cancel{2}^{1}}{7} \times \frac{1}{\cancel{4}_{2}} = \mathbf{\frac{1}{14}}$

3. (a) $\frac{1}{4} \div \frac{1}{2} = \frac{1}{\cancel{4}_{2}} \times \cancel{2}^{1} = \mathbf{\frac{1}{2}}$ (b) $\frac{8}{9} \div \frac{1}{3} = \frac{8}{\cancel{9}_{3}} \times \cancel{3}^{1} = \mathbf{\frac{8}{3}}$ (c) $\frac{3}{4} \div \frac{1}{6} = \frac{3}{\cancel{4}_{2}} \times \cancel{6}^{3} = \mathbf{\frac{9}{2}}$

4. (a) $\frac{1}{6} \div \frac{2}{3} = \frac{1}{\cancel{6}_{2}} \times \frac{\cancel{3}^{1}}{2} = \mathbf{\frac{1}{4}}$ (b) $\frac{3}{4} \div \frac{9}{10} = \frac{\cancel{3}^{1}}{\cancel{4}_{2}} \times \frac{\cancel{10}^{5}}{\cancel{9}_{3}} = \mathbf{\frac{5}{6}}$ (c) $\frac{4}{5} \div \frac{5}{8} = \frac{4}{5} \times \frac{8}{5} = \mathbf{\frac{32}{25}} = \mathbf{1\frac{7}{25}}$

5. (a) $3 \div \frac{1}{6} = 3 \times 6 = \mathbf{18}$ (b) $\frac{2}{3} \div \frac{1}{6} = \frac{2}{3} \times 6 = \mathbf{4}$

6. Number of periods $= 4 \div \frac{1}{2} = 4 \times 2 = \mathbf{8}$

7. Number of bricks $= 3 \div \frac{1}{4} = 3 \times 4 = \mathbf{12}$

8. Number of pieces of string $= 3 \div \frac{1}{5} = 3 \times 5 = \mathbf{15}$

9. Number of packages $= 6 \div \frac{2}{3} = 6 \times \frac{3}{2} = 3 \times 3 = \mathbf{9}$

10. Number of kg left $= \frac{1}{5} \times 2$ kg $= \mathbf{\frac{2}{5}}$ **kg**

11. Total cut $= \frac{4}{5}$ m $\times 6 = \frac{24}{5}$ m $= 4\frac{4}{5}$ m; Amount left $= 5$ m $- 4\frac{4}{5}$ m $= \mathbf{\frac{1}{5}}$ **m**

Part 2 – Order of Operations (pp. 11-14)

(A) Mixed Operations without Parentheses I

- Do mixed operations involving addition and subtraction with fractions without parentheses.
- Do mixed operations involving multiplication and division with fractions without parentheses.

In *Primary Mathematics 5A*, students learned how to solve expressions using whole numbers with more than two terms using order of operation. This is extended here to fractions.

If the problem does not have parentheses to indicate which operation is done first, then we follow the convention of doing multiplication or division from left to right first, and then addition or subtraction from left to right.

Since addition and multiplication are commutative ($a+b=b+a$), if the problem only contains addition or multiplication, the terms can be added or multiplied in any order. Since division of fractions involves multiplication by the reciprocal, once all the division problems have been changed into multiplication, the problem can be done in any order, and can be simplified in any order.

$$\frac{3}{5}\times\frac{4}{9}\div\frac{3}{10}\div 2=\frac{\cancel{3}^{1}}{\cancel{5}_{1}}\times\frac{4}{9}\times\frac{\cancel{10}^{\cancel{2}^{1}}}{\cancel{3}_{1}}\times\frac{1}{\cancel{2}_{1}}=\frac{4}{9}$$

If the problem has multiplication and division along with addition or subtraction, the multiplication and division part can be solved together as a unit if all the division operations are changed into multiplication by the reciprocal. For example:

$$2\times 3\div 9+\frac{1}{2}=\underline{2\times\cancel{3}^{1}\times\frac{1}{\cancel{9}_{3}}}+\frac{1}{2}=\frac{2}{3}+\frac{1}{2}=\frac{4}{6}+\frac{3}{6}=\frac{7}{6}$$

Page 11

Discuss this page. The diagram shows that to solve this expression we first multiply $\frac{3}{4}$ by 4, and then add $\frac{1}{4}$ to the product.

3, $3\frac{1}{4}$

Tell your student that mathematicians have agreed that, where there is no indication of what operation should be done first, we should first multiply and divide from left to right, then add and subtract from left to right.

You can have your student solve the problem by adding first. He will get a different answer (16).

Learning Tasks 1-2, p. 12

1. **7**

2. (a) $\frac{1}{3}+\frac{3}{4}+\frac{1}{2}=\frac{4}{12}+\frac{9}{12}+\frac{6}{12}=\frac{19}{12}=\mathbf{1\frac{5}{12}}$

   (b) $\frac{1}{3}+\frac{5}{6}-\frac{3}{4}=\frac{4}{12}+\frac{10}{12}-\frac{9}{12}=\mathbf{\frac{5}{12}}$

   (c) $\frac{1}{5}+\frac{7}{10}-\frac{3}{4}=\frac{4}{20}+\frac{14}{20}-\frac{15}{20}=\mathbf{\frac{3}{20}}$

   (d) $\frac{8}{9}-\frac{1}{6}-\frac{1}{2}=\frac{16}{18}-\frac{3}{18}-\frac{9}{18}=\frac{4}{18}=\mathbf{\frac{2}{9}}$

   (e) $\frac{1}{2}-\frac{2}{5}+\frac{3}{10}=\frac{5}{10}-\frac{4}{10}+\frac{3}{10}=\frac{4}{10}=\mathbf{\frac{2}{5}}$

   (f) $\frac{5}{8}-\frac{1}{2}+\frac{3}{4}=\frac{5}{8}-\frac{4}{8}+\frac{6}{8}=\mathbf{\frac{7}{8}}$

Learning Task 3, p. 12

Tell your student that 5 is the same as $\frac{5}{1}$.

So $\frac{7}{9}\times 5\times\frac{3}{8}=\frac{7}{9}\times\frac{5}{1}\times\frac{3}{8}=\frac{7\times 5\times 3}{9\times 8}=\frac{3\times 5\times 7}{9\times 8}=\frac{3}{9}\times\frac{5\times 7}{8}$

We can simplify $\frac{3}{9}$ to $\frac{1}{3}$. Since we can use any number in the numerator with any number in the denominator to simplify, we can record this process more simply as

$\frac{7}{\cancel{9}_3}\times 5\times\frac{\cancel{3}^1}{8}=\frac{35}{24}=\mathbf{1\frac{11}{24}}$

Learning Tasks 4-7, pp 12-13

4. $\mathbf{\frac{3}{5}}$

5. **1**

6. $\mathbf{\frac{5}{12}}$

7. (a) $\cancel{3}^1\times\frac{1}{2}\times\frac{5}{\cancel{6}_2}=\mathbf{\frac{5}{4}}$

   (b) $\frac{1}{\cancel{3}_1}\times\frac{\cancel{3}^1}{\cancel{4}_1}\times\cancel{8}^2=\mathbf{2}$

   (c) $\frac{4}{9}\div 4\div\frac{3}{5}=\frac{\cancel{4}^1}{9}\times\frac{1}{\cancel{4}_1}\times\frac{5}{3}=\mathbf{\frac{5}{27}}$

   (d) $\frac{3}{8}\div\frac{1}{2}\div 3=\frac{\cancel{3}^1}{\cancel{8}_4}\times\cancel{2}^1\times\frac{1}{\cancel{3}_1}=\mathbf{\frac{1}{4}}$

   (e) $14\div 2\times\frac{2}{7}=\cancel{14}^2\times\frac{1}{\cancel{2}_1}\times\frac{\cancel{2}^1}{7_1}=\mathbf{2}$

   (f) $\frac{3}{5}\times\frac{4}{9}\div\frac{3}{10}=\frac{\cancel{3}^1}{\cancel{5}_1}\times\frac{4}{9}\times\frac{\cancel{10}^2}{\cancel{3}_1}=\mathbf{\frac{8}{9}}$

Workbook Exercise 4

(B) Mixed Operations without Parentheses II

➢ Do mixed operations involving all four operations with fractions without parentheses.

In this section, expressions will include addition and subtraction as well as multiplication and division. Multiplication and division should be done first.

In some of these problems, calculations involving addition or subtraction are easier if the fraction is changed into a mixed number. For example, in task 8, your student might find it easier to change $\frac{15}{4}$ into a mixed number to add to the whole number 4. Your student can leave the answer as a mixed number.

As you have your student work through these learning tasks with you, you can point out that if there are 3 or 4 multiplication and division operations next to each other, they can be solved together as a unit, as was done in the previous section, rather than strictly left to right, if all the division operations are changed into multiplication by the reciprocal. For example:

$$2 \times 3 \div 9 + \frac{1}{2} = \underline{2 \times \cancel{3}^{1} \times \frac{1}{\cancel{9}_{3}}} + \frac{1}{2} = \frac{\cancel{2}^{4}}{\cancel{3}_{6}} + \frac{\cancel{1}^{3}}{\cancel{2}_{6}} = \frac{7}{6} = 1\frac{1}{6}$$

If there are several multiplication or division operations separated by an addition or subtraction operation, they can be recorded together, rather than first one and then the other, since they do not affect each other. For example:

$$4 \div \frac{2}{5} + 5 \div \frac{5}{8} = \underline{\cancel{4}^{2} \times \frac{5}{\cancel{2}_{1}}} + \underline{\cancel{5}^{1} \times \frac{8}{\cancel{5}_{1}}} = 10 + 8 = 18$$

You can also let your student cut down on the number of steps recorded by showing equivalent fractions in one step, rather than two.

$\frac{1}{3} + \frac{1}{2} = \frac{2}{6} + \frac{3}{6} = \frac{5}{6}$ we can write $\frac{\cancel{1}^{2}}{\cancel{3}_{6}} + \frac{\cancel{1}^{3}}{\cancel{2}_{6}} = \frac{5}{6}$

However, if your student gets confused and starts multiplying instead of adding have her write the intermediate step.

Learning Tasks 8-13, pp. 13-14

8. $4 + \cancel{6}^{3} \times \frac{5}{\cancel{8}_{4}} = 4 + \mathbf{\frac{15}{4}}$

$= 4 + 3\frac{3}{4}$

$= \mathbf{7\frac{3}{4}}$

9. $1 - \frac{4}{5} \div 6 = 1 - \frac{\cancel{4}^{2}}{5} \times \frac{1}{\cancel{6}_{3}}$

$= 1 - \mathbf{\frac{2}{15}}$

$= \mathbf{\frac{13}{15}}$

10. (a) $3 - \frac{1}{3} \div 4 = 3 - \frac{1}{3} \times \frac{1}{4}$

$= 3 - \frac{1}{12}$

$= \mathbf{2\frac{11}{12}}$

(b) $7 + \cancel{5}^{1} \times \frac{9}{\cancel{10}_{2}} = 7 + \frac{9}{2}$

$= 7 + 4\frac{1}{2}$

$= \mathbf{11\frac{1}{2}}$

(c) $4 \div \frac{2}{5} + 5 \div \frac{5}{8}$

$= \cancel{4}^{2} \times \frac{5}{\cancel{2}_{1}} + \cancel{5}^{1} \times \frac{8}{\cancel{5}_{1}}$

$= 10 + 8$

$= \mathbf{18}$

(d) $8 \times 4 - 6 \div \frac{2}{3} = 32 - \cancel{6}^{3} \times \frac{3}{\cancel{2}_{1}}$

$= 32 - 9$

$= \mathbf{23}$

(e) $2 \times 3 \div 9 + \frac{1}{2} = 2 \times \cancel{3}^{1} \times \frac{1}{\cancel{9}_{3}} + \frac{1}{2}$

$= \frac{\cancel{2}^{4}}{\cancel{3}_{6}} + \frac{\cancel{1}^{3}}{\cancel{2}_{6}}$

$= \frac{7}{6} = \mathbf{1\frac{1}{6}}$

(f) $4 \div 6 \times 6 + \frac{2}{5} = 4 \times \frac{1}{\cancel{6}_{1}} \times \cancel{6}^{1} + \frac{2}{5}$

$= 4 + \frac{2}{5}$

$= \mathbf{4\frac{2}{5}}$

11. $\frac{3}{8} - \frac{\cancel{3}^{1}}{4} \times \frac{1}{\cancel{3}_{1}} = \frac{3}{8} - \mathbf{\frac{1}{4}}$

$= \mathbf{\frac{1}{8}}$

12. $\frac{5}{6} + \frac{2}{3} \div 4 \times \frac{1}{2} = \frac{5}{6} + \frac{\cancel{2}^{1}}{3} \times \frac{1}{4} \times \frac{1}{\cancel{2}_{1}}$

$= \frac{\cancel{5}^{10}}{\cancel{6}_{12}} + \mathbf{\frac{1}{12}}$

$= \mathbf{\frac{11}{12}}$

13. (a) $\frac{3}{4}+\underline{\frac{\cancel{2}^{1}}{5}\times\frac{1}{\cancel{4}_{2}}}=\frac{3}{4}+\frac{1}{10}$

$=\frac{15}{20}+\frac{2}{20}$

$=\mathbf{\frac{17}{20}}$

(b) $\frac{3}{5}-\underline{\frac{\cancel{3}^{1}}{\cancel{4}_{2}}\times\frac{\cancel{2}^{1}}{\cancel{9}_{3}}}=\frac{3}{5}-\frac{1}{6}$

$=\frac{18}{30}-\frac{5}{30}$

$=\mathbf{\frac{13}{30}}$

(c) $\frac{1}{8}+\frac{1}{2}\div\frac{1}{4}=\frac{1}{8}+\underline{\frac{1}{\cancel{2}_{1}}\times\cancel{4}^{2}}$

$=\frac{1}{8}+2$

$=\mathbf{2\frac{1}{8}}$

(d) $\frac{7}{9}-\frac{1}{5}\div\frac{3}{10}=\frac{7}{9}-\underline{\frac{1}{\cancel{5}_{1}}\times\frac{\cancel{10}^{2}}{3}}$

$=\frac{7}{9}-\frac{\cancel{2}^{6}}{\cancel{3}_{9}}$

$=\mathbf{\frac{1}{9}}$

(e) $\frac{2}{3}+\underline{\frac{5}{6}\div10}\times\frac{2}{3}$

$=\frac{2}{3}+\underline{\frac{\cancel{5}^{1}}{6}\times\frac{1}{\cancel{10}_{2}}}\times\frac{2}{3}$

$=\frac{2}{3}+\underline{\frac{1}{\cancel{12}_{6}}\times\frac{\cancel{2}^{1}}{3}}$

$=\frac{\cancel{2}^{12}}{\cancel{3}_{18}}+\frac{1}{18}$

$=\mathbf{\frac{13}{18}}$

(f) $\frac{5}{8}-\frac{5}{8}\times\frac{4}{5}\div2=\frac{5}{8}-\underline{\frac{\cancel{5}^{1}}{\cancel{8}_{2}}\times\frac{\cancel{4}^{1}}{\cancel{5}_{1}}\times\frac{1}{2}}$

$=\frac{5}{8}-\frac{1}{4}$

$=\frac{5}{8}-\frac{2}{8}$

$=\mathbf{\frac{3}{8}}$

 **Workbook Exercise 5**

(C) Mixed Operations with Parentheses

➢ Do mixed operations involving all four operations with fractions with parentheses.

If the expression contains parentheses, the rules for order of operations are applied first to the expression in parentheses to replace it with a single term, and then to the entire expression.

Learning Tasks 14-15, p. 14

14. $\left(\frac{4}{5}-\frac{1}{2}\right)\div 4=\left(\frac{8}{10}-\frac{5}{10}\right)\div 4=\mathbf{\frac{3}{10}}\div 4=\frac{3}{10}\times\frac{1}{4}=\mathbf{\frac{3}{40}}$

15. (a) $\left(\frac{3}{5}+\frac{1}{3}\right)\div\frac{2}{5}=\left(\frac{9}{15}+\frac{5}{15}\right)\div\frac{2}{5}=\frac{\cancel{14}^{7}}{\cancel{15}_{3}}\times\frac{\cancel{5}^{1}}{\cancel{2}_{1}}=\mathbf{\frac{7}{3}}$

(b) $\frac{3}{4}\div\left(\frac{3}{4}-\frac{\cancel{1}^{2}}{\cancel{2}_{4}}\right)=\frac{3}{4}\div\frac{1}{4}=\frac{3}{4}\times 4=\mathbf{3}$

(c) $\frac{4}{7}\times\left(\frac{3}{4}+\frac{1}{8}\right)=\frac{4}{7}\times\left(\frac{6}{8}+\frac{1}{8}\right)=\frac{\cancel{4}^{1}}{7}\times\frac{7}{\cancel{8}_{2}}=\mathbf{\frac{1}{2}}$

(d) $\left(\frac{1}{3}+\frac{5}{12}\right)\times\frac{4}{9}=\left(\frac{4}{12}+\frac{5}{12}\right)\times\frac{4}{9}=\frac{\cancel{9}^{1}}{\cancel{12}_{3}}\times\frac{\cancel{4}^{1}}{\cancel{9}_{1}}=\mathbf{\frac{1}{3}}$

(e) $\frac{2}{3}\times\left(\frac{\cancel{1}^{2}}{\cancel{2}_{4}}+\frac{1}{4}\right)-\frac{3}{8}=\frac{\cancel{2}^{1}}{\cancel{3}_{1}}\times\frac{\cancel{3}^{1}}{\cancel{4}_{2}}-\frac{3}{8}=\frac{\cancel{1}^{4}}{\cancel{2}_{8}}-\frac{3}{8}=\mathbf{\frac{1}{8}}$

(f) $\frac{2}{5}+\left(\frac{\cancel{1}^{2}}{\cancel{3}_{6}}+\frac{\cancel{1}^{3}}{\cancel{2}_{6}}\right)\div\frac{3}{4}=\frac{2}{5}+\frac{5}{6}\div\frac{3}{4}=\frac{2}{5}+\frac{5}{\cancel{6}_{3}}\times\frac{\cancel{4}^{2}}{3}=\frac{\cancel{2}^{18}}{\cancel{5}_{45}}+\frac{\cancel{10}^{50}}{\cancel{9}_{45}}=\mathbf{\frac{68}{45}}$

Workbook Exercise 6

Practice (p. 15)

Practice 1B, p. 15

1. (a) $\frac{2}{3}+\frac{1}{4}-\frac{1}{2}=\frac{8}{12}+\frac{3}{12}-\frac{6}{12}$ $=\mathbf{\frac{5}{12}}$

   (b) $\frac{7}{8}-\frac{1}{4}+\frac{1}{2}=\frac{7}{8}-\frac{2}{8}+\frac{4}{8}$ $=\mathbf{\frac{9}{8}}$ or $\mathbf{1\frac{1}{8}}$

   (c) $2\times\frac{4}{9}\div\frac{2}{3}=\cancel{2}^1\times\frac{4}{\cancel{9}_3}\times\frac{\cancel{3}^1}{\cancel{2}_1}$ $=\mathbf{\frac{4}{3}}$

   (d) $\frac{3}{5}\div 6\times\frac{5}{6}=\frac{\cancel{3}^1}{\cancel{5}_1}\times\frac{1}{\cancel{6}_2}\times\frac{\cancel{5}^1}{6}$ $=\mathbf{\frac{1}{12}}$

   (e) $\frac{3}{4}\times\frac{2}{3}\div\frac{1}{2}=\frac{\cancel{3}^1}{\cancel{4}_1}\times\frac{\cancel{2}^1}{\cancel{3}_1}\times\cancel{2}^1$ $=\mathbf{1}$

   (f) $\frac{5}{6}\div\frac{3}{4}\div\frac{5}{9}=\frac{\cancel{5}^1}{\cancel{6}_{\cancel{3}\,1}}\times\frac{\cancel{4}^2}{\cancel{3}_1}\times\frac{\cancel{9}^{\cancel{3}\,1}}{\cancel{5}_1}$ $=\mathbf{2}$

2. (a) $6+4\times\frac{3}{4}=6+3$ $=\mathbf{9}$

   (b) $\frac{3}{\cancel{4}_1}\times\cancel{8}^2-\cancel{6}^2\times\frac{2}{\cancel{3}_1}=6-4$ $=\mathbf{2}$

   (c) $3+6\div\frac{2}{7}=3+\cancel{6}^3\times\frac{7}{\cancel{2}_1}$ $=3+21$ $=\mathbf{24}$

   (d) $\frac{5}{6}\div 10+2=\frac{\cancel{5}^1}{6}\times\frac{1}{\cancel{10}_2}+2$ $=\frac{1}{12}+2$ $=\mathbf{2\frac{1}{12}}$

   (e) $2+\frac{8}{9}\div\frac{2}{3}=2+\frac{\cancel{8}^4}{\cancel{9}_3}\times\frac{\cancel{3}^1}{\cancel{2}_1}$ $=2+\frac{4}{3}$ $=\mathbf{3\frac{1}{3}}$

   (f) $7-\frac{9}{10}\div\frac{3}{5}=7-\frac{\cancel{9}^3}{\cancel{10}_2}\times\frac{\cancel{5}^1}{\cancel{3}_1}$ $=7-\frac{3}{2}$ $=\mathbf{5\frac{1}{2}}$

3. (a) $6\times\left(1-\frac{3}{4}\right)=\cancel{6}^3\times\frac{1}{\cancel{4}_2}$ $=\frac{3}{2}=\mathbf{1\frac{1}{2}}$

   (b) $\left(\frac{3}{4}-\frac{\cancel{1}^2}{\cancel{2}_4}\right)\div 3=\frac{1}{4}\times\frac{1}{3}$ $=\mathbf{\frac{1}{12}}$

(c) $\frac{2}{5}\times\left(\frac{\cancel{3}^{6}}{\cancel{4}_{8}}-\frac{3}{8}\right)=\frac{\cancel{2}^{1}}{5}\times\frac{3}{\cancel{8}_{4}}$

$=\mathbf{\frac{3}{20}}$

(d) $\left(\frac{\cancel{1}^{2}}{\cancel{4}_{8}}+\frac{3}{8}\right)\div\frac{5}{6}=\frac{\cancel{5}^{1}}{\cancel{8}_{4}}\times\frac{\cancel{6}^{3}}{\cancel{5}_{1}}$

$=\mathbf{\frac{3}{4}}$

(e) $\frac{4}{9}\div\left(2\div\frac{3}{4}\right)=\frac{4}{9}\div\left(2\times\frac{4}{3}\right)$

$=\frac{4}{9}\div\frac{8}{3}$

$=\frac{\cancel{4}^{1}}{\cancel{9}_{3}}\times\frac{\cancel{3}^{1}}{\cancel{8}_{2}}$

$=\mathbf{\frac{1}{6}}$

(f) $\frac{1}{7}\div\left(\frac{1}{\cancel{3}_{1}}\times\frac{\cancel{6}^{2}}{7}\right)=\frac{1}{7}\div\frac{2}{7}$

$=\frac{1}{\cancel{7}_{1}}\times\frac{\cancel{7}^{1}}{2}$

$=\mathbf{\frac{1}{2}}$

4. (a) $(20-8)\times\frac{3}{4}\div 3$

$=\cancel{12}^{1}\times\frac{3}{\cancel{4}_{1}}\times\frac{1}{\cancel{3}_{1}}$

$=\mathbf{3}$

(b) $(8+4)\div\frac{1}{2}\times\frac{5}{6}=\cancel{12}^{2}\times 2\times\frac{5}{\cancel{6}_{1}}$

$=\mathbf{20}$

(c) $(20+12)\div 12\times\frac{3}{8}$

$=\cancel{32}^{\cancel{4}^{1}}\times\frac{1}{\cancel{12}_{\cancel{4}_{1}}}\times\frac{\cancel{3}^{1}}{\cancel{8}_{1}}$

$=\mathbf{1}$

(d) $(12+4)\div\frac{4}{5}\div 8=\cancel{16}^{\cancel{2}^{1}}\times\frac{5}{\cancel{4}_{2}}\times\frac{1}{\cancel{8}_{1}}$

$=\frac{5}{2}=\mathbf{2\frac{1}{2}}$

(e) $\frac{3}{8}\times\left(\frac{5}{6}-\frac{1}{2}\right)\times\frac{2}{5}$

$=\frac{3}{8}\times\left(\frac{5}{6}-\frac{3}{6}\right)\times\frac{2}{5}$

$=\frac{\cancel{3}^{1}}{\cancel{8}_{4}}\times\frac{\cancel{2}^{1}}{\cancel{6}_{1}}\times\frac{\cancel{2}^{1}}{5}$

$=\mathbf{\frac{1}{20}}$

(f) $\frac{2}{3}\div\frac{4}{9}\div\left(\frac{1}{2}-\frac{3}{8}\right)=\frac{2}{3}\div\frac{4}{9}\div\left(\frac{4}{8}-\frac{3}{8}\right)$

$=\frac{2}{3}\div\frac{4}{9}\div\frac{1}{8}$

$=\frac{2}{\cancel{3}_{1}}\times\frac{\cancel{9}^{3}}{\cancel{4}_{1}}\times\cancel{8}^{2}$

$=\mathbf{12}$

5. (a) $8 - \underline{6 \times \frac{2}{3} \div 2}$

$= 8 - \underline{\cancel{6}^{2} \times \frac{\cancel{2}^{1}}{\cancel{3}_{1}} \times \frac{1}{\cancel{2}_{1}}}$

$= 8 - 2$

$= \mathbf{6}$

(b) $16 - \underline{4 \times 2} + 4 \div \frac{1}{2} = 16 - 8 + \underline{4 \times 2}$

$= 16 - 8 + 8$

$= \mathbf{16}$

(c) $\frac{2}{5} \times (18 - 3) + \frac{3}{10}$

$= \underline{\frac{2}{\cancel{5}_{1}} \times \cancel{15}^{3}} + \frac{3}{10}$

$= 6 + \frac{3}{10}$

$= \mathbf{6\frac{3}{10}}$

(d) $\frac{4}{5} - \left(\frac{3}{4} - \frac{2}{3}\right) \times 2 = \frac{4}{5} - \left(\frac{9}{12} - \frac{8}{12}\right) \times 2$

$= \frac{4}{5} - \underline{\frac{1}{\cancel{12}_{6}} \times \cancel{2}^{1}}$

$= \frac{\cancel{4}^{24}}{\cancel{5}_{30}} - \frac{\cancel{1}^{5}}{\cancel{6}_{30}}$

$= \mathbf{\frac{19}{30}}$

(e) $\left(\frac{5}{6} - \frac{3}{4}\right) \div \frac{2}{3} + \frac{3}{4}$

$= \underline{\frac{1}{12} \div \frac{2}{3}} + \frac{3}{4}$

$= \frac{1}{\cancel{12}_{4}} \times \frac{\cancel{3}^{1}}{2} + \frac{3}{4}$

$= \frac{1}{8} + \frac{\cancel{3}^{6}}{\cancel{4}_{2}}$

$= \mathbf{\frac{7}{8}}$

(f) $\frac{5}{9} \div \frac{5}{6} - \frac{4}{5} \times \frac{3}{4} = \underline{\frac{\cancel{5}^{1}}{\cancel{9}_{3}} \times \frac{\cancel{6}^{2}}{\cancel{5}_{1}}} - \underline{\frac{\cancel{4}^{1}}{5} \times \frac{3}{\cancel{4}_{1}}}$

$= \frac{2}{3} - \frac{3}{5}$

$= \frac{10}{15} - \frac{9}{15}$

$= \mathbf{\frac{1}{15}}$

Part 3 - Word Problems (pp. 16-19)

(A) Word Problems I

- Solve word problems involving fractions.

Most of these problems can be solved by drawing models with units, then finding the value of a unit, and then using the value of a unit to solve the problem. If there is a before situation and an after situation they should both be diagrammed, taking care to show any relationships in the units between the two situations.

You may want to give your student the problem and have him solve it without looking at the text, and then compare solutions and discuss. Few of the problems, if any, have only one method of arriving at the answer. At least one method will be shown in this guide, sometimes more. Your student may come up with another method.

p. 16

The arrow can read *of the total*.

$\frac{7}{15} \longrightarrow 700$ ml

$\frac{1}{15} \longrightarrow 700 \div 7 = 100$ ml

$\frac{1}{5} = \frac{3}{15} \longrightarrow 100 \times 3 =$ **300 ml**

$\frac{2}{3} = \frac{10}{15} \longrightarrow 100 \times 10 =$ **1000 ml**

OR:

700 ml is $\frac{7}{15}$ of what?

$700 \div \frac{7}{15} = 700 \times \frac{15}{7} = 1500$ ml

The tank holds 1500 ml.

$\frac{1}{5} \times 1500$ ml $=$ **300 ml**

$\frac{2}{3} \times 1500$ ml $= 1000$ ml

Learning Tasks 1-2, p. 17

Discuss the various possible approaches for solving each of these problems.

1. (b) 5 units = 35
   1 unit = $35 \div 5 = 7$
   12 units = $7 \times 12 = 84$
   He bought **84** chairs.

   OR:
   35 is $\frac{5}{12}$ of what?
   $35 \div \frac{5}{12} = 35 \times \frac{12}{5} = 84$

   OR:
   $\frac{5}{12} \longrightarrow 35$
   $\frac{1}{12} \longrightarrow 35 \div 5 = 7$
   $\frac{12}{12} \longrightarrow 7 \times 12 = 84$

2. (b) 3 units = \$90
   1 unit = $\$90 \div 3 = \$30$
   10 units = $\$30 \times 10 = \$300$
   He had **\$300** at first.

   OR: \$90 is $\frac{3}{10}$ of what?
   $\$90 \div \frac{3}{10} = \$90 \times \frac{10}{3} = \$300$

   OR:
   $\frac{3}{10} \longrightarrow \$90$
   $\frac{1}{10} \longrightarrow \$90 \div 3 = \$30$
   $\frac{10}{10} \longrightarrow \$30 \times 10 = \$300$

Workbook Exercise 7

(B) Word Problems II

➢ Solve word problems involving fractions.

Learning Tasks 3-6, pp. 18-19

3. The value of 3 white units (of the top bar's total of 5 units) is the same as the value of the 2 white units of the middle bar in the diagram.

   The lowest common multiple of 3 and 2 is 6. So we can get equal units by dividing each unit of the top bar in half, and dividing each unit of the middle bar into thirds. Then the 3 white units of the top bar are now 6 smaller units, and the 2 units of the middle bar are also 6 smaller units.

   The resulting total has 10 units, shown in the bottom bar, 4 units spent on the doll and 3 on the musical box.

   One more unit was spent on the doll than on the music box. So, one of these units is \$8. 3 units, the money she has left, is therefore \$24.

   1 unit = 8. Money she had left = 3 units = $\$8 \times 3 =$ **\$24**

   OR: Fraction spent on doll $= \frac{1}{2} \times \left(1 - \frac{2}{5}\right) = \frac{1}{2} \times \frac{3}{5} = \frac{3}{10}$

   Difference $= \frac{2}{5} - \frac{3}{10} = \frac{1}{10} \rightarrow \$8$

   Total money $= \$8 \div \frac{1}{10} = \$80$

   Fraction of money left $= 1 - \frac{4}{10} - 1 - \frac{4}{10} - \frac{3}{10} = \frac{3}{10}$

   Amount left $\frac{3}{10} \times \$80 = \$24$

4. **120**

   or: Fraction of the book she read on Tuesday $= \frac{1}{2} - \frac{2}{5} = \frac{5}{10} - \frac{4}{10} = \frac{1}{10}$

   Total number of pages $= 12 \div \frac{1}{10} = 12 \times 10 = 120$

6. 3rd to 4th step in the solution given: Since $\frac{2}{8}$ is 4 jugs, and $\frac{3}{8}$ is 4 jugs 5 cups, then $\frac{1}{8}$ must be 5 cups.

Workbook Exercise 8

Practice (pp. 20-21)

Practice 1C, p. 20

1. Fraction that are children $= 1 - \frac{2}{3} - \frac{1}{4} = \frac{1}{12}$

   Number of children $= \frac{1}{12} \times 300 = \mathbf{25}$

2. Fraction of members that are new female $= \frac{3}{10} \times \frac{2}{7} = \frac{3}{35}$

   Number of new females $= \frac{3}{35} \times 350 = \mathbf{30}$

3. Remainder $= \frac{1}{4}$

   Fraction given away $= \frac{2}{5} \times \frac{1}{4} = \frac{1}{10}$

   Number given away $= \frac{1}{10} \times 500 = \mathbf{50}$

4. 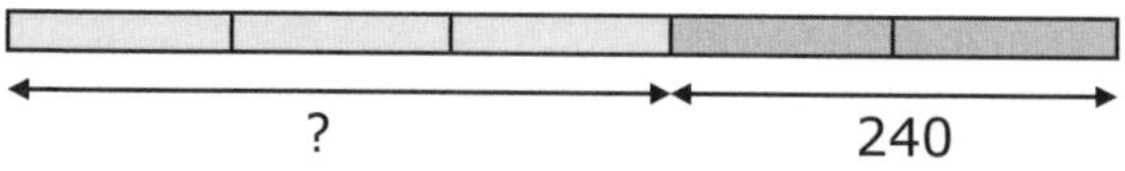

   2 units $= 240$

   1 unit $= \frac{240}{2} = 120$

   3 units $= 120 \times 2 = 360$

   There were **360** chicken satay sticks.

   OR: Total sticks

   $= 240 \div \frac{2}{5} = 240 \times \frac{5}{2} = 600$

   Number of chicken satay sticks

   $= \frac{3}{5} \times 600 = 360$

5. He spent $\frac{2}{5}$ of his money.

   $\frac{2}{5} \longrightarrow \$30$, $\frac{1}{5} \longrightarrow \$30 \div 2 = \$15$, $\frac{5}{5} \longrightarrow \$15 \times 5 = \$75$

   He had **\$75** at first.

6. He had $\frac{3}{5}$ of his money left.

   $\frac{3}{5} \longrightarrow \$12$, $\frac{1}{5} \longrightarrow \$12 \div 3 = \$4$, $\frac{2}{5} \longrightarrow \$4 \times 2 = \$8$

   He spent **\$8** on the storybook.

7. $\frac{1}{4} \longrightarrow \$120$, $\frac{4}{4} \longrightarrow \$120 \times 4 = \$480$

   He had **\$480** at first.

8. 8 units $= 480$
   1 unit $= 489 \div 8 = 60$
   2 units $= 60 \times 2 = 120$
   He has **120** more foreign stamps than U.S. stamps.

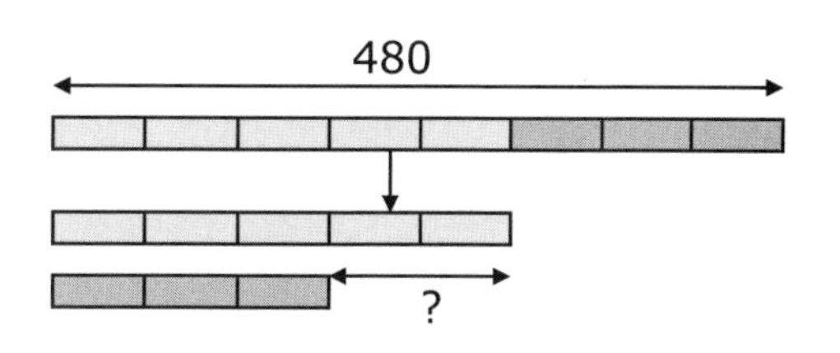

   or: Fraction that are foreign $= \frac{3}{8}$.

   Fraction more U.S. than foreign $= \frac{5}{8} - \frac{3}{8} = \frac{1}{4}$. $\frac{1}{4} \times 480 =$ **120**

9. Divide a bar into thirds. The remainder is two third. One fourth of the remainder is one half of one of the thirds. So divide each unit into half to give 6 units.
   6 units $= 24$
   3 units $= 24 \div 2 = 12$

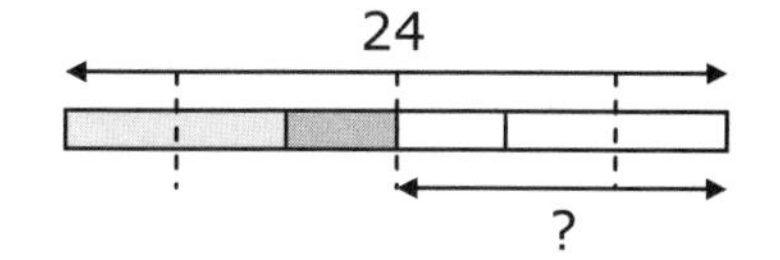

   OR: Remainder $= \frac{2}{3}$. Fraction of remainder not used $= \frac{3}{4}$

   Fraction left $= \frac{3}{4} \times \frac{2}{3} = \frac{1}{2}$. $\frac{1}{2} \times 24 = 12$

   12 lb of flour were left.

Practice 1D, p 21

1. $\frac{1}{4} \longrightarrow \$450 + \$150 = \$600$

   $\frac{4}{4} \longrightarrow \$600 \times 4 = \$2400$

   His total savings was **$2400**.

2. Fraction remaining $= 1 - \frac{1}{3} - \frac{1}{4} = \frac{5}{12}$

   $\frac{5}{12} \longrightarrow \$600,\ \frac{1}{12} \longrightarrow \$120,\ \frac{1}{4} = \frac{3}{12} \longrightarrow \$120 \times 3 = \$360$

   He gave his mother **$360**.

3. 2 units $= 3 \times \$4 = \$12$
   1 unit $= \$12 \div 2 = \$6$
   3 units $= \$6 \times 3 = \$18$

   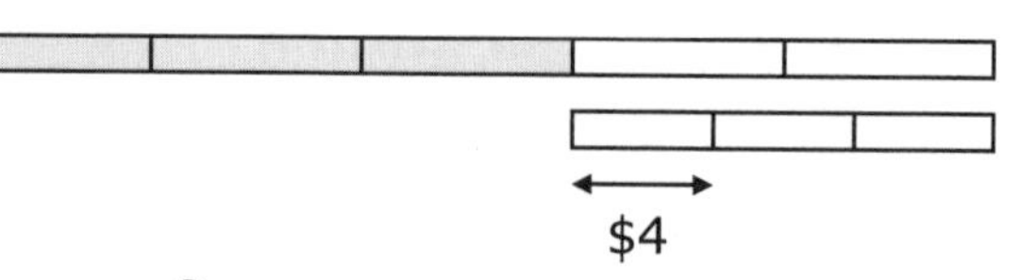

   OR: Cost of shirts $= \$12$. Remainder $= \frac{2}{5}$

   $\frac{2}{5} \longrightarrow \$12,\ \frac{1}{5} \longrightarrow \$6,\ \frac{3}{5} \longrightarrow \$6 \times 3 = \$18$

   The handbag cost **$18**.

4. Divide a bar up into fourths. The remainder is one fourth. Since she spent half the remainder on the calculator, divide it into two units. The dictionary is 5 units more than the calculator.

   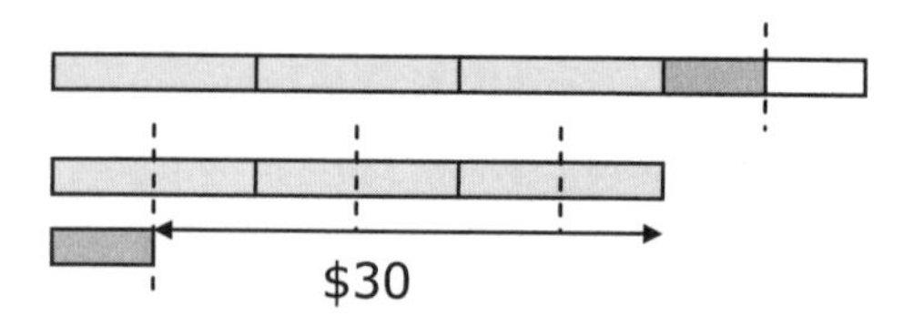

   5 units $= \$30$
   1 unit $= \$30 \div 5 = \$6$
   6 units $= \$6 \times 6 = \$36$

   OR: Remainder $= \frac{1}{4}$. Fraction spent on calculator $= \frac{1}{2} \times \frac{1}{4} = \frac{1}{8}$

   Fraction more spent on dictionary than calculator $= \frac{3}{4} - \frac{1}{8} = \frac{5}{8}$

   $\frac{5}{8} \longrightarrow \$30.\ \frac{1}{8} \longrightarrow \$6.\ \frac{3}{4} = \frac{6}{8} \longrightarrow \$6 \times 6 = \$36$

   The dictionary cost **$36**.

5. Fraction of tarts left $= \frac{3}{4} \times \frac{2}{5} = \frac{3}{10}$

$\frac{3}{10} \longrightarrow 150$, $\frac{1}{10} \longrightarrow 50$, $\frac{3}{5} = \frac{6}{10} \longrightarrow 6 \times 50 = 300$

He sold **300** tarts.

6. Fraction spent $= \frac{1}{4} + \left(\frac{1}{2} \times \frac{3}{4}\right) = \frac{5}{8}$

$\frac{5}{8} \longrightarrow \$10$, $\frac{1}{8} \longrightarrow \$2$ Fraction left $= \frac{3}{8}$ $\frac{3}{8} \longrightarrow \$2 \times 3 = \$6$

She had **$6** left.

7. Divide his money into 5 units.

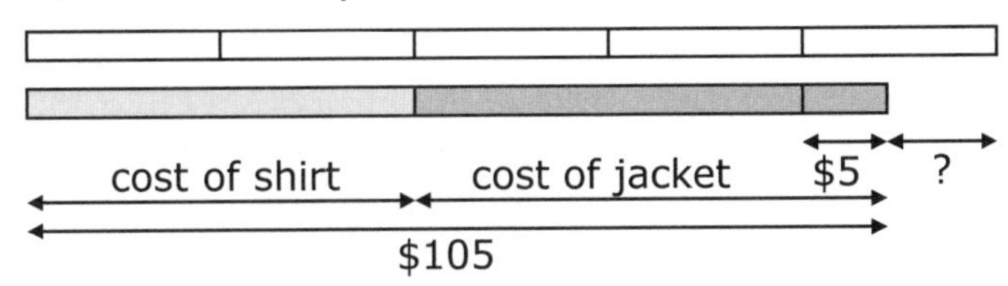

4 units $= \$105 - \$5 = \$100$
1 unit $= \$100 \div 4 = \$25$
Amount left $= 1$ unit $- \$5$
$= \$25 - \$5 =$ **$20**

8.

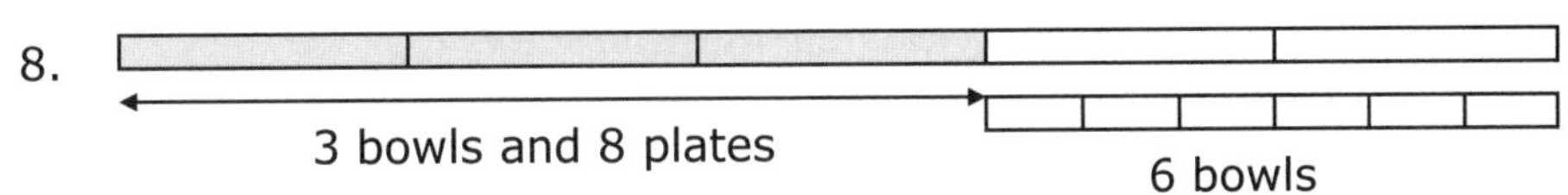

2 units = 6 bowls
1 unit = 3 bowls
3 units = 3 bowls and 8 plates, so 2 units = 8 plates and 1 unit = 4 plates
5 units $= 4 \times 5 = 20$ plates

OR: Remainder $= \frac{2}{5} \longrightarrow 6$ bowls

$\frac{1}{5} = 3$ bowls

So the 8 plates cost $\frac{3}{5} - \frac{1}{5} = \frac{2}{5}$ of her money.

$\frac{2}{5} \longrightarrow 8$ plates

$\frac{1}{5} \longrightarrow 4$ plates

$\frac{5}{5} \longrightarrow 4 \times 5 = 20$ plates.

She can buy **20** plates.

US> Unit 2 3d> Unit 1
Circles

Part 1 – Radius and Diameter (US> pp. 22-25, 3d> pp. 6-9)

(A) Radius and Diameter

- Identify the center, diameter, and radius of a circle.
- Measure the radius or diameter of a circle.
- Construct circles of a given radius or diameter.
- Find the diameter given the radius.
- Find the radius, given the diameter.

In earlier levels of *Primary Mathematic*, students learned how find the perimeter of figures made from rectangles, and the area of figures made from triangles and rectangles. In this unit they will learn to find the perimeter and area of circles, semicircles, and quarter circles, as well as the area or perimeter of composite figures which include circles, semicircles, or quarter circles.

In this part, they will learn to find the center, radius, and diameter of a circle.

A circle is a set of points which are all the same distance from a given point, the center. The center is usually labeled with the letter "O" here.

A radius is any line segment from the center of the circle to a point on the circle. A circle has an infinite number of radii (plural for radius), all the same length. The term *radius* is also used to mean the *length* of the radius.

A diameter is a line segment that has its endpoints on the circle and passes through the center of the circle. The term diameter is also used to mean the length of the diameter.

Your student will not learn a formal definition for radius or diameter at this time, but will learn to recognize and measure the radius or diameter of a circle.

The diameter of a circle is twice its radius.
$\text{Diameter} = \text{Radius} \times 2$
$\text{Radius} = \text{Diameter} \div 2$

The circumference of a circle is the distance around, or the perimeter, of the circle.

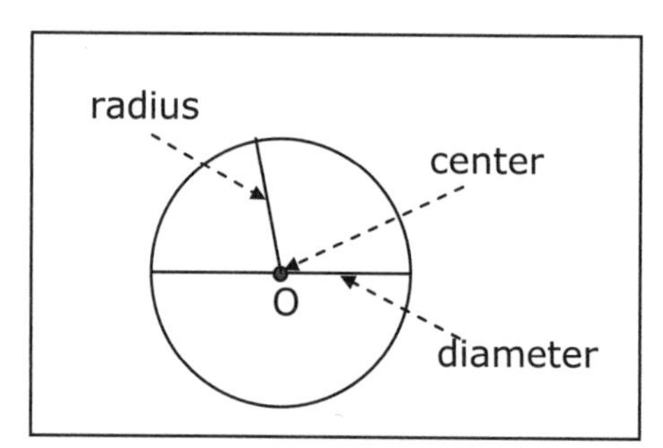

Use a piece of cardboard, a tack or pin, and some string. Place a piece of paper on the cardboard and stick a tack through the paper into the cardboard. Tie the string in a loop so that the doubled length is less than the distance from the tack to the edge of the paper. Have your student loop the string around the tack and the pencil and draw a circle, keeping the string tight and trying to draw a straight line. The string pulls the pencil around in a circle.

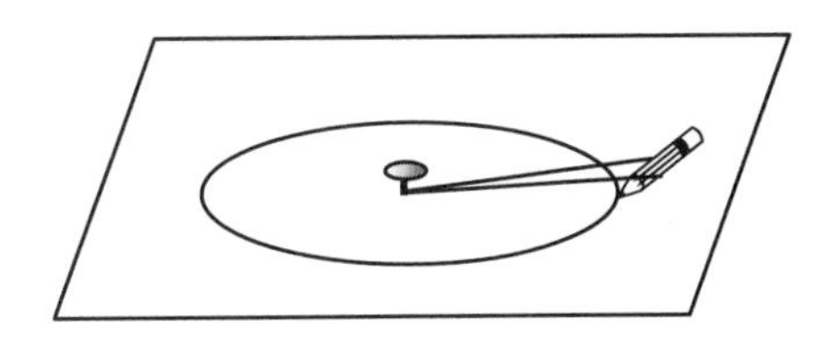

Point out that the distance from the tack to the line is always the same. The curved line is called the circumference.

Show your student a compass and have her practice drawing circles with a compass.

US> page 22, 3d> p. 6
Have your student draw a circle, a radius, and a diameter.

Draw a circle with various chords (line segments that join two points on a circle). Ask your student to identify the center, radius, and diameter.

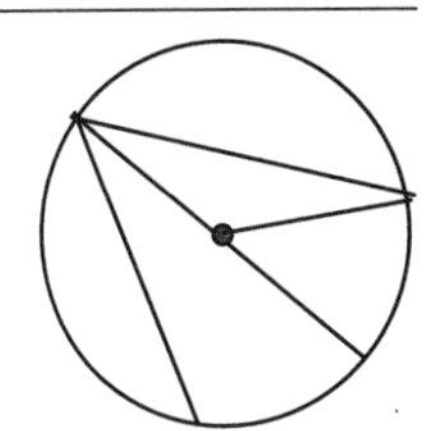

Learning Tasks 1-7, US> pp. 23-25, 3d> pp. 7-9

1. A **3 cm** B **4 cm** C **6 cm**

2. **radius** = **5 cm, diameter** = **10 cm**

6. (a) **8 cm** (b) **9 cm**

7. (a) **B** (b) **D**

(c)

Circle	Radius	Diameter
A	8 m	**16 m**
B	**10 m**	20 m
C	**8 cm**	16 cm
D	7 cm	**14 cm**

US> Workbook Exercise 9 **3d> Workbook Exercise 1**

Part 2 – Circumference (US› pp. 26-29, 3d› pp. 10-13)

(A) Circumference

- Relate the circumference of a circle to its diameter.
- Find the circumference of a circle given its diameter or radius.

The ratio of the circumference of a circle to its diameter is a constant; that is, it is always the same for every circle. Mathematicians have found that it is impossible to find the exact value of the quotient $\frac{\text{circumference}}{\text{diameter}}$ as a ratio of two whole numbers. They use the Greek letter π (which is sometimes written as "pi" and is pronounced like "pie") to represent this quotient. Some calculators give the approximate value of 3.141592654. In this book, 3.14, 3.142, or $\frac{22}{7}$ are used as an approximation for the value of π.

In this section, the formula for circumference is given as
Circumference $= \pi \times$ Diameter
If we use C for circumference, and d for diameter, we can write this as
$C = \pi d$
The formula for circumference is often given as
$C = 2\pi r$ where r is the radius.
Your student should know both of these formulas.

US› page 26, 3d› page 10
Learning Task 1, US› p. 27, 3d› p. 11

If your student hasn't already learned about π, you may want to have him actually do this activity and learning task 1, using several circles, without first letting him see the text. Even if he has seen the text, he might be interested in "proving" it for himself – actually measuring the circumference and diameter of some circles and finding their ratio. His ratios may not be as close as 3.14. You can tell him that mathematicians have come up with various methods to find the ratio that depend on mathematical properties rather than just measurement, and have found that the ratio is an unending decimal, 3.14159265358979323846264... so an approximation has to be used for this ratio.

1. A: **3.14** B: **3.1428....** C: **3.14**
   The quotient is always approximately the same.

Rewrite the formula given here as $C = \pi d$. Tell your student that C stands for circumference and d for the length of the diameter. This is a mathematical formula, where the letters

$C = \pi d$

stand for specific measurements, and relates C to d. For any value of d, there is only one value for C. Since we can only approximate π, C will be an approximation too.

Ask your student for a formula for the circumference using the radius instead of the diameter. Since the diameter is twice the radius, we can write this as $d = 2r$. So $C = \pi 2r$. Tell your student that even though π is not an unknown value, as r is, since it always stands for the same value we still write it after the whole number in formulas like this. $C = 2\pi r$

$C = 2\pi r$

Learning Tasks 2-8, US› pp. 27-29, 3d› pp. 11-13

2. **188.4** cm
3. **157** cm
4. **88** cm
5. $C = \pi \times 70$ cm $= \frac{22}{7} \times 70$ cm $=$ **220 cm**
6. $D = 2 \times 4$ m $= 8$ m
   $C = \pi \times 8$ m $= 3.14 \times 8$ m $=$ **25.12 m**

7. (a) $\pi \times 49$ cm $= \frac{22}{7} \times 49$ cm $=$ **154 cm**
   (b) $\pi \times 28$ cm $= \frac{22}{7} \times 28$ cm $=$ **88 cm**
   (c) $\pi \times 14$ cm $= \frac{22}{7} \times 14$ cm $=$ **44 m**

8. (a) $\pi \times 10$ m $= 3.14 \times 10$ m $=$ **31.4 m**
   (b) $\pi \times 6$ cm $= 3.14 \times 6$ cm $=$ **18.84 cm**
   (c) $\pi \times 12$ m $= 3.14 \times 12$ m $=$ **37.68 m**

US› Workbook Exercise 10 **3d› Workbook Exercise 2**

(B) Perimeter

- Find the perimeter of a semicircle and quarter circle and related shapes.
- Find the perimeter of a compound shape make up of rectangles, triangles, semicircles, and/or quarter circles.

A common error when finding the perimeter of a semicircle or quarter circle is to forget to add in the length of the straight sides.

You can use P to stand for Perimeter.

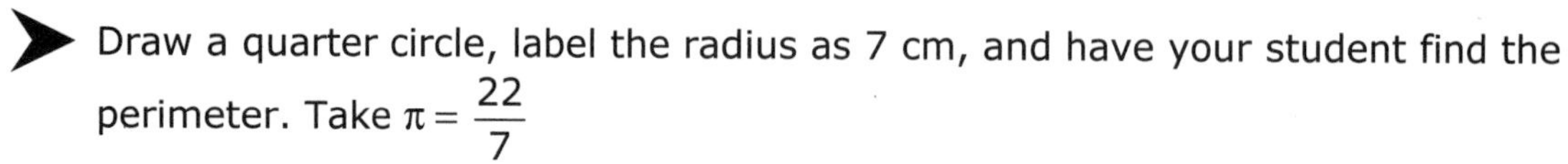

Draw a quarter circle, label the radius as 7 cm, and have your student find the perimeter. Take $\pi = \frac{22}{7}$

$$P = \frac{1}{4} \times C + (2 \times \text{the radius})$$

$$= \left(\frac{1}{\cancel{4}_{\cancel{2}_1}} \times \frac{\cancel{22}^{11}}{\cancel{7}_1} \times \cancel{14}^{\cancel{2}^1} \text{ cm} \right) + (2 \times 7 \text{ cm}) = 11 \text{ cm} + 14 \text{ cm} = 25 \text{ cm}$$

7 cm

Learning Task 9-11, US› p. 29, 3d› p. 13

9. $P = \frac{1}{2}C + d = (\frac{1}{2} \times 3.14 \times 4 \text{ m}) + 4 \text{ m} = 6.28 \text{ m} + 4 \text{ m} = \mathbf{10.28 \text{ m}}$

10. Length $= 3 \times \frac{1}{2}$ the circumference of a circle with diameter 10 cm

$$= 3 \times \frac{1}{2} \times \pi \times 10 \text{ cm} = 15 \text{ cm} \times \pi = \mathbf{15\pi \text{ cm}}$$

11. The two semicircles make a whole circle.
Perimeter = circumference of the circle + the two sides of the rectangle

$$= (\frac{22}{7} \times 14 \text{ cm}) + (2 \times 30 \text{ cm}) = 44 \text{ cm} + 60 \text{ cm} = \mathbf{104 \text{ cm}}$$

US› Workbook Exercise 11 **3d› Workbook Exercise 3**

Practice (US> p. 30, 3d> p. 14)

US> Practice 2A, p. 30   3d> Practice 1A, p. 14

1. $C = \pi \times d = 3.14 \times 20 \text{ cm} = \mathbf{62.8 \text{ cm}}$

2. $C = \pi \times 2 \times r = \frac{22}{7} \times 2 \times 35 \text{ cm} = \mathbf{220 \text{ cm}}$

3. $C = \pi \times d = 3.14 \times 23 \text{ cm} = 72.22 \text{ cm} \approx \mathbf{72.2 \text{ cm}}$

4. The diameter is 8 cm.
   $C = 3.14 \times 8 \text{ cm} = \mathbf{25.12 \text{ cm}}$

5. Length $= 4 \times$ half the circumference of a circle of diameter 14 cm
   $= 4 \times \frac{1}{2} \times \frac{22}{7} \times 14 \text{ cm} = \mathbf{88 \text{ cm}}$

6. The perimeter is half the circumference of the larger circle plus half the circumference of the two smaller circles. The two smaller circles together make a whole circle.
   $P = (\frac{1}{2} \times \pi \times 20 \text{ cm}) + (\pi \times 10 \text{ cm}) = (10 \text{ cm} \times \pi) + (10 \text{ cm} \times \pi) = \mathbf{20\pi \text{ cm}}$

Part 3 – Area (US› pp. 31-35, 3d› pp. 15-19)

(A) Area of a Circle

- Relate the area of a circle to its radius.
- Find the area of a circle given its diameter.

The formula that is commonly used for area of a circle is

$A = \pi r^2$

Where A is area and r is the radius.

A common error to watch out for is using the diameter rather than the radius in this formula when the diameter, instead of the radius, is given in the problem.

US› page 31, 3d› page 15
Learning Task 1, US› pp. 32-33, 3d› pp. 16-17

If your student is a "hands-on" type, she may want to do task 1. There is a circle in the appendix divided into 24 equal parts that you can copy, cut out, and use.

The figure formed is almost a rectangle. The smaller the sections, the straighter the sides will be. The area of the rectangle will be the same as the area of the circle.

Using r for radius, the length of the rectangle is $\frac{1}{2} \times 2 \times \pi \times r$ and the width is r. The area of the rectangle is length $\times$ width.

Area of the rectangle $= (\frac{1}{2} \times 2 \times \pi \times r) \times r = \pi \times r \times r$.

Remind your student (from *Primary Mathematics 6A*) that we can write $r \times r$ as r^2. So the formula for the area of a circle is

$A = \pi r^2$, where A is the Area and r is the radius

After your student determines the area of the circle at the end of task 1, tell her that she can use estimation to quickly check if her answer is reasonable, using 3 for π.

Area of circle $= 3.14 \times 10$ cm $\times 10$ cm $=$ **314** cm^2

Estimated area $= 3 \times 10 \times 10 = 300$

Learning Tasks 2-7, US› pp. 33-34, 3d› pp. 17-18

2. **616** cm^2
3. **50.24** cm^2
4. $A = \frac{22}{7} \times 7 \times 7 = \mathbf{154\ m^2}$

   Estimation: $3 \times 7 \times 7 = 3 \times 49 \approx 3 \times 50 = 150$
5. $A = 3.14 \times 6\text{ m} \times 6\text{ m} = \mathbf{113.04\ m^2}$
6. (a) $\frac{22}{7} \times 14\text{ cm} \times 14\text{ cm} = \mathbf{616\ cm^2}$

   Estimation: $3 \times 10 \times 20 = 600$ (rounding one up and one down will give a closer estimation.

   (b) $\frac{22}{7} \times 21\text{ cm} \times 21\text{ cm} = \mathbf{1386\ cm^2}$

   Estimation: $3 \times 20 \times 20 = 1200$

   (c) $\frac{22}{7} \times 14\text{ m} \times 14\text{ m} = \mathbf{616\ m^2}$
7. (a) $3.14 \times 3\text{ cm} \times 3\text{ cm} = \mathbf{28.26\ cm^2}$

   (b) $3.14 \times 5\text{ cm} \times 5\text{ cm} = \mathbf{78.5\ cm^2}$

   (c) $3.14 \times 8\text{ cm} \times 8\text{ cm} = \mathbf{200.96\ m^2}$

US› Workbook Exercise 12 **3d› Workbook Exercise 4**

(B) Area of Semicircles and Quarter Circles

- Find the area of a semicircle or quarter circle.
- Find the area of a circle given its diameter.
- Find the area of compound figures made up of semicircles and quarter circles.

Learning Tasks 8-10, US pp. 34-35, 3d pp. 18-19

8. (a) Radius = 6 cm

$$\text{Area} = \frac{1}{2} \times \pi \times 6 \text{ cm} \times 6 \text{ cm}$$
$$= \frac{1}{2} \times 3.14 \times 36 \text{ cm}$$
$$= \mathbf{56.52 \text{ cm}^2}$$

(b) Radius = 10 cm

$$\text{Area} = \frac{1}{2} \times \pi \times 10 \text{ cm} \times 10 \text{ cm}$$
$$= \frac{1}{2} \times 3.14 \times 100 \text{ cm}$$
$$= \mathbf{157 \text{ cm}^2}$$

9. (a)

$$\text{Area} = \frac{1}{4} \times \pi \times 2 \text{ m} \times 2 \text{ m}$$
$$= \frac{1}{4} \times 3.14 \times 4 \text{ m}$$
$$= \mathbf{3.14 \text{ m}^2}$$

(b)

$$\text{Area} = \frac{1}{4} \times \pi \times 10 \text{ cm} \times 10 \text{ cm}$$
$$= \frac{1}{4} \times 3.14 \times 100 \text{ cm}$$
$$= \mathbf{78.5 \text{ cm}^2}$$

10. (a) The shaded area consists of 4 quarter circles, which together make one whole circle. The radius is 6 cm.
Area $= \pi \times 6 \text{ cm} \times 6 \text{ cm} = 3.14 \times 36 \text{ cm} =$ **113.04 cm²**

(b) The shaded area consists of 4 quarter circles, which together make one whole circle. The radius is 3 m.
Area $= \pi \times 3 \text{ m} \times 3 \text{ m} = 3.14 \times 9 \text{ m} =$ **28.26 m²**

US› Workbook Exercises 13-14 **3d› Workbook Exercises 5-6**

(C) Area of Compound Figures

- Find the area of a compound figure made up of rectangles, triangles, semicircles, and/or quarter circles.

Learning Tasks 11-12, US p. 35, 3d pp. 19

11. Area = area of semicircle + area of rectangle + area of triangle

$$= (\frac{1}{2} \times 3.14 \times 10 \text{ m} \times 10 \text{ m}) + (50 \text{ m} \times 20 \text{ m}) + (\frac{1}{2} \times 10 \text{ m} \times 20 \text{ m})$$
$$= 157 \text{ m}^2 + 1000 \text{ m}^2 + 100 \text{ m}^2$$
$$= \mathbf{1257 \text{ m}^2}$$

12. Area = area of large semicircle of radius 2 cm − area of small semicircle of radius 1 cm

$$= (\frac{1}{2} \times \pi \times 2 \text{ cm} \times 2 \text{ cm}) - (\frac{1}{2} \times \pi \times 1 \text{ cm} \times 1 \text{ cm})$$
$$= (2 \text{ cm}^2 \times \pi) - (\frac{1}{2} \text{ cm}^2 \times \pi) = \mathbf{1\frac{1}{2}\pi \text{ cm}^2}$$

US› Workbook Exercises 15-16 **3d› Workbook Exercises 7-8**

Practice (US› pp. 36-37, 3d› pp. 20-21)

US› Practice 2B, p. 36 **3d› Practice 1B, p. 20**

1. Area $= \pi \times 6$ cm $\times 6$ cm $= 3.14 \times 36$ cm^2 = **113.04 cm^2**

2. Radius = 14 m

   Area $= \pi \times 14$ m $\times 14$ m $= \frac{22}{7} \times 14$ m $\times 14$ m = **616 m^2**

3. (a) Circumference $= \pi \times 4$ cm $= 3.14 \times 4$ cm = **12.56 cm**

   (b) Radius = 2 cm
   Area $= \pi \times 2$ cm $\times 2$ cm $= 3.14 \times 2$ cm $\times 2$ cm = **12.56 cm^2**

4. Radius = 1 m

   Area $= \frac{1}{2} \times \pi \times 1$ m $\times 1$ m $= \frac{1}{2}$ m$^2 \times 3.14$ = **1.57 m^2**

5. Area $= \frac{1}{4} \times \pi \times 10$ in. $\times 10$ in. $= \frac{1}{4} \times 3.14 \times 100$ in.^{2} = **78.5 in.^{2}**
   (**3d›** in.^{2} = cm^2)

6. The diameter of the circle is the same as the side of the square. If the area of the square is 36 cm^2, then its side is 6 cm, and the radius of the circle is 3 cm.
   Area $= \pi \times 3$ cm $\times 3$ cm $= 3.14 \times 9$ cm^2 = **28.26 cm^2**
   Circumference $= \pi \times 6$ cm $= 3.14 \times 6$ cm = **18.84 cm**

7. The four quarter circles make a whole circle.

   Area $= \pi \times 7$ cm $\times 7$ cm $= \frac{22}{7} \times 7$ cm $\times 7$ cm = **154 cm^2**

US> Practice 2C, p. 37   3d> Practice 1C, p. 21

1. (a) Area = area of square + area of two circles

$= (14 \text{ cm} \times 14 \text{ cm}) + (2 \times \frac{22}{7} \times 7 \text{ cm} \times 7 \text{ cm})$

$= 196 \text{ cm}^2 + 308 \text{ cm}^2 = \mathbf{504\ cm^2}$

(b) Perimeter = circumference of two circles

$= 2 \times \frac{22}{7} \times 14 \text{ cm} = \mathbf{88\ cm}$

2. Area = area of semicircle with radius 5 m + area of triangle

$= (\frac{1}{2} \times 3.14 \times 5 \text{ m} \times 5 \text{ m}) + (\frac{1}{2} \times 6 \text{ m} \times 8 \text{ m})$

$= 39.25 \text{ m}^2 + 24 \text{ m}^2 = \mathbf{63.25\ m^2}$

Perimeter = half the circumference + the two sides of the triangle

$= (\frac{1}{2} \times 3.14 \times 10 \text{ m}) + 6 \text{ m} + 8 \text{ m} = 15.7 \text{ m} + 14 \text{ m} = \mathbf{29.7\ m}$

3. Area = area of square − area of semicircle

$= (8 \text{ cm} \times 8 \text{ cm}) - (\frac{1}{2} \times 3.14 \times 4 \text{ cm} \times 4 \text{ cm})$

$= 64 \text{ cm}^2 - 25.12 \text{ cm}^2 = \mathbf{38.88\ cm^2}$

Perimeter = length of 3 sides of the square + half the circumference

$= (3 \times 8 \text{ cm}) + (\frac{1}{2} \times 3.14 \times 8 \text{ cm}) = 24 \text{ cm} + 12.56 \text{ cm} = \mathbf{36.56\ cm}$

4. Area = area of quarter circle with radius 2 m + area of circle with radius 1 m

$= (\frac{1}{4} \times \pi \times 2 \text{ m} \times 2 \text{ m}) + (\pi \times 1 \text{ m} \times 1 \text{ m}) = \pi \text{ m}^2 + \pi \text{ m}^2 = \mathbf{2\pi\ m^2}$

Perimeter = a quarter the circumference of circle with diameter 4 m
+ circumference of circle with diameter 2 m

$= (\frac{1}{4} \times \pi \times 4 \text{ m}) + (\pi \times 2 \text{ m}) = \pi + 2\pi = \mathbf{3\pi\ m}$

5. Area = area of large circle with radius 4 cm
− area of small circle with radius 2 cm

$= (\pi \times 4 \text{ cm} \times 4 \text{ cm}) - (\pi \times 2 \text{ cm} \times 2 \text{ cm}) = 16\pi \text{ cm}^2 - 4\pi \text{ cm}^2 = \mathbf{12\pi\ cm^2}$

US› Unit 3 3d› Unit 2
Graphs

Part 1 – Pie Charts (US› pp. 38-41, 3d› pp. 22-25)

(A) Pie Charts

- Understand pie charts.
- Read and interpret pie charts with data given as whole numbers.

A pie chart is used to show the composition of a set of data such that each component is represented as part of a whole. The data are represented by the proportional parts of a circle.

Three forms of pie charts are introduced in this unit; ones that display numbers, (e.g., learning task 1), ones that display fractions (e.g., p. 22), and ones that display percentages (e.g., learning task 5).

Although it is not specifically taught here, you may want to include a lesson on how to use degrees to construct pie charts. A whole circle is 360°. Once the fraction of the whole is found for each piece of data, we can multiply that fraction by 360° to find the central angle used for that component on the pie chart. So for the pie chart on p. 38 (**3d›** p. 22), we can use the fractions to determine what their central angle is so that we can construct a pie chart.

Size S: $\frac{1}{4} \times 360° = 90°$ Size M: $\frac{1}{2} \times 360° = 180°$

Size XL: $\frac{1}{12} \times 360° = 30°$ Size L: $\frac{1}{6} \times 360° = 60°$

US› p. 33, 3d› p. 22

Discuss this page. Make sure your student understands how to get from the information in the table to the data in the pie chart. To get the fractions, we find the part out of the whole. Your student should see that the circle represents the whole, which is the total number of shirts sold.

$$\frac{1}{4} + \frac{1}{2} + \frac{1}{12} + \frac{1}{6} = 1$$

Point out that the lines bordering the section representing $\frac{1}{4}$ make a right angle at the center.

Make two copies of the fraction circle chart in the appendix.

Have your student make a table containing information showing approximately how many hours he spends on certain activities during the day. For example, 8 hours for sleeping, 6 hours for school, etc. Have about 4-6 activities totaling 24 hours.

Then have him express the time spent for each activity as a fraction of the day. Have him show the fractions on the fraction circle chart. For example, make a section $\frac{1}{3}$ of the circle and label it "Sleep, $\frac{1}{3}$".

Have him make another pie chart showing the original data. The lines on the chart will be the same, but instead of one section marked as "Sleep, $\frac{1}{3}$", it will be marked as "Sleep, 8 h". Ask him to compare the charts and tell you what information we can get from each chart and under what circumstances we might want to show numbers versus fractions.

Learning Tasks 1-2, US› p. 39, 3d› p. 23

1. (a) **plastic**
   (b) $200 - 80 - 30 - 40 = \mathbf{50}$
   (c) $\frac{80}{200} = \mathbf{\frac{2}{5}}$
   (d) $\frac{80}{40} = \mathbf{2}$

2. (a) The angle at the center for the games is 90°, which is $\mathbf{\frac{1}{4}}$ of the total.
   (b) $\frac{1}{4} \longrightarrow \$3000$ (handcraft)
   $1 \longrightarrow \$3000 \times 4 = \mathbf{\$12,000}$
   (c) $\$12,000 - (2 \times \$3000) - \$4800 = \mathbf{\$1200}$
   (d) $4800 : 3000 = \mathbf{8 : 5}$

Have your student find the fraction of the total for each item in these two graphs, redraw them (roughly) and write in the fractions (or write in pencil on the text page). The fractions should add up to 1.

US› Workbook Exercise 17 **3d› Workbook Exercise 9**

(B) Fraction Pie Charts

➢ Read and interpret pie charts with data given as fractions.

Learning Tasks 3-4, US› p. 40, 3d› p. 24

3. (a) US› **toast** 3d› **bread**
   (b) $1-\frac{3}{5}-\frac{1}{4}-\frac{1}{10}=\frac{20}{20}-\frac{12}{20}-\frac{5}{20}-\frac{2}{20}=\mathbf{\frac{1}{20}}$
   (c) $\frac{3}{5}\times 40=\mathbf{24}$
   (d) $\frac{1}{4}=\mathbf{25\%}$
4. (a) $\mathbf{\frac{1}{2}}$
   (b) $\frac{1}{4}=\mathbf{25\%}$
   (c) $\frac{1}{4}-\frac{1}{8}=\mathbf{\frac{1}{8}}$
   (d) $\frac{1}{2}\longrightarrow 1{,}200$
   $\frac{1}{4}\longrightarrow 1{,}200\div 2=\mathbf{600}$

Have your student find the percentage of the total for each item in these two graphs, redraw them (roughly), and write in the fractions (or write in pencil on the text page). The percentages should add up to 100%.

US› Workbook Exercise 18 **3d› Workbook Exercise 10**

(C) Percentage Pie Charts

➢ Read and interpret pie charts with data given as percentages.

Copy the percentage circle chart in the appendix. Have your student collect some data involving 4-5 items. For example, you could give her a handful of coins and have her record the number of each coin. Have her express the percentage for each item. The total percentage should be 100%.

Have her draw a pie chart showing the percentages for each item. Use the percentage pie chart at the back of the book, or have her construct a chart by converting the percentages into angles. The whole circle represents 100%, or 360°.

Learning Tasks 5-6, US› p. 41, 3d› p. 25

5. (a) **swimming**

   (b) $100\% - 30\% - 20\% - 35\% = \mathbf{15\%}$

   (c) $\frac{30}{100} \times 200 = \mathbf{60}$

   (d) $35\% = \frac{35}{100} = \mathbf{\frac{7}{20}}$

6. (a) US› **shirts** 3d› **blouses**

   (b) $50\% - 15\% = \mathbf{35\%}$

   (c) $50\% - 20\% = \mathbf{30\%}$

   (d) $30\% \rightarrow \$60$

   $100\% \rightarrow \$\frac{60}{30} \times 100 = \mathbf{\$200}$

US› Workbook Exercise 19 **3d› Workbook Exercise 11**

Review (US› pp. 42-53, 3d› pp. 26-37)

Reviews in *Primary Mathematics* cover material from all previous levels. Reviews are particularly important in Primary Mathematics 6B since students are finishing up their primary education in preparation for more advanced mathematics. These reviews will allow you to see if your student is weak in any topic.

You may wish to have your student work through all four reviews (two in the text and two in the workbook) now, or you can to assign a page of review daily for more continuous review as you proceed with the next units.

The reviews in the text tend to be a bit more challenging than the reviews in the workbook, and the problems can be good opportunities for discussion of concepts and solutions. If your student has difficulty with a problem, have him explain his reasoning and approach before simply giving him the correct answers so that you can see exactly what type of misunderstanding he has.

There are usually several methods to solve a problem. The solutions in this guide show only one or two methods. The method shown may not be the best method for your student – for example, sometimes a fraction method is shown as an example on an easier problem, and sometimes a bar method, which is normally the best method. Don't assume the method shown is *the* required method for the problem. Your student may find a different, valid way to solve some of the problems. You can compare and discuss different methods.

Review A, (US pp. 42-47, 3d› pp. 26-31)

1. **Two million, three hundred forty thousand**
2. **0.57**
3. **2**
4. **7** $(7 \times 17 = 119)$
5. **0.09, 0.123, 0.25, 0.5**
6. **5.59 kg**
7. $0.125 = \frac{125}{1000} = \mathbf{\frac{1}{8}}$
8. $\mathbf{\frac{3}{8}}$
9. **2**

US› 10.

$$\frac{2}{9} \div \left(\frac{4}{9} + \frac{2}{3}\right) \times \frac{7}{8} = \frac{2}{9} \div \left(\frac{4}{9} + \frac{6}{9}\right) \times \frac{7}{8}$$
$$= \frac{2}{9} \div \frac{10}{9} \times \frac{7}{8}$$
$$= \frac{\overset{1}{2}}{\cancel{9}_1} \times \frac{\overset{1}{\cancel{9}}}{10} \times \frac{7}{\cancel{8}_4}$$
$$= \mathbf{\frac{7}{40}}$$

3d› 10. **21.49**

11. **600.93**

12. **41.86**

13. $\underline{15 \div 3} + (\underline{9-6}) \times 4 = 5 + \underline{3 \times 4} = \underline{5+12} = \mathbf{17}$

14. **35,000**

15. **67.5**

16. (a) $1\frac{1}{3}$ h $= 1\frac{1}{3} \times 60$ min $= 60$ min $+ 20$ min $=$ **80 min**

    (b) 0.02 kg $= 0.02 \times 1{,}000$ g $=$ **20 g**

17. 2 ℓ = 2000 ml
    $\frac{2000}{250} = 8$
    8 packets are needed
    (**3d›** packets → cartons)

18. 3 boxes → \$20
    30 boxes → \$20 × 10 = \$200
    She received **\$200**.
    (**3d›** boxes → jars)

19. 1 unit = blue marbles
    2 units = 72 − 20 = 52
    1 unit = 52 ÷ 2 = 26
    There were **26** blue marbles.

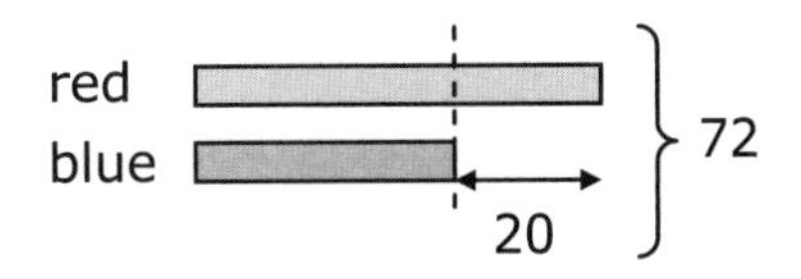

20. 5 mangoes weigh 2 kg − 0.4 kg = 1.6 kg
    Average weight $= \frac{1.6}{5}$ kg $=$ **0.32 kg**

21. Jane's weight = 36 kg + 4 kg = 40 kg
    Average weight $= \frac{36+40}{2} = \frac{76}{2} = \mathbf{38\ kg}$

22. Total weight of 3 boys = 35.6 × 3 = 106.8 kg
    Weight of 2 boys = 106.8 − 34.8 = 72
    Average weight of 2 boys $= \frac{72}{2} = \mathbf{36\ kg}$

23. Fraction left $= 1 - \frac{2}{5} - \frac{1}{4} = \frac{20}{20} - \frac{8}{20} - \frac{5}{20} = \mathbf{\frac{7}{20}}$

24. Since $\frac{1}{3}$ of the girls can swim, and girls are $\frac{1}{3}$ of all the students, divide each third into thirds. Swimmers are 4 out of 9 units. So the fraction of students that can swim is $\mathbf{\frac{4}{9}}$.

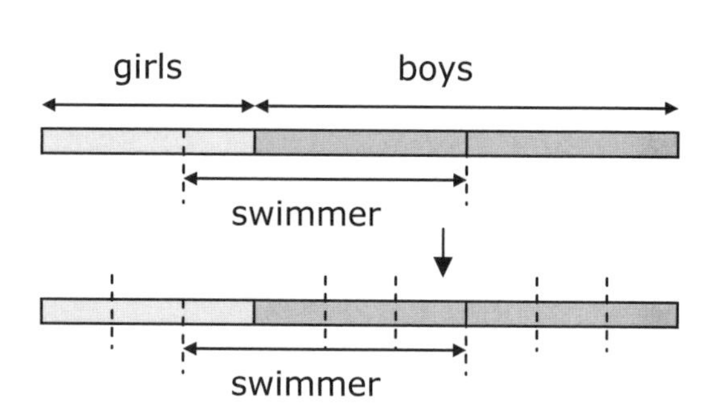

OR:

Fraction of students who are girls that can swim $= \frac{1}{3} \times \frac{1}{3} = \frac{1}{9}$

Fraction of students that are boys $= 1 - \frac{1}{3} = \frac{2}{3}$

Fraction of students who are boys that can swim $= \frac{1}{2} \times \frac{2}{3} = \frac{1}{3}$

Fraction of students that can swim $= \frac{1}{9} + \frac{1}{3} = \frac{1}{9} + \frac{3}{9} = \frac{4}{9}$

25. 5 units = \$50
1 unit = \$10
2 units = \$20
He had **\$20** left

book
money left
Radio = \$50

OR:

Fraction spent on radio $= 1 - \frac{1}{8} - \frac{1}{4} = \frac{5}{8}$

$\frac{5}{8} \longrightarrow \$50$

$\frac{1}{8} \longrightarrow \$50 \div 5 = \$10$

$\frac{2}{8} \longrightarrow \$10 \times 2 = \$20$

or: $50 \div \frac{5}{8} = 50 \times \frac{8}{5} = \$80$ = all his money

$\frac{1}{4} \times \$80 = \$20$ = money he had left

26. $3 \text{ units} = 270$

$4 \text{ units} = \frac{270}{3} \times 4 = 360$

There are **360** girls.

270
boys
girls

27. $9 \text{ units} = 36$
$1 \text{ unit} = 36 \div 9 = 4$
There are **4** more boys than girls.

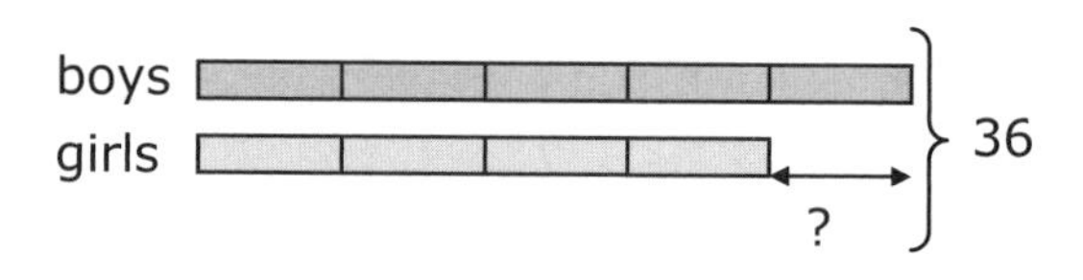

28. Fraction of stamps that is Canadian, $= 1 - \frac{3}{4} = \frac{1}{4}$

    Percentage of stamps that are Canadian = **25%**
    (**3d›** Canadian → Malaysian)

29. Amount of increase = $250 – $200 = $50

    Percent increase $= \frac{50}{200} \times 100\% =$ **25%**

30. Amount of discount = 30% of $40 $= \frac{3}{10} \times \$40 = \$12$

    Selling price = $40 – $12 = **$28**

31. Distance = Speed × Time = 60 km/h × 2 h = **120 km**

32. Cost for Thursday and Friday = $50 × 2 = $100
    Cost for Saturday and Sunday = $70 × 2 = $140
    Total cost = $100 + $140 = **$240**

33. John bought 3 more books than Peter. Together they bought 11 books.
    3 books cost $1.95.
    1 book costs $1.95 ÷ 3 = $0.65
    11 books cost $0.65 × 11 = **$7.15**

34.

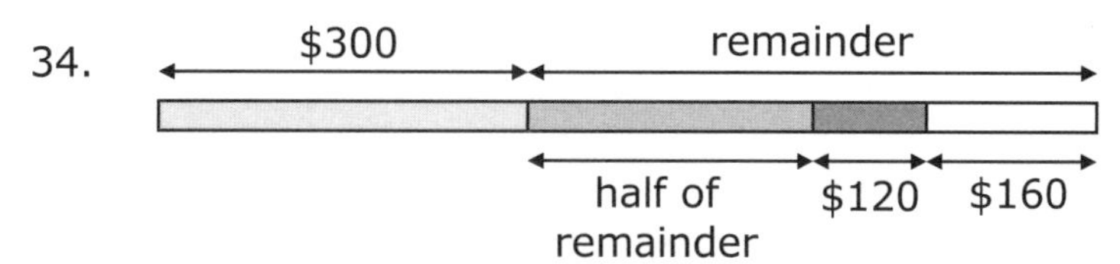

Half of remainder = $120 + $160 = $280
Remainder = $280 × 2 = $560
Salary = $300 + $560 = **$860**

35. $\frac{3}{4} \longrightarrow \$1800$

    $\frac{4}{4} \longrightarrow \$\frac{1800}{3} \times 4 = \$2400$

    $\frac{2}{5} \longrightarrow \frac{2}{5} \times \$2400 =$ **$960**

36. **US›** **3d›**
    Tyrone Gopal
    Ryan Raju

    Tyrone Gopal
    Ryan Raju

    The new ratio will be **3 : 4**

37. She saves 60% of the remainder.
The remainder is 30%.

60% of $30\% = \frac{6}{10} \times 30\% = 18\%$

18% of the salary is $360.

$18\% \longrightarrow \$360$

$100\% \longrightarrow \$\frac{360}{18} \times 100 = \$2000$

Her monthly salary is **$2000**.

38.

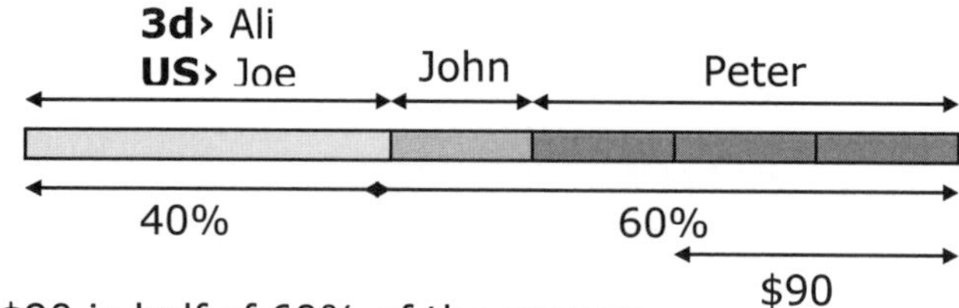

$90 is half of 60% of the money.

$30\% \longrightarrow \$90$

$40\% \longrightarrow \$\frac{90}{30} \times 40 = \$120$

Joe receives **$120**.

39. $\frac{2}{5}$ of the trip $= 30$ km

All of the trip $= \frac{30}{2} \times 5 = 75$ km

Total time $= 6$ h

Average speed $= \frac{75 \text{ km}}{6 \text{ h}}$ $=$ **12.5 km/h**

4 h   2 h 30 min

40. (a)

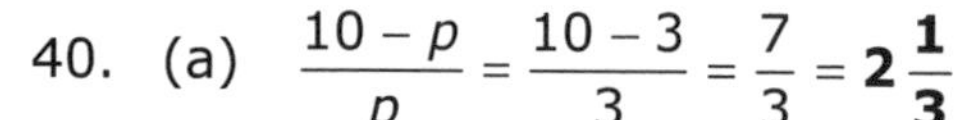

$\frac{10 - p}{p} = \frac{10 - 3}{3} = \frac{7}{3} = \mathbf{2\frac{1}{3}}$

(b) $5p^2 - 9 = (5 \times 3 \times 3) - 9$
$= 45 - 9$
$= \mathbf{36}$

41. Total weight of 3 boxes $= 3x$ kg
Total weight of 2 boxes $= (3x - 2)$ kg

Average weight of 2 boxes $= \mathbf{\frac{3x - 2}{2}}$ **kg**

42. Perimeter of triangle $= 12 + 14 + 10 = 36$ cm
Side of square $= 36 \div 4 = 9$ cm
Area of square $= 9 \times 9 =$ **81 cm²**

43. Perimeter $= (\frac{1}{2} \times 3.14 \times 10 \text{ cm}) + (3 \times 10 \text{ cm}) = 15.7 \text{ cm} + 30 \text{ cm} =$ **45.7 cm**

44. **D** does not have a line of symmetry. (A has a vertical line of symmetry, B has one going from top left to bottom right corner, C has a horizontal one.

45. 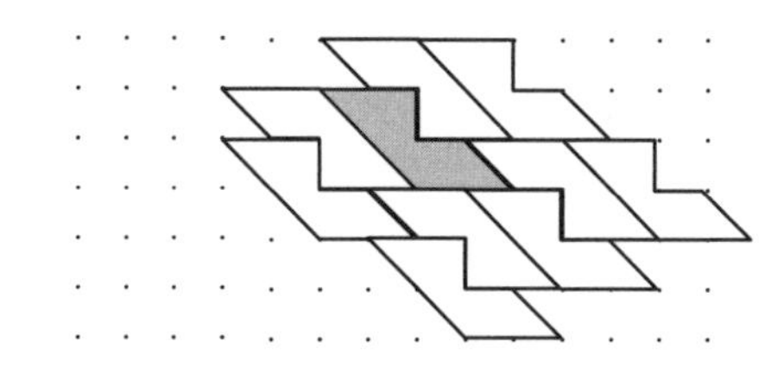

46. (a) **Thursday** (b) $\frac{40-38}{40} \times 100\% = \mathbf{5\%}$

(c) Total pupils $= 40 + 37 + 36 + 34 + 38 = 185$

Average attendance $= \frac{185}{5} = \mathbf{37}$

47. (a) $50\% - 20\% - 12\% = \mathbf{18\%}$

(b) $\frac{20}{100} = \mathbf{\frac{1}{5}}$

(c) $12\% \longrightarrow 18$

$100\% \longrightarrow \frac{18}{12} \times 100 = \mathbf{150}$

 **Review B, US› 48-53, 3d› pp. 32-37**

1. **4**
2. **1000**
3. (a) **10,000** (b) **0.06**
4. **36**
5. **2.53**
6. **9.009**
7. $\frac{1}{2}$ of $\frac{2}{3} = \mathbf{\frac{1}{3}}$
8. **1000**
9. (a) $0.048 = \frac{48}{1000} = \mathbf{\frac{6}{125}}$ (b) $36\% = \frac{36}{100} = \mathbf{\frac{9}{25}}$

10. $\frac{31}{20}$ is greater than 1; all the others are less than 1.

$\frac{12}{25}$ is less than $\frac{1}{2}$; the other two are greater than $\frac{1}{2}$.

$\frac{62}{100} = \frac{31}{50}$; $\frac{3}{5} = \frac{30}{50}$

In order: $\mathbf{\frac{12}{25}, \frac{3}{5}, \frac{62}{100}, \frac{31}{20}}$

11. (a) $64 - (\underline{24 - 18}) \times 10$
$= 64 - \underline{6 \times 10}$
$= \underline{64 - 60}$
$= \mathbf{4}$

3d› (b) $8 + \underline{16 \div 2} \times 4$
$= 8 + \underline{8 \times 4}$
$= 8 + 32$
$= \mathbf{40}$

US› (b) $\frac{3}{10} + \frac{1}{6} \div \left(\frac{5}{6} - \frac{4}{5}\right)$
$= \frac{3}{10} + \frac{1}{6} \div \underline{\left(\frac{25}{30} - \frac{24}{30}\right)}$
$= \frac{3}{10} + \underline{\frac{1}{6} \div \frac{1}{30}}$
$= \frac{3}{10} + \frac{1}{6} \times 30$
$= \frac{3}{10} + 5$
$= \mathbf{5\frac{3}{10}}$

12. **100**

13. 10:15 a.m. to 12:00 noon is 1 h 45 min.
12:00 noon to 9:30 p.m. is 9 h 30 min.
The shop is open 1 h 45 min + 9 h 30 min = **11 h 15 min**

14. $\frac{3}{4}\ \ell \longrightarrow$ 4 glasses

$1\ \ell \longrightarrow \frac{4}{3} \times 4$ glasses

$3\ \ell \longrightarrow \frac{4}{3} \times 4 \times 3 =$ **16** glasses

4 glasses

15. 1 kg 300 g − 450 g = 1300 g − 450 g = **850 g**
Or: 1 kg 300 g − 450 g = 1 kg − 450 g + 300 g = 550g + 300 g = 850 g

16. $2 $\longrightarrow$ 5 oranges

$24 $\longrightarrow \frac{5}{2} \times 24 =$ **60** oranges

17. $40 $\longrightarrow$ 1

$350 $\longrightarrow \frac{1}{40} \times 350 = 8.75$

She will get **8** of them.

18. Number of post cards $= \frac{4.80}{0.30} =$ **16**

19. Total of 3 numbers $= 45 \times 3 = 135$
Total of 2 of the numbers $= 47 \times 2 = 94$
Third number $= 135 - 94 =$ **41**

20. 8 ℓ $\longrightarrow$ 1 min

200 ℓ $\longrightarrow \frac{1}{8} \times 200 = 25$ min

It will take **25** min to fill the tank. (**3d›** gal → ℓ)

21. Fraction left $= \frac{1}{3} \times \frac{1}{2} = \mathbf{\frac{1}{6}}$

22. The remainder is $\frac{3}{4}$. $\frac{1}{2}$ of the remainder $= \frac{1}{2}$ of $\frac{3}{4} = \frac{1}{2} \times \frac{3}{4} = \frac{3}{8}$

Fraction spent $= \frac{1}{4} + \frac{3}{8} = \frac{2}{8} + \frac{3}{8} = \mathbf{\frac{5}{8}}$

23. (a) **12** (x 4) (b) **7** (÷ 7)

24. 12 units = 60

1 unit $= \frac{60}{12}$

7 units $= \frac{60}{12} \times 7 = 35$

The longest piece is **35 yd**.
(**3d›** yd → m)

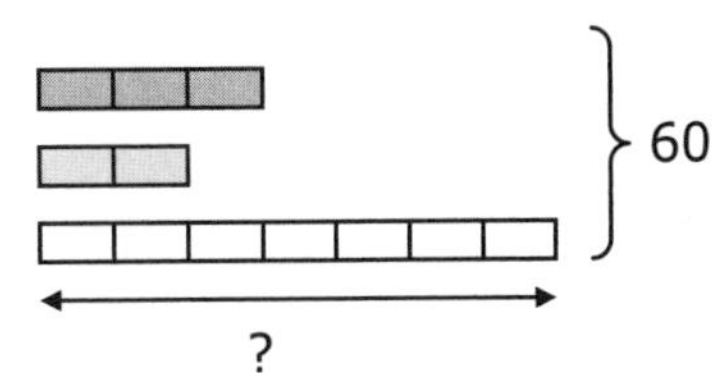

25. Amount of increase $= 2800 - 2500 = 300$

Percentage increase $= \frac{300}{2500} \times 100\% =$ **12%**

26. Total number of stamps $= 600 + 200 = 800$

    Percentage of stamps that are Singapore stamps $= \frac{600}{800} \times 100\% =$ **75%**

27. 15% of $\$30 = \frac{15}{100} \times 30 =$ **$4.50**

28. Average speed $= \frac{50\text{ m}}{40\text{ s}} = \frac{5}{4}$ m / s $=$ **1.25 m/s**

29. Total stickers $= 130 + 50 = 180$
    3 units $= 180$
    1 unit $= 180 \div 3 = 60$
    Kara (Devi) had 50 and ended up with 60, so Jack (Samy) gave her **10** stickers.

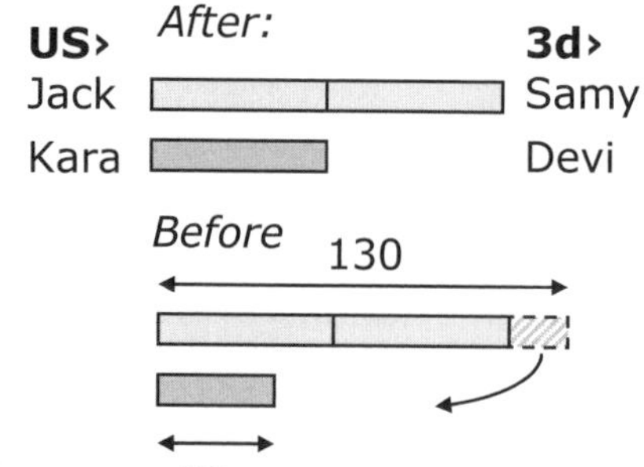

30. Number sold at 3 for $\$2 = \frac{3}{5} \times 100 = 60$

    $3 \longrightarrow \$2$
    $60 \longrightarrow \$2 \times 20 = \$40$
    Remainder $= 40$ cards
    $40 \times \$0.75 = \$30$
    Total money $= \$40 + \$30 = \$70$
    Amount of money he made $= \$70 - \$60 =$ **$10**

31. 1 unit $= 24$
    2 units $= 48 =$ remainder
    $\frac{1}{3}$ of remainder $= \frac{1}{3} \times 48 = 16$
    There are **16** yellow beads.

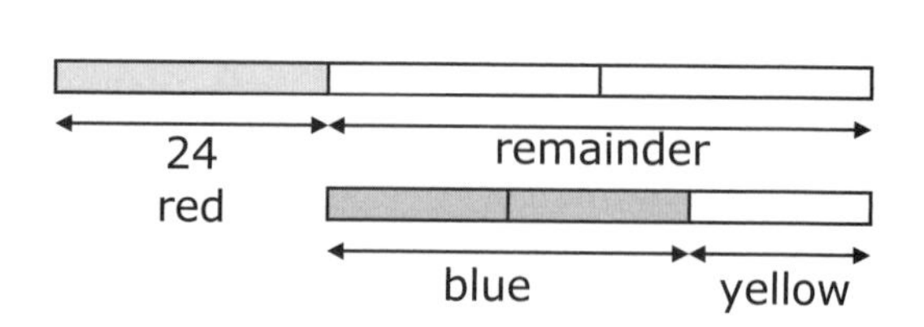

32. The number of boys does not change.

	boys : girls	
before	1 : 1	= 4 : 4
after	4 : 3	= 4 : 3

    The number of girls is reduced by 1 unit.
    1 unit $= 8$
    3 units $= 8 \times 3 = 24$
    24 girls remained in the band.

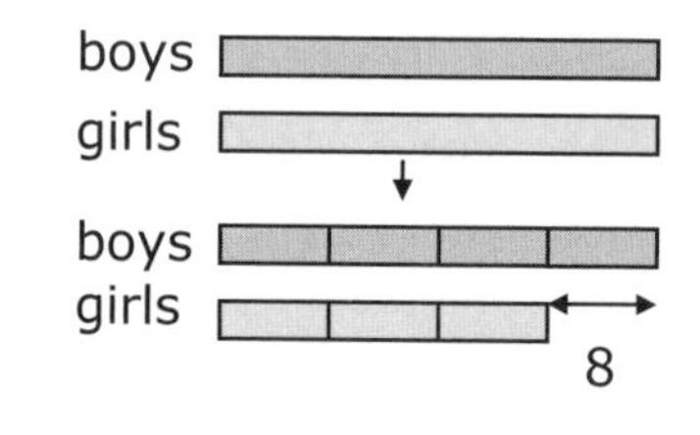

33. Total weight $= 40 \times 2 = 80$
    8 units $= 80$
    1 unit $= 80 \div 8 = 10$
    5 units $= 10 \times 5 = 50$
    US› John weighs **50 lb**. **3d›** John weighs **50 kg**.

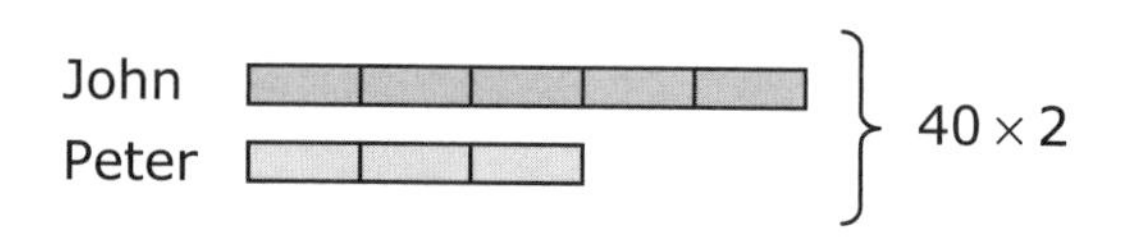

34. 2 units = \$60
8 units = \$60 × 4 = \$240
They saved **\$240.**

Mary \$60
Susan

35. 10% of the boys = 10% of 60% = $\frac{1}{10}$ x 60% = 6%

30% of the girls = 30% of 40% = $\frac{3}{10}$ x 40% = 12%

Percentage of the students that walk = 6% + 12% = **18%**

36. The base (100%) is February, since we are finding the percent more than in February.
Difference = \$75 – \$60 = \$15

Percentage difference = $\frac{15}{60} \times 100\% = 25\%$

He saved **25%** more in January than in February.

37. 40 min = $\frac{40}{60}$ h = $\frac{2}{3}$ h

20 min = $\frac{20}{60}$ h = $\frac{1}{3}$ h

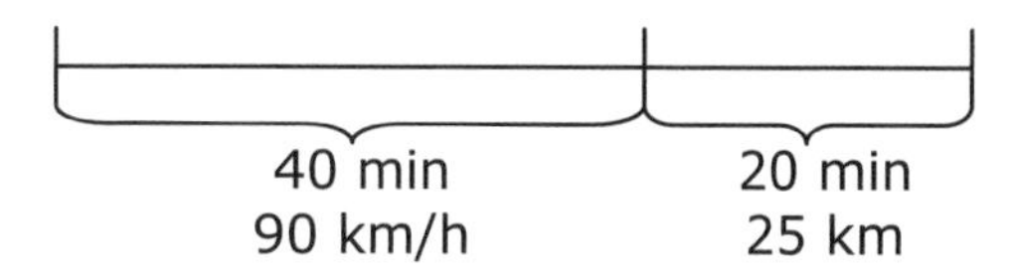

Distance for 1st part = 90 km/h × $\frac{2}{3}$ h = 60 km

Total distance = 60 km + 25 km = 85 km
Total time = 1 h
Average speed = **85 km/h**

38. Length of the rectangle = $\frac{72}{6}$ = 12 in. = base of triangle

Area of triangle = $\frac{1}{2} \times 12 \times 8$ = **48 in.²**

(**3d›** in. → cm)

39. Base of triangle = 5 + 7 = 12 cm
Height of triangle = 9 + 7 = 16 cm
Shaded area = area of triangle – area of quarter circle

$$= (\frac{1}{2} \times 12 \times 16) - (\frac{1}{4} \times \frac{22}{7} \times 7 \times 7)$$

= 96 – 38.5 = **57.5 cm²**

40. Perimeter = 2 × circumference of the quarter circle with radius 10 cm

$$= 2 \times \frac{1}{4} \times 3.14 \times 2 \times 10 = \mathbf{31.4\ cm}$$

41. Two lines of symmetry:

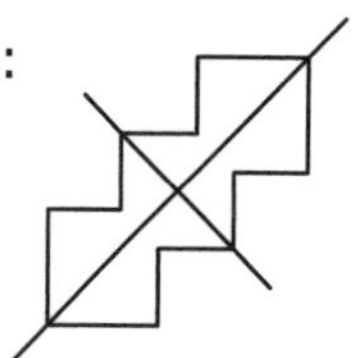

42. **9**

43. The net has to have two triangles and 3 rectangles. A has one rectangle and 4 triangles, so it is not a net of the solid. B and D are not nets of the solid because the side of the smaller rectangle does not match in length to a side of the triangle. **C** is a net of the solid.

US› 44. (a) Number choosing the Art Club $= 2 \times 20 = \mathbf{40}$

(b) **25%** (quarter circle)

(c) Computer Club and Drama Club together are the same as Chess Club, or 20.
Number choosing the Drama Club $= 20 - 12 = \mathbf{8}$

(d) Total $= 4 \times 20 = \mathbf{80}$

3d› 44. (a) Number choosing the school band $= 2 \times 20 = \mathbf{40}$

(b) **25%** (quarter circle)

(c) Brownies and Red Cross together are the same as Boy Scouts, or 20.
Number choosing the Red Cross $= 20 - 12 = \mathbf{8}$

(d) Total $= 4 \times 20 = \mathbf{80}$

45. (a) Increase $= \$3000 - \$1200 = \mathbf{\$1800}$

(b) Average $= \dfrac{2000 + 1200 + 3000 + 2400 + 800}{5} = \dfrac{9400}{5} = \mathbf{\$1880}$

(c) Number sold in April $= \$2400 \div \$4 = \mathbf{600}$

US› Unit 4 3d› Unit 3
Volume

Part 1 – Solving Problems (US› pp. 54-58, 3d› pp. 38-42)

(A) Volume

- Find the volume of a cube given its side.
- Find the edge of a cuboid given its volume.
- Find the volume of a solid made up of unit cubes.
- Find the volume of a cuboid.
- Find an unknown dimension of a cuboid given the volume and two dimensions.
- Find an unknown dimension of a cuboid given its volume and the area of a face perpendicular to the unknown dimension.

This unit is a review of concepts learned in Primary Mathematics 4 and 5.

A cuboid is the name given here to a rectangular prism.

The volume of a cuboid is equal to the length × width × height. A formula for volume is:

$V = lwh$ Where V = volume, l = length, w = width, and h = height.

If we know the volume and two of its sides, we can find the other side with division. For example, if we are given the length and width, we can find the height.

$$\text{height} = \frac{\text{Volume}}{\text{length} \times \text{width}}$$

If we know the volume and the area of one face, we can find the dimension perpendicular to the face. For example:

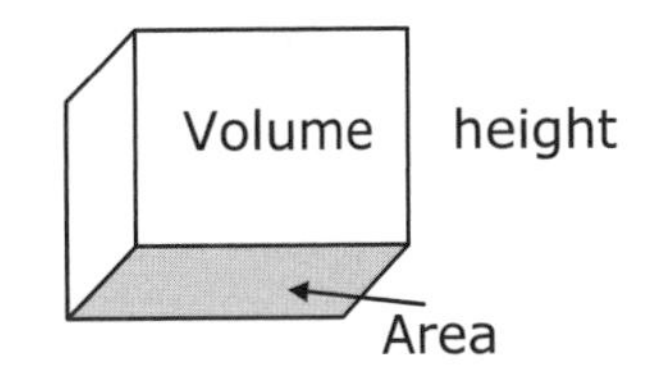

$$\text{height} = \frac{\text{Volume}}{\text{Area}}$$

In a cube, the lengths of the sides are equal so the volume is the cube of the length of a side. Students will be given a volume of a cube and asked to find the length of its side. They should know the cubes of the numbers 1, 2, 3, 4, 5 and 10, so that they can easily find the side of cubes with volumes of 1, 8, 27, 64, 125, and 1000 cubic units, and be able to use estimation and trial and error to find the side if they are given a volume which is the cube of 6, 7, 8, or 9.

US› p. 54, 3d› p. 38

He needs **125** 1 cm cubes to build a cube of edge 5 cm.

➤ Ask your student to find the volume of cubes of edges from 1 to 10.

The numbers in the second column (1, 8, 27...) are called perfect cubes. Encourage your student to memorize them.

Edge of cube units	Volume cubic units
1	1
2	8
3	27
4	64
5	125
6	216
7	343
8	512
9	729
10	1000

US› p. 55, 3d› p. 39

The edge of a cube with 729 1-cm cubes is **9 cm**.

Learning Tasks 1-3, US› p. 55, 3d› p. 39

1. $\text{Volume} = 10 \times (2 \times 2 \times 2) = \mathbf{80\ cm^3}$
2. $\text{Number of cubes needed for 10 cm sides} = 10 \div 2 = 5$
   $\text{Number of cubes needed for 6 cm side} = 6 \div 2 = 3$
   $\text{Total cubes needed} = 5 \times 5 \times 3 = \mathbf{75}$
3. **15 cm**

➤ Draw a box on the board and label the sides 15 cm, 12 cm, and 4 cm. Tell your student that this is an empty box and ask her to find how many cubes of edge 2 cm can be fit into this box. To solve this, she needs to determine how many blocks fit along each length. Only 7 cubes fit along the width, leaving a 1 cm gap. So the total number of cubes that can be fit into the box is $7 \times 6 \times 2 = 84$.

Your student may suggest finding the total volume ($15\text{ cm} \times 12\text{ cm} \times 4\text{ cm} = 720\text{ cm}^3$) and dividing by the volume of an individual 2-cm cube ($720\text{ cm}^3 \div 8\text{ cm}^3 = 90$). This method will only work if the lengths of all of the sides of the box are multiples of the side of the cube.

US› Workbook Exercise 20 **3d› Workbook Exercise 12**

(B) Volume and Liters

- Convert the volume of a liquid from cm^3 to liters and vice versa.
- Solve multi-step word problems involving the volume of a liquid in a rectangular tank.

This section is also a review, except that the problems involving volume in *Primary Mathematics 5* were only 2-step. Problems in this section are multi-step.

$$1 \text{ liter} = 1000 \text{ cm}^3$$

Fill a liter jar with water. Give your student a 1000-block from a base-10 set. Tell your student that if we had a container that fit around this block, we could fill it with the water from the jar. Ask your student for the volume of the water in cubic centimeters.

$$\text{Volume of water} = 10 \text{ cm} \times 10 \text{ cm} \times 10 \text{ cm} = 1000 \text{ cm}^3 = 1 \text{ liter}$$

Ask your student for the volume of water in liters in a tank measuring $25 \text{ cm} \times 10 \text{ cm} \times 4 \text{ cm}$. It would also be 1 liter.

Ask your student for the number of milliliters in a liter. There are 1000. So $1 \text{ ml} = 1 \text{ cm}^3$

Point out that 1000 cm^3 is not the same as 1 m^3. You can show students a meter stick and tell students that a cubic meter would have 1 m edges. 1 m = 100 cm, so 1 m × 1 m × 1 m = 100 cm × 100 cm × 100 cm = 1,000,000 cm^3. A container with a capacity of 1 m^3 would hold more water than 1 liter. It would hold 1000 liters.

Ask your student to convert some values in cubic centimeters to liters and vice versa.

1200 cm^3 = 1 ℓ 200 ml
4 ℓ 5 ml = 4005 cm^3

Learning Tasks 4-5, US› p. 56, 3d› p. 40

4. If the tank is half full, then the height of the oil is half the height of the tank. **4.4 ℓ**
5. In this task, note that the volume is left as 162×1000 in writing the fraction. This makes it easier to simplify the fraction. We can start simplifying by crossing out the same number of zeros in the numerator as in the denominator.

Once we know what $\frac{2}{3}$ of the height is, we can find the full height with a unitary approach, or with division. (36 is $\frac{2}{3}$ of what?; 36 ÷ $\frac{2}{3}$ = what?). The unitary approach shown below is more intuitive than division of a fraction.

Height of water level $= \frac{162 \times \cancel{1000}^{2}}{9\cancel{0} \times \cancel{50}} =$ **36** cm

$\frac{2}{3} \longrightarrow 36$ cm

$\frac{1}{3} \longrightarrow \frac{36}{2}$ cm

$1 \longrightarrow \frac{36}{2} \times 3$ cm $= 54$ cm

Height of the tank = **54** cm

 **US› Workbook Exercise 21** **3d› Workbook Exercise 13**

(C) Volume and Displacement

- Solve multi-step word problems involving the displacement of a liquid by a solid.

This section is a review, except that the problems involving volume in *Primary Mathematics 5* were only 2-step. Problems in this section are multi-step.

The volume of the water displaced is the same as the volume of the solid. The solid must be totally immersed.

If your student did not do *Primary Mathematics 5B*, and you have a displacement can or a graduated cylinder, you can do some experiments to find the volume of some solids. Fill the cylinder to a specific height, and add some small solids to the cylinder. The rise in the height of water is the same as the volume of the solid. If you have rectangular solids, you can measure it to determine its volume, change to milliliters, and see if it is the same as the rise of liquid in the cylinder.

Learning Tasks 6-7, US› p. 57, 3d› p. 41

6. Volume of stone = **1750** cm^3

7. Increase in height of water level = $\frac{3000}{50 \times 40} = \frac{3}{2}$ cm = **1.5** cm

   To find the height of the new water level, we need to first find the original height of the water level.

   Original height = $\frac{1}{2} \times 40$ cm = 20 cm

   Height of new water level = 20 + 1.5 = **21.5** cm

US› Workbook Exercise 22 **3d› Workbook Exercise 14**

(D) Volume and Rate of Flow

➢ Solve multi-step word problems involving the rate of flow of a liquid.

Problems involving the rate of flow of a liquid are new here.

If we are given the rate of flow, such as the number of liters per minute, and the total volume, we can use rate concepts to find the time it takes for that volume to flow out of or into the tank. For example, if the rate of flow is 10 ℓ/min then it takes one tenth of a minute for 1 liter to flow. Once we know how long it takes for one liter to flow, we can find the time for any number of liters.

Rate was covered in *Primary Mathematics 5B*, and then again in *Primary Mathematics 6A* in the context of speed.

Review rate and rate problems.

A rate involves two quantities that correspond to each other. It is usually expressed as one quantity per unit of another quantity.

Ask your student for an example of a rate. Speed is an example of rate. If a car goes 50 miles in 1 hour, the rate (speed) of the car is 50 miles per hour.

The flow of water is also a rate. We can say that water fills a tank (flows into the tank) at a rate of 50 liters per minute.

How much water will be in the tank after 1 minute? (50 ℓ) How much will be in the tank after 2 minutes? (100 ℓ)

A tank is filled from a faucet. 200 liters flow into the tank in 5 minutes. How many liters will be in the tank after 8 minutes?

We can use an arrow diagram to solve this. The change in minutes is given, and we need to find the new volume, so put the minutes first in the arrow diagram, and the volume after the arrow.

$$5 \text{ min} \longrightarrow 200\ \ell$$

Then we find the value of the second quantity for a unitary value of the first quantity — how many liters flow in 1 minute.

$$1 \text{ min} \longrightarrow \frac{200}{5}\ \ell$$

Then we find the value for the second quantity (liters) for the new value for the first quantity (8 min) by multiplying the number of liters that flow in 1 minute by 8.

$$8 \text{ min} \longrightarrow \frac{200}{5}\ \ell \times 8 = 320\ \ell$$

The tank will have 320 liters of water.

If we are given the dimensions of the tank, we can find how high the water level will be, since 320 liters $=$ 320,000 cm^3.

Using the same flow rate of 200 liters in 3 minutes, how long will it take to fill up the tank with 300 liters?

Here, a change in the liters is given, and we need to find the new number of minutes, so we put liters first in the arrow diagram.

$200\ \ell \longrightarrow 5$ min

Find out how long it takes for 1 liter to flow.

$1\ \ell \longrightarrow \frac{5}{200}$ min

Then find the number of minutes for 300 liters.

$300\ \ell \longrightarrow \frac{5}{2\not{0}\not{0}} \times 3\not{0}\not{0}$ min

It will take 7.5 minutes to put 300 liters in the tank.

$= 7.5$ min

Point out that by not solving the intermediate step immediately, we can sometimes simplify the fraction, making the calculations simpler.

Learning Tasks 8-9, US› p. 58, 3d› p. 41

8. We can use the unitary method to solve the second step.

$12\ \ell \longrightarrow 1$ min

$1 \longrightarrow \frac{1}{12}$ min

$240\ \ell \longrightarrow \frac{1}{12} \times 240$ min $=$ **20** min

or $(8 \times 5 \times 6)\ \ell \longrightarrow \frac{1}{12} \times 8 \times 5 \times 6 = \frac{\not{8}^{4} \times 5 \times \not{6}^{1}}{\not{12}\ \not{2}_{1}}$ min $= 20$ min

Point out that the time taken is liters divided by liters/min

9. **0.65** min

US› Workbook Exercise 23 **3d› Workbook Exercise 15**

Practice (US pp. 59-61, 3d> pp. 43-45)

US> Practice 4A, p. 59 3d> Practice 3A, p. 43

1. Side of cube = 6 cm
   Area of one face = 6 cm × 6 cm = **36 cm²**

2. Width = 15 cm
   Length = 15 cm × 2 = 30 cm
   Height = $\frac{3600 \text{ cm}^3}{15 \text{ cm} \times 30 \text{ cm}}$ = **8 cm**

3. (a) AB = $\frac{400}{10 \times 10}$ = **4** cm (b) XY = $\frac{768}{96}$ = **8** cm

4. (a) Area of the face of each cube = 36 cm^2 ÷ 4 = 9 cm^2
   Edge of cube = 3 cm (since 3 × 3 = 9)
   OR:
   Edge of the shaded face (which is a square) = 6 cm (since 6 × 6 = 36)
   Edge of cube = 6 cm ÷ 2 = 3 cm
   The volume of each cube is therefore 3 cm × 3 cm × 3 cm = **27 cm³**.
   (b) Since there are 12 cubes, and each cube has a volume of 27 cm^3, then the total volume is 12 × 27 cm^3 = **324 cm³**.
   OR:
   Since the edge of a cube is 3 cm, the edges of the cuboid are 6 cm, 9 cm, and 6 cm, so the volume is 6 cm × 9 cm × 6 cm = 324 cm^3.

5. (a) Volume of 1 cube = 2 cm × 2 cm × 2 cm = 8 cm^3
   Volume of the figure = 4 × 8 cm^3 = **32 cm³**
   (b) 18 faces would be painted, 4 on the front, 4 on the back, 3 on the bottom, and 7 going around from one side to the other.
   Area of 1 face = 2 cm × 2 cm = 4 cm^2
   Area of 18 faces = 18 × 4 cm^2 = **72 cm²**

US> Practice 4B, p. 60 3d> Practice 3B, p. 44

1. Height of water = $\frac{9000 \text{ cm}^3}{50 \text{ cm} \times 40 \text{ cm}}$ = **4.5 cm**

2. Height of water in first tank = $\frac{2}{3}$ × 6 cm = 4 cm
   Volume of water = 18 cm × 18 cm × 4 cm = 1296 cm^3
   Height of water in second tank = $\frac{1296 \text{ cm}^3}{12 \text{ cm} \times 10 \text{ cm}}$ = **10.8 cm**

3. (a) Capacity $= 60 \text{ cm} \times 50 \text{ cm} \times 56 \text{ cm} = 168{,}000 \text{ cm}^3 =$ **168 ℓ**

   (b) 8 ℓ ⟶ 1 min

   168 ℓ ⟶ $\frac{1}{8} \times 168 = 21$ min

   It will take **21 min** to fill the tank.

4. $\frac{3}{4}$ of a full tank = 60 ℓ

   $\frac{1}{4}$ of a full tank = $\frac{60}{3}$ ℓ

   $\frac{4}{4}$ of a full tank = $\frac{60}{3} \times 4 = 80$ ℓ $= 80{,}000 \text{ cm}^3$

   Height of tank = $\frac{80{,}000}{50 \times 40} =$ **40 cm**

US› Practice 4C, p. 61 3d› Practice 3C, p. 45

1. Volume of cube $= 10 \text{ cm} \times 10 \text{ cm} \times 10 \text{ cm} = 1000 \text{ cm}^3$

   Height water rises = $\frac{1000}{25 \times 25} = 1.6$ cm

   New height of water = 10 cm + 1.6 cm = **11.6 cm**

2. (a) Capacity of tank $= 50 \text{ cm} \times 50 \text{ cm} \times 42 \text{ cm} =$ **105,000 cm³**

   (b) Height without stone = $\frac{2}{3} \times 42 \text{ cm} = 28$ cm

   Height with stone = $\frac{3}{4} \times 42 \text{ cm} = 31.5$ cm

   Change in height = 31.5 cm − 28 cm = 3.5 cm

   Volume of stone $= 50 \text{ cm} \times 50 \text{ cm} \times 3.5 \text{ cm} =$ **8750 cm³**

3. Capacity of tank $= 25 \text{ cm} \times 70 \text{ cm} \times 36 \text{ cm} = 63{,}000 \text{ cm}^3$

   Volume of water needed $= 63{,}000 \text{ cm}^3 - 4{,}500 \text{ cm}^3 = 58{,}500 \text{ cm}^3 = 58.5$ ℓ

   9 ℓ → 1 min

   58.5 ℓ → $\frac{1}{9} \times 58.5 =$ **6.5 min**

4. Amount of water added in 3 min = 10 ℓ × 3 = 30 ℓ $= 30{,}000 \text{ cm}^3$

   Volume of water that would be needed without the stone to fill the tank to 18 cm $= 50 \times 40 \times 18 = 36{,}000 \text{ cm}^3$

   Volume of stone $= 36{,}000 \text{ cm}^3 - 30{,}000 \text{ cm}^3 =$ **6000 cm³**

Workbook Review 3
Workbook Review 4

US› Unit 5 3d› Unit 4
Triangles and 4-Sided Figures

Part 1 – Finding Unknown Angles (US› pp. 62-65, 3d› pp. 46-49)

(1) Finding Unknown Angles I

- Review angle properties of straight lines, triangles, and quadrilaterals.
- Find unknown angles in problems related to triangles and quadrilaterals.

In *Primary Mathematics 5*, the students learned the following angle properties of lines, triangles, and 4-sided figures:

The sum of adjacent angles along a straight line resulting from the intersection of lines with a straight line is 180°.
(∠'s on a st. line)

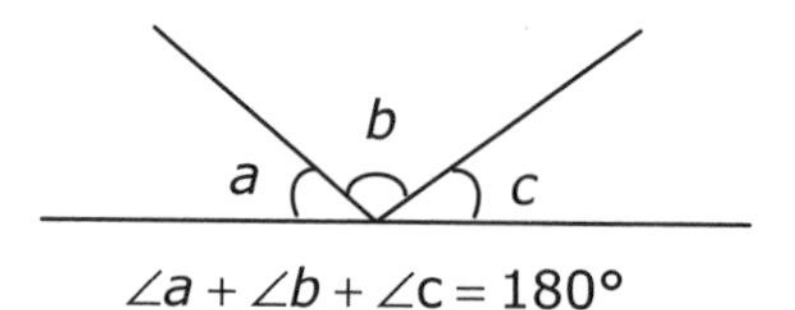

$\angle a + \angle b + \angle c = 180°$

Angles opposite each other at the intersection of two lines are equal.
(vert. opp. ∠'s)

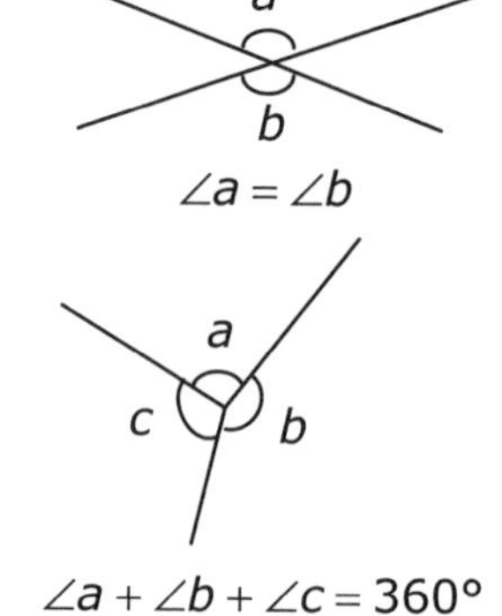

$\angle a = \angle b$

The sum of angles around a point of intersection of 2 or more lines is 360°.
(∠'s around a point)

$\angle a + \angle b + \angle c = 360°$

The sum of the three angles of a triangle is 180°. (∠ sum of a Δ)

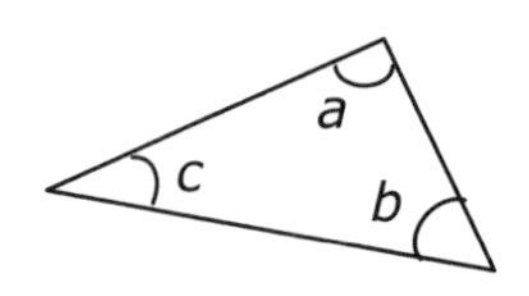

$\angle a + \angle b + \angle c = 180°$

When one angle of a triangle is a right angle, the other two angles add up to 90°.
(right Δ).

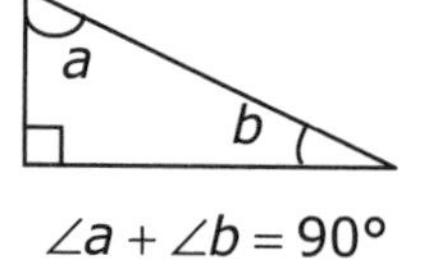

$\angle a + \angle b = 90°$

The exterior angle of a triangle is equal to the sum of the interior opposite angles.
(ext. ∠ of a Δ)

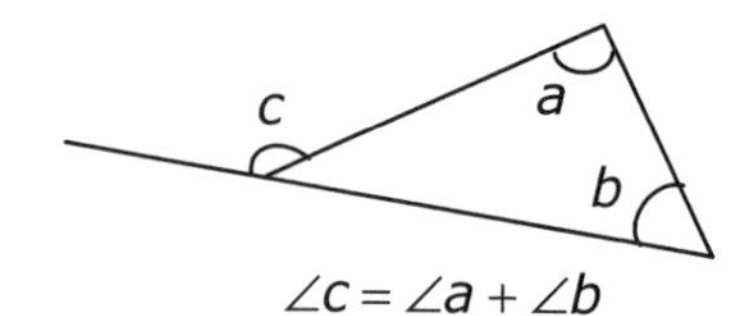

$\angle c = \angle a + \angle b$

In an isosceles triangle (two sides are equal) the angles opposite the equal sides are equal.
(iso. Δ)

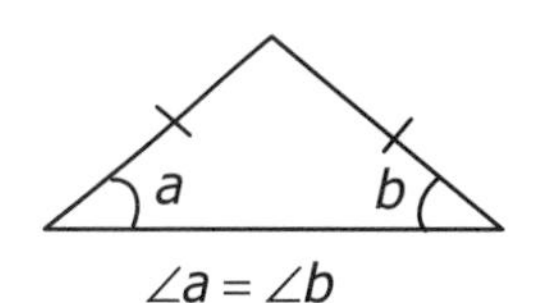

$\angle a = \angle b$

We can identify a triangle as an isosceles triangle if we know that two sides are equal or that two angles are equal.

In an equilateral triangle (a triangle with all sides equal) each angle is 60°.
(equ. Δ)

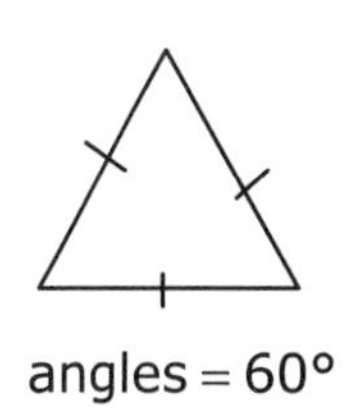

angles = 60°

We can identify a triangle as an equilateral triangle if we know that the three sides are equal, that two angles are equal while the third angle is 60°, or that the triangle has two equal angles of 60°.

A parallelogram is a 4-sided figure with 2 pairs of parallel lines. The parallel lines are equal in length.

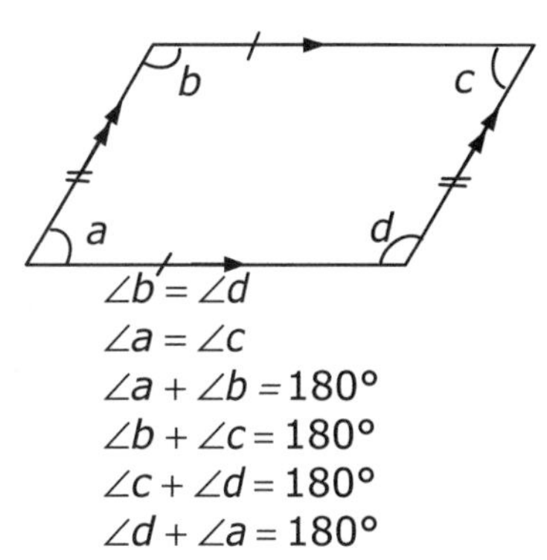

$\angle b = \angle d$
$\angle a = \angle c$
$\angle a + \angle b = 180°$
$\angle b + \angle c = 180°$
$\angle c + \angle d = 180°$
$\angle d + \angle a = 180°$

Parallel lines can be marked with arrows. Sides marked with the same number of arrows are parallel to each other. Equal sides can be marked with short cross-lines; sides marked with the same number of lines are equal.

In a parallelogram the opposite angles are equal.
(opp. ∠'s of //)

In a parallelogram, the sum of each pair of angles between two parallel lines is 180°.
(inside ∠'s)

A rectangle is a parallelogram where all the angles are 90°.

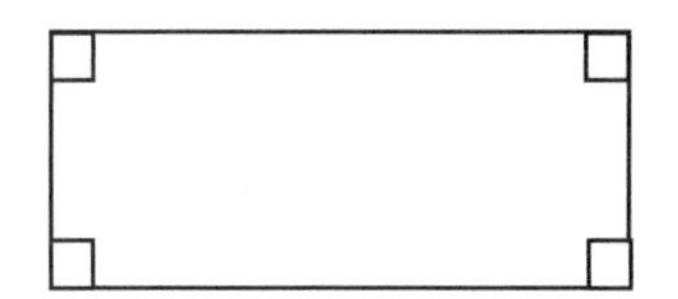

90° are marked with a little square at the angle.

A rhombus is an equilateral parallelogram with 4 equal sides. It can be divided into two isosceles triangles. The angles opposite the equal sides are equal.

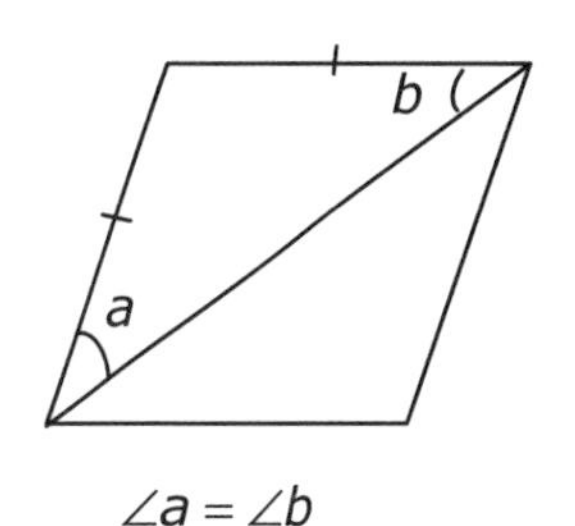

$\angle a = \angle b$

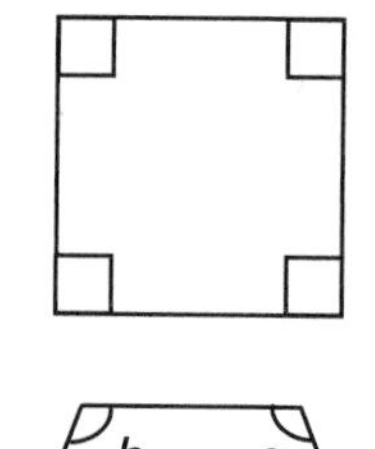

A square is a rhombus where all the angles are 90°. (It is therefore also a parallelogram and a rectangle.)

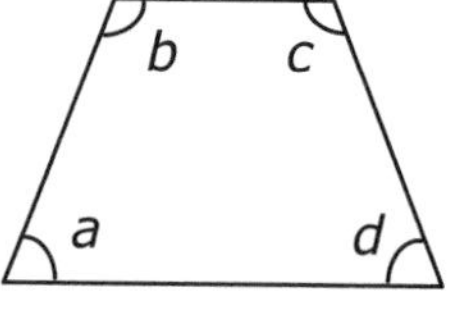

$\angle a + \angle b = 180°$
$\angle c + \angle d = 180°$

A trapezoid is a 4-sided figure with only one pair of parallel sides. The parallel sides are not equal in length. The non-parallel sides may or may not be equal in length; if they are, then the trapezoid is called an equilateral trapezoid. In the 3rd edition of *Primary Mathematics*, a trapezoid is called a trapezium (British English). The term trapezoid (American English) will be used in this guide.

In a trapezoid, the sum of each pair of angles between two parallel lines is 180°.

In this unit, students will use these properties to find unknown angles in figures composed of triangles and 4-sided figures. No new angle properties are taught here, but the figures are generally more complicated than those encountered in earlier levels.

The illustrated figures are not drawn to scale, so students cannot use a protractor to measure the angles.

Students are not required to write down the reasons for each step of their solutions. However, they should be encouraged to give the reasons verbally.

Different steps for arriving at the value of the unknown angle are possible. This guide will show one possible solution. Your student may use different steps.

US› Page 62, 3d› Page 46

Use this page to review the angle properties of an equilateral triangle and a parallelogram. Ask your student questions about triangles and parallelograms.

Name the triangle in this figure.	CDE
What is the sum of all the angles of a triangle?	180°
We say that $\angle q$ is opposite which two angles in the triangle?	∠CED and ∠EDC
What can we say about $\angle q$ in relation to these to opposite angles?	$\angle q = \angle CED + \angle EDC$
What is an equilateral triangle? (After your student answer, mark each side with a short cross-line. Tell student that this means the sides are the same length.)	A triangle where all the sides and all the angles are equal.
Can we say anything about the relationship between $\angle q$ and $\angle p$?	They are on a straight line. $\angle q + \angle p = 180°$
What is a parallelogram?	It is a 4-sided figure with two pairs of parallel and equal sides.
Name the parallelogram in this figure. (Draw arrows and cross-lines to indicate parallel and equal sides. Remind your student that sides marked with the same number of cross-lines are equal to each other, and sides with the same number of arrows are parallel to each other.)	ABCE
Which two angles of the parallelogram are equal? (Point out that, although it is not separately labeled, ∠AEC = ∠s.)	$\angle r = \angle q$ ∠AEC = ∠s
Which pairs of angles add up to 180°?	$\angle r + \angle s = 180°$ $\angle r + \angle AEC = 180°$ $\angle q + \angle s = 180°$ $\angle q + \angle AEC = 180°$ $\angle q + \angle p = 180°$
What is a trapezoid?	A 4-sided figure with only one pair of parallel lines.
Name the trapezoid in this figure.	ABDE
What do you know about the angles of a trapezoid?	The sum of each pair of angles between two parallel lines is 180°.

Find the size of the angles, and explain your reasoning.

$\angle p = \mathbf{60°}$	CDE is an equilateral triangle
$\angle q = \mathbf{120°}$	$\angle p$ and $\angle q$ are on a straight line. $\angle q = 180° - 60°$
$\angle r = \mathbf{120°}$	$\angle r$ and $\angle q$ are on opposite angles of the parallelogram. $\angle r = \angle q = 120°$
$\angle s = \mathbf{60°}$	$\angle s$ and $\angle r$ are between two parallel lines. $\angle s = 180° - 120° = 60°$

Learning Tasks 1-3, US› p. 63, 3d› p. 47

Use these to review properties of isosceles triangles and rhombuses. For example:

What kind of a triangle is WXY?	Isosceles
Why?	It has two equal sides.
What can you say about the angles of an isosceles triangle?	The two angles opposite the equal sides are equal. The sum of all three angles is 180°.
What is a rhombus (in task 3)	A parallelogram with all sides equal.
So does a rhombus have the same angle properties as a parallelogram?	Yes.

1. ΔXYX is an isosceles triangle.
   The sum of the angles is 180° and $\angle XWY = \angle WYX$
   $\angle XWY = (180° - 38°) \div 2 = \mathbf{71°}$
   $\angle WYZ$ is the exterior angle of a triangle.
   Interior opposite angles are $\angle WXY$ and $\angle XWY$.
   $\angle WYZ = \angle WXY + \angle XWY = 38° + 71° = \mathbf{109°}$

2. $\angle BAD = \mathbf{98°}$
   $\angle BCD = \mathbf{132°}$

3. Opposite angles of a rhombus are equal.
   So $\angle WZY = \angle WXY = \mathbf{84°}$
   XW = XY, therefore WXY is an isosceles triangle, and $\angle XWY = \angle XYW$
   $\angle XWY = (180° - 84°) \div 2 = \mathbf{48°}$

US› Workbook Exercise 24 **3d› Workbook Exercise 16**

(B) Finding Unknown Angles II

➢ Find unknown angles in problems related to triangles and quadrilaterals.

Learning Tasks 4-7-3, US> pp. 64-65, 3d> pp. 48-49

Copy the figures on a separate sheet of paper or a white-board. Since they are not to scale, they don't have to be exact copies. Guide your student to work out the intermediate steps and mark the respective angles in the figures. Encourage her to find the unknown angles in more than one way. When different steps are used, the angles involved in the intermediate steps may be different. Then discuss the steps given in the text.

For example, in task 4 your student could find $\angle YZW = 180° - 2 \times 52° = 76°$ and then $\angle ZWX = 76° + 52° = 128°$ (ext. $\angle$ of a Δ).

4. $\angle ZWV = \mathbf{52°}$ (iso. Δ)
   $\angle ZWX = 180° - 52° = \mathbf{128°}$ ($\angle$s on a st. line)
   $\angle XYZ = \mathbf{128°}$ (opp. $\angle$s of //)
   OR:
   $\angle VZW = 180° - (2 \times 52°) = 76°$ (isosceles ΔZWV)
   $\angle ZWX = 76° + 52° = 128°$ (ext. $\angle$ of a Δ)

5. $\angle ACE = \mathbf{45°}$ (ΔACE is a right iso. Δ)
   $\angle ACD = 90° + 45° = \mathbf{135°}$ ($\angle ACE = 90°$)
   $\angle CDA = (180° - 135°) \div 2 = \mathbf{22.5°}$ (iso. Δ)

6. $\angle QRT = \mathbf{62°}$ (opp. $\angle$s of //)
   $\angle QRS = 90° + 62° = \mathbf{152°}$
   $\angle RSQ = (180° - 152°) \div 2 = \mathbf{14°}$ (iso. Δ)

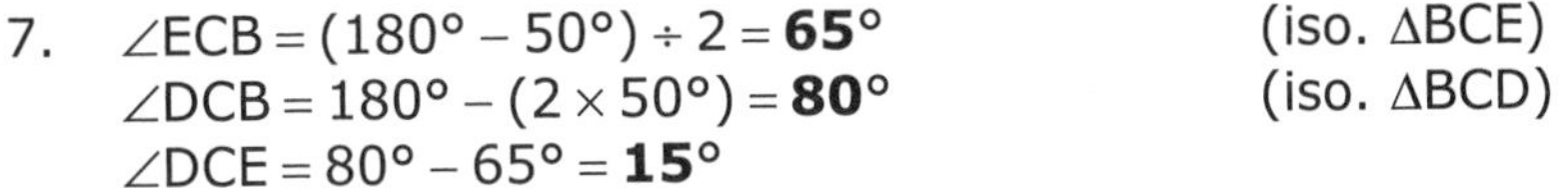

7. $\angle ECB = (180° - 50°) \div 2 = \mathbf{65°}$ (iso. ΔBCE)
   $\angle DCB = 180° - (2 \times 50°) = \mathbf{80°}$ (iso. ΔBCD)
   $\angle DCE = 80° - 65° = \mathbf{15°}$

US> Workbook Exercise 25 **3d> Workbook Exercise 17**

Practice (US pp. 66-67, 3d› pp. 50-51)

US› Practice 5A, p. 66 3d› Practice 4A, p. 50

1. $\angle a = 180° - 130° = \mathbf{50°}$ (inside $\angle$'s)
   $\angle b = 180° - 50° - 72° = \mathbf{58°}$ ($\angle$ sum of a Δ)
2. $\angle TZS = 90° - 52° = 38°$ (right Δ)
   $\angle p = \mathbf{38°}$ (vert. opp. $\angle$'s)
   $\angle q = 180° - (2 \times 38°) = \mathbf{104°}$ (iso. ΔXYZ)
3. $\angle ABC = 90° - 30° = 60°$ (right Δ)
   $\angle DBC = 60° - 40° = 20°$
   $\angle x = (180° - 20°) \div 2 = \mathbf{80°}$ (iso. Δ)
4. $\angle SPQ = 82°$ (opp. $\angle$s of a //)
   $\angle PQT = 180° - (2 \times 82°) = 16°$ (iso. Δ)
   $\angle PQR = 180° - 82° = 98°$ (inside $\angle$'s)
   $\angle m = 98° - 16° = \mathbf{82°}$
5. $\angle FGH = (180° - 48°) \div 2 = 66°$ (iso. Δ)
   $\angle EFG = 180° - 66° = 114°$ (inside $\angle$'s)
   $\angle h = 114° - 48° = \mathbf{66°}$

US› Practice 5B, p. 67 3d› Practice 4B, p. 51

1. $\angle JKM = 60° + 60° = 120°$ (ext. $\angle$ of an equ. Δ)
   $\angle p = 180° - 120° = \mathbf{60°}$ (inside $\angle$'s)
   $\angle q = 180° - 56° = \mathbf{124°}$ (inside $\angle$'s)
2. $\angle BAD = 180° - 124° = 56°$ (inside $\angle$'s)
   $\angle BAE = 180° - 90° = 90°$ (inside $\angle$'s)
   $\angle a = 90° - 56° = \mathbf{34°}$
   $\angle b = \mathbf{56°}$ (opp. $\angle$'s of //, $\angle BAD$ is opp.)
3. $\angle x = 180° - 55° = \mathbf{125°}$ (inside $\angle$'s)
   $\angle VWU = 125°$ (vert. opp. $\angle$'s)
   $\angle y = (180° - 125°) \div 2 = \mathbf{27.5°}$ (iso. Δ)
4. $\angle IJH = 48°$ (opp $\angle$'s of //)
   $\angle JIH = (180° - 48°) \div 2 = 66°$ (iso. Δ)
   $\angle m = 90° - 66° = \mathbf{24°}$
5. $\angle PRS = 45°$ (right iso. ΔPSR)
   $\angle TRS = 45° - 20° = 25°$
   $\angle RST = 180° - (2 \times 25°) = 130°$ (iso. ΔRST)
   $\angle w = 130° - 90° = \mathbf{40°}$

Review (US pp. 68-82, 3d› pp. 52-66)

Review C, US pp. 68-72, 3d› pp. 52-56

1. (a) **30,030** (b) **3,040,000**
2. (a) **100** (b) **0.09**
3. **3400**
4. $3594 \div 597 \approx 3600 \div 600 = \mathbf{6}$
5. $100 \div 3 = \frac{100}{3} = \mathbf{33\frac{1}{3}}$
6. Cost for first 50 T-shirts = 50 × \$9 = \$450
   Cost for remaining 30 T-shirts = 30 × \$8 = \$240
   Total cost = \$450 + \$240 = **\$690**
7. Remainder $= \frac{2}{3}$; fraction each of his children received $= \frac{1}{3} \times \frac{2}{3} = \mathbf{\frac{2}{9}}$
8. $\frac{2}{3}$ full → 60 ℓ

   $\frac{1}{3}$ full → $60 \div 2 = 30$ ℓ

   $\frac{3}{3}$ full → $30 \times 3 = 90$ ℓ

   $\frac{3}{5} \times 90$ ℓ $= 54$ ℓ

   There is **54 ℓ** of water in the container when it is $\frac{3}{5}$ full.

US› 9. (a)

$$\frac{3}{4} + \frac{1}{12} \times 4 \div \frac{2}{3}$$
$$= \frac{3}{4} + \frac{1}{\cancel{12}_{\cancel{3}_1}} \times \cancel{4}^1 \times \frac{\cancel{3}^1}{2}$$
$$= \frac{3}{4} + \frac{1}{2}$$
$$= \mathbf{1\frac{1}{4}}$$

(b)

$$6 \div \frac{3}{5} + \frac{2}{5} \times \frac{5}{6}$$
$$= \cancel{6}^2 \times \frac{5}{\cancel{3}} + \frac{\cancel{2}^1}{\cancel{5}_1} \times \frac{\cancel{5}^1}{\cancel{6}_3}$$
$$= 10 + \frac{1}{3}$$
$$= \mathbf{10\frac{1}{3}}$$

3d› 9. 24 : 6 : 15 = **8 : 2 : 5**

10. John's savings : David's savings = **6 : 1**

11. Peter's money $= \mathbf{\frac{5}{3}}$ of John's money

12. Total money $= \$32 + \$48 = \$80$; Percentage spent $= \frac{32}{80} \times 100\% =$ **40%**

13. The remainder is $\frac{3}{4}$. 20% of $\frac{3}{4} = 20\%$ of $75\% = \frac{20}{100} \times 75 = 15\%$
15% of the circle is colored red.

14. Percentage that take the bus = 25%
Percentage that walk = 100% – 15% – 25% – 20% = **40%**

15. $2.5\% = \frac{2.5}{100} = \frac{25}{1000} = \mathbf{\frac{1}{40}}$

16. 20% of \$14.50 $= \frac{2}{10} \times \$14.50 =$ **\$2.90**

17. Time = 2 h; Speed $= \frac{8\text{ km}}{2\text{ h}} =$ **4 km/h**

18. Extra money earned $= \frac{2000}{400} \times \$3 = \$15$
Regular money earned $= 2000 \times \$0.03 = \$60$
Total money earned $= \$60 + \$15 =$ **\$75**

19. 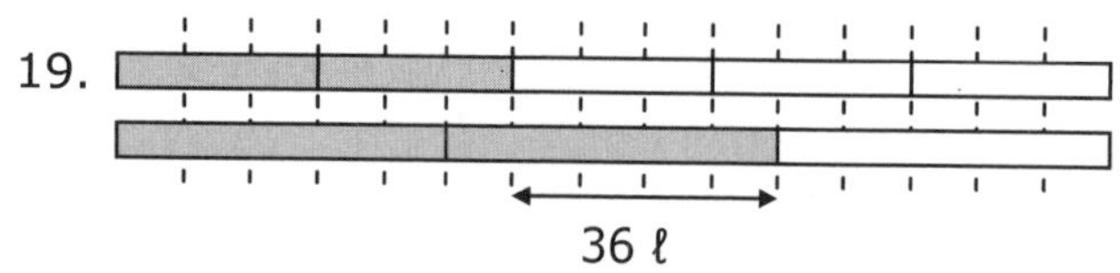

One bar shows the tank $\frac{2}{5}$ full, and the other shows it $\frac{2}{3}$ full. The lowest common multiple of 5 and 3 is 15; divide each bar into 15 to get equal units.
4 units = 36 ℓ
1 unit $= \frac{36}{4}$ ℓ
15 units $= \frac{36}{4} \times 15 = 135$ ℓ
The capacity is **135 ℓ**.

Or: $\frac{2}{3} - \frac{2}{5} = \frac{10}{15} - \frac{6}{15} = \frac{4}{15}$
$\frac{4}{15}$ of a full tank = 36 ℓ
all of a full tank $= \frac{36}{4} \times 15$
$= 135$ ℓ

20. (a) New ratio = 3 : 6 = **1 : 2**
(b) 3 units = 12
1 unit = 12 ÷ 3 = 4
5 units = 4 × 5 = 20
20 beads were removed.

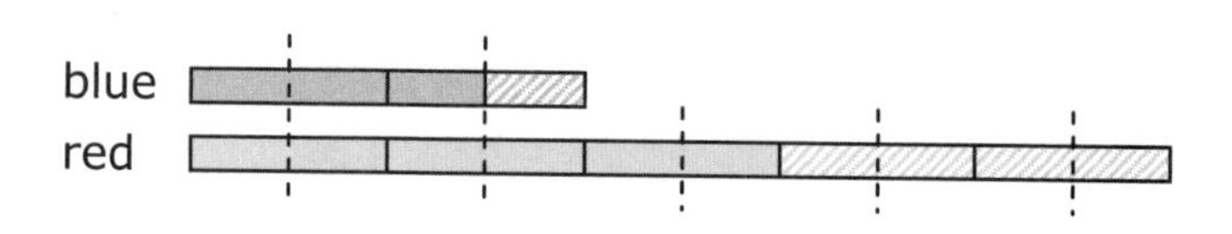

21. Perimeter = 2 x (width + length)
= 2 x 5 units = 10 units
10 units = 40 cm
1 unit = 4 cm
2 units = $2 \times 4 = 8$ cm = width
3 units = $3 \times 4 = 12$ cm = length
Area = $8 \times 12 =$ **96 cm²**

width / length

22. Distance for second part
$= 72 \text{ km/h} \times \frac{1}{2} \text{ h} = 36 \text{ km}$
Total distance = 36 km × 3 = 108 km
Total time = $1\frac{1}{2} + \frac{1}{2} = 2$ h
Average speed = $\frac{108 \text{ km}}{2 \text{ h}} =$ **54 km/h**

$1\frac{1}{2}$ h $\frac{1}{2}$ h, 72 km/h

23. John's time = $\frac{80 \text{ km}}{60 \text{ km/h}} = \frac{4}{3} \text{ h} = 1 \text{ h } 20 \text{ min}$
John left 20 min earlier, but they arrived at the same time.
David's time = 1 h 20 min – 20 min = 1 h
David's speed = **80 km/h**

24. $9t - 6t + t - 2 = \mathbf{4t - 2}$

25. Cost of shampoo = $\$3n$
Cost of toothpaste = $5 \times \$2 = \$10$
Total cost = $\$(3n + 10)$
Change = $\$50 - \$(3n + 10) =$ **$(40 – 3*n*)**

26. $90° + x = 150°$ (vert. opp. ∠s)
$x = 150° - 90° =$ **60°**

27. ∠QRP = 45° (right iso. Δ)
∠PSR = ∠RPS (iso. Δ)
∠QRP = ∠PSR + ∠RPS = 2 × ∠RPS (ext. ∠ of a Δ, ∠PRS = ∠RPS)
∠RPS = ∠PRQ ÷ 2 = 45° ÷ 2 = **22.5°**

28. ∠BED = 180° - 80° = 100° (int. ∠'s)
∠*x* = 180° - 100° = 80

29. Base of Δ = 20 – 9 = 11 cm; Height of Δ = 11 cm
Area = $\frac{1}{2} \times 11 \times 11 =$ **60.5 cm²**

30. Area = $3 \times \frac{1}{2} \times \pi \times 2 \times 2 =$ **6π m²**

31. Volume of Cuboid A $= 9 \times 4 \times 4 = 144$ cm^3
Volume of Cuboid B $= 144$ cm^3
Height of Cuboid B $= \frac{144}{6 \text{ x } 3} =$ **8 cm**

32. Height of water $= \frac{1}{2} \times 30 = 15$ cm
Volume of water $= 40 \times 30 \times 15 = 18{,}000$ cm^3 $= 18$ ℓ
10 ℓ $\longrightarrow$ 1 min
18 ℓ $\longrightarrow \frac{1}{10} \times 18$ min $= 1.8$ min
It will take **1.8 min** to empty the tank.

33. (a) Average $= \frac{1.2 + 2.6 + 2.4 + 3.0 + 1.8}{5} = \frac{11}{5} =$ **2.2 (US› gal, 3d› ℓ)**
(b) **C**
(c) $\frac{2.4}{4} = \frac{24}{40} = \mathbf{\frac{3}{5}}$

Review D, US pp. 73-77, 3d› pp. 57-61

1. (a) **600** (b) **1000**
2. (a) $(84 - \underline{4 \times 15}) \div 3$
$= \underline{(84 - 60)} \div 3$
$= \underline{24 \div 3}$
$=$ **8**

(b) $\underline{7 \times 8} - \underline{42 \div 7}$
$= \underline{56 - 6}$
$=$ **50**
3. **13.28**
4. (a) **0.375** (b) **0.82**
5. The first three have the same numerator. The one with the largest denominator, $\frac{3}{15}$, is the smallest of those. $\frac{3}{15} = \frac{1}{5}$, so it is smaller than the last fraction. $\mathbf{\frac{3}{15}}$ is the smallest.
6. **1.4**
7. 4 h before 2:00 p.m. is 10:00 a.m. 35 min before that is 9:25 a.m. The bus left at **9:25 a.m**.
8. (a) $8\% = \frac{8}{100} = \mathbf{\frac{2}{25}}$ (b) $4.28 = 4\frac{28}{100} = \mathbf{4\frac{7}{25}}$
9. (a) $\frac{8}{25} = \frac{32}{100} =$ **32%** (b) $0.45 \times 100\% =$ **45%**

10. 2 kg = 2000 g $\qquad \frac{275}{2000} = \mathbf{\frac{11}{80}}$

US› 11. $4 \div \frac{7}{8} \times \left(\frac{1}{6} + \frac{1}{8}\right) = 4 \div \frac{7}{8} \times \left(\frac{4}{24} + \frac{3}{24}\right) = 4 \times \frac{8}{7} \times \frac{7}{24} = \mathbf{\frac{4}{3}}$

3d› 11. $\frac{180}{500} \times 100\% = \mathbf{36\%}$

12. (a) **5** (b) **6** : 9 : **15**

13. 3 ⟶ \$1
15 ⟶ \$1 × 5 = \$5
He paid **\$5**.

14. 2 units = \$603 – \$115 = \$488
1 unit = \$488 ÷ 2 = \$244
David had **\$244**.

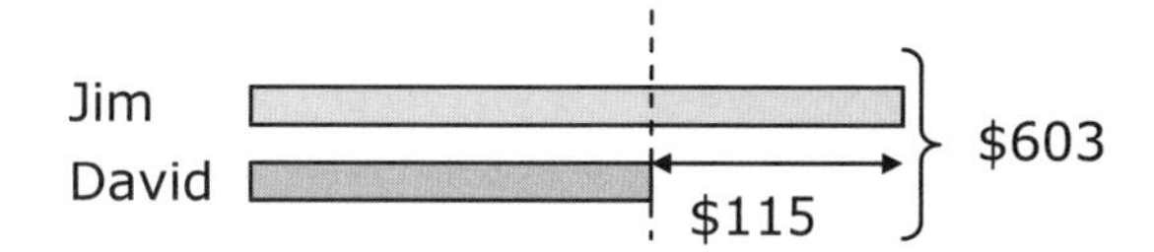

15. Number of men = 144 – 56 = 88
Fraction of the people who are men $= \frac{88}{144} = \mathbf{\frac{11}{18}}$

16. If Betty received twice as much as Annie, she received $\frac{2}{3}$ of the half-pizza, and Annie received $\frac{1}{3}$ of it.
Fraction of the whole pizza Betty received $= \frac{2}{3} \times \frac{1}{2} = \mathbf{\frac{1}{3}}$

17. $\frac{1}{2}$ kg = 500 g
100 g ⟶ \$0.90
500 g ⟶ \$0.90 × 5 = **\$4.50**

18. She had 85% of her money left.
15% ⟶ \$60
1% ⟶ $\$\frac{60}{15}$
85% ⟶ $\$\frac{60}{15} \times 85 = \mathbf{\$340}$

19. (a) Sale price is 70% of usual price.
Sale price = 70% × \$55 = $\frac{7}{10} \times \$55 = \mathbf{\$38.50}$
(b) 70% of usual price = \$42
100% of usual price = $\$\frac{42}{70} \times 100 = \mathbf{\$60}$

20. 1 km = 1,000 m
200 m → 1 min
1000 m → $1 \times 5 = 5$ min
It will take him **5 min** to cycle 1 km.

21.

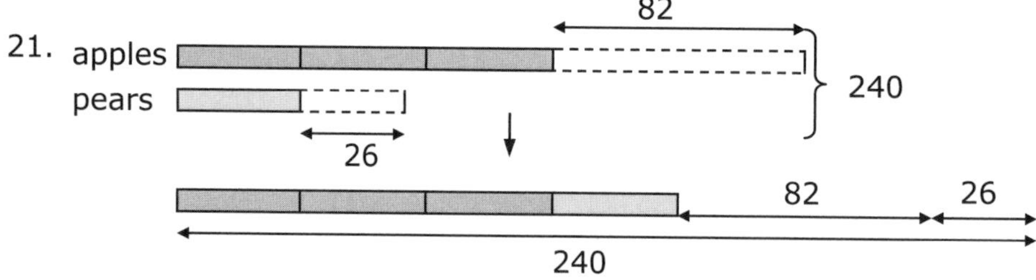

4 units = $240 - 82 - 26 = 132$

3 units = $\frac{132}{4} \times 3 = 99$

Number of apples he had at first = $99 + 82 =$ **181**

22. 4 units = $600 - 40 = 560$
1 unit = $560 \div 4 = 140$
Alan received **140** stamps.

Alan
Dave
Linda
600
40

23. 7 units = \$350

3 units = \$$\frac{350}{7} \times 3 =$ \$150

They spent **\$150**.

John
Mary
\$350

24. Number of pineapple tarts
= $24 + 18 = 42$
Number of apple tarts
= $84 - 24 - 42 = 18$
pineapple : cherry : apple
= 42 : 24 : 18 = 21 : 12 : 9 = **7 : 4 : 3**

cherry
pineapple
apple
24
24
18
84

25. Number of goldfish = $4 \times 20 = 80$
Number of angelfish = $2 \times 30 = 60$
Total number of fish at first
= $80 + 60 =$ **140**

20
goldfish
angelfish
30

OR: Total number of fish = $20 \div \frac{1}{4} + 30 \div \frac{1}{2} = 20 \times 4 + 30 \times 2 = 80 + 60 = 120$

26.

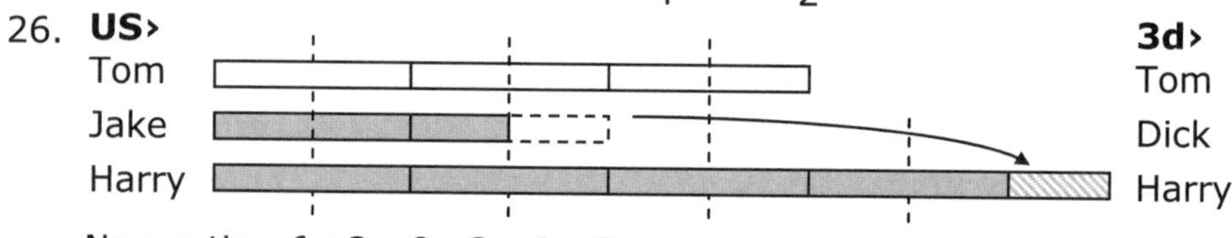

New ratio = 6 : 3 : 9 = **2 : 1 : 3**

27. **US›** **3d›**

Dan — Ali

Jason — Rahim

$15 $10 $15

1 unit $= \$15 + \$10 + \$15 = \$40$
3 units $= \$40 \times 3 = \$120$
Dan (Ali) had **$120** at first.

28. Remainder $= 60\%$

Percentage used to make pizzas $= 35\%$ of $60\% = \frac{35}{100} \times 60\% = \mathbf{21\%}$

29. Jimmy's time $= \frac{1}{2}$ h

Distance = Jimmy's speed × Jimmy's time $= 12$ km/h $\times \frac{1}{2}$ h $= 6$ km

Steve's time $= \frac{\text{Distance}}{\text{Halim's speed}} = \frac{6 \text{ km}}{15 \text{ km/h}} = \frac{6}{15} \text{ h} = \frac{2}{5} \text{ h} = \frac{2}{5} \times 60 \text{ min} = 24 \text{ min}$

Steve reached Town B at **10:24 a.m.** (**3d›** Steve → Halim)

30. David's time = Peter's time $= \frac{10 \text{ km}}{5 \text{ km/h}} = 2$ h

David's distance $= 10 - 2 = 8$ km

David's speed $= \frac{8 \text{ km}}{2 \text{ h}} =$ **4 km/h**

31. $4a + 6 + 8a - 3 - a = 4a + 8a - a + 6 - 3 = \mathbf{11a + 3}$

32. Area = area of semicircle + triangle + square
$= (\frac{1}{2} \times 3.14 \times 10 \times 10) + (\frac{1}{2} \times 10 \times 10) + (10 \times 10)$
$= 157 + 50 + 100$
$= \mathbf{307\ cm^2}$

33. Volume of tank A $= 36 \times 8 = 288\ cm^3$
Volume of tank B $= 5 \times 3 \times 12 = 180\ cm^3$
Volume remaining in A after filling B $= 288 - 180 = 108\ cm^3$
Height of remaining water $= \frac{108}{36} =$ **3 cm**

34. $\angle ACB = 90° - 48° = 42°$ (right Δ)
$\angle DCE = 42°$ (vert. opp. $\angle$)
$\angle CDE = 180° - 32° - 42° = \mathbf{106°}$ ($\angle$ sum of a Δ)

35. **C** (It is the only one with 4 triangles and 1 square.)

36.

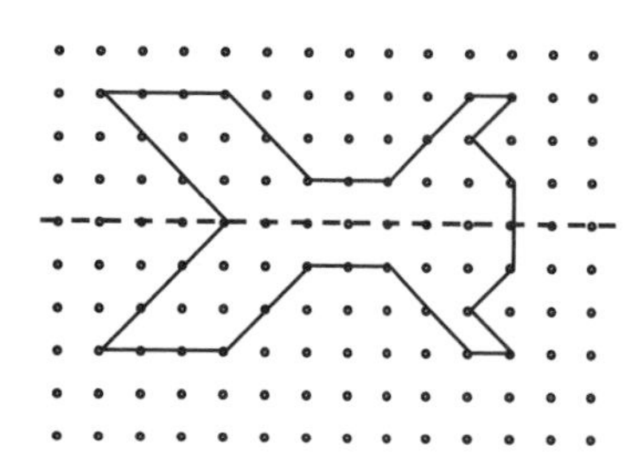

37. (a) **50 ℓ**

(b) Average $= \frac{150 + 200 + 175 + 150 + 125 + 100}{6} = \frac{900}{6} =$ **150 ℓ**

(c) $\$1.15 \times 200 =$ **\$230**

Review E, US pp. 78-82, 3d› pp. 62-66

1. $2400 \div 3000 = 24 \div 30 =$ **0.8**
2. $6.5 \times 4000 =$ **26,000**
3. $796.8 \div 19.2 \approx 800 \div 20 = 80 \div 2 =$ **40**
4. Divisions are 25 g. Arrow is slightly past first division past 400. Closest value is **430 g**.
5. 3 whole squares, 3 half squares, and half of three squares are shaded.

   Number of squares shaded $= 3 + (3 \times \frac{1}{2}) + (\frac{1}{2} \times 3) = 6$

   Fraction shaded $= \frac{6}{10} = \mathbf{\frac{3}{5}}$
6. $\frac{4}{5}$ and $\frac{9}{10}$ are less than 1; the rest are greater than 1.

   $\frac{4}{5} = \frac{8}{10}$ which is less than $\frac{9}{10}$. So $\mathbf{\frac{4}{5}}$ is smallest.
7. $\frac{2}{25} = \frac{8}{100} =$ **0.08**
8. $2.08 = \mathbf{2\frac{2}{25}}$
9. $2\frac{1}{4} = 2.25$ Order is **2 m, $2\frac{1}{4}$ m, 2.49 m, 2.6 m**
10. 2 h = 120 min

    $\frac{45}{120} = \frac{9}{24} = \mathbf{\frac{3}{8}}$
11. $2 \div \frac{1}{4} = 2 \times 4 = 8$ There are **8** one-fourth quarts in 2 quarts. (**3d›** quarts → liters)

12. $3 \longrightarrow \$2$ (There are 15 groups of 3.)
$45 \longrightarrow \$2 \times 15 = \$30$
She received **$30**.

13. (**3d›** shrimps → prawn, beef → mutton)
Cost of 3 kg of shrimps $= 3 \times \$9 = \$27$
Cost of 3 kg of beef = Total cost − cost of 3 kg of shrimps
$= \$46.50 - \$27 = \$19.50$
Cost of 1 kg of beef $= \$19.50 \div 3 =$ **$6.50**

14. Total time = 45 min
5 min $\longrightarrow$ 225 words
45 min $\longrightarrow 225 \times 9 = 2025$ words
She types **2025** words.

15. $\frac{2}{3}$ of the number $= 12$
$\frac{1}{3}$ of the number $= 12 \div 2 = 6$
The number $= 6 \times 3 = 18$
$\frac{1}{2} \times 18 = \mathbf{9}$

16. $\frac{3}{5}$ of the total cupcakes went in the box.
$\frac{2}{5}$ of the total cupcakes $= 8$
$\frac{1}{5}$ of the total cupcakes $= 8 \div 2 = 4$
$\frac{3}{5}$ of the total cupcakes $= 4 \times 3 = 12$
She put **12** cup cakes in the box.

17. $\frac{3}{8}$ of the bottle still needs to be filled.
$\frac{5}{8}$ of a bottle $= 10$ glasses
$\frac{1}{8}$ of a bottle $= 10 \div 5 = 2$ glasses
$\frac{3}{8}$ of a bottle $= 2 \times 3 = 6$ glasses
6 more glasses of water are needed.

18. Number of girls $= 40 - 24 = 16$
Number of boys : Number of girls $= 24 : 16 =$ **3 : 2**

19. Total weight $= 60$ kg $\times 2 = 120$ kg
5 units $= 120$ kg
2 units $= \frac{120}{5} \times 2 = 48$ kg
The boy weighs **48 kg**.

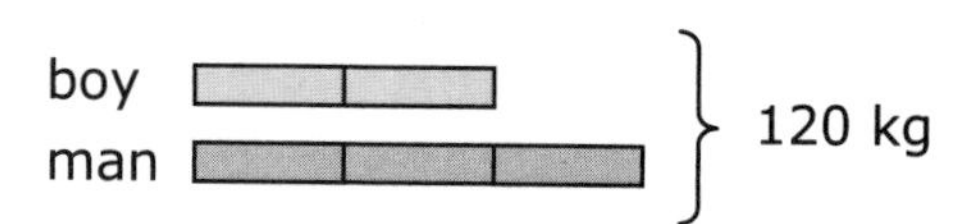

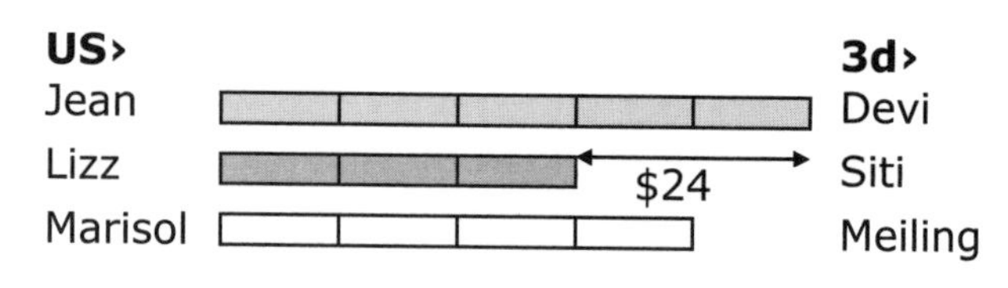

20. 2 units $= \$24$
4 units $= \$24 \times 2 = \$48$
Marisol received **$48**.

21. Number left $= 800 - 750 = 50$
Percentage left $= \frac{50}{800} \times 100\% =$ **6.25%**

22. Percentage of boys $= 100\% - 45\% = 55\%$
Percentage more boys than girls $= 55\% - 45\% = 10\%$
Amount more boys than girls $= 10\%$ of $120 =$ **12**

23. The number this year is 120% of the number last year.
120% of the number last year $= 1800$
100% of the number last year $= \frac{1800}{120} \times 100 =$ **1500**

24. 45 min $= \frac{3}{4}$ h
Distance $= 80$ km/h $\times \frac{3}{4}$ h $=$ **60 km**

25. Total number of stamps $= 100 + 140 = 240$
After:
4 units $= 240$
1 unit $= 240 \div 4 = 60$
3 units $= 60 \times 3 = 180$

US› 3d›
Jared Gopal
Ryan Samy

Jared ends up with 180 stamps and Ryan ends up with 60 stamps. If Jared started with 140 and Ryan (Samy) started with 100, Ryan gave Jared **40** stamps.

26.
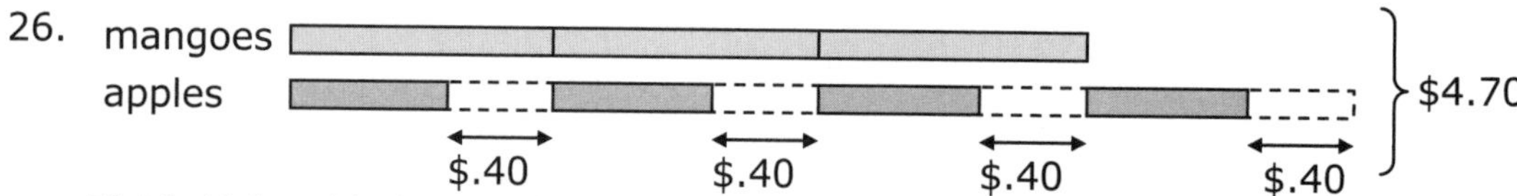

If $0.40 is added to each apple, the resulting cost would be the cost of 7 mangoes.
Cost of 7 mangoes $= \$4.70 + (4 \times \$0.40) = \$6.30$
Cost of 1 mango $= \$6.30 \div 7 =$ **$0.90**

27. A costs $\$5 + \$2 = \$7$ more than C
B costs \$2 more than C.
A and B cost $\$7 + \$2$ more than C
A and B cost \$9 more than C
3 units $= \$19.50 - \$9 = \$10.50$
1 unit $= \$10.50 \div 3 = \$3.50$
Book C costs **\$3.50**.

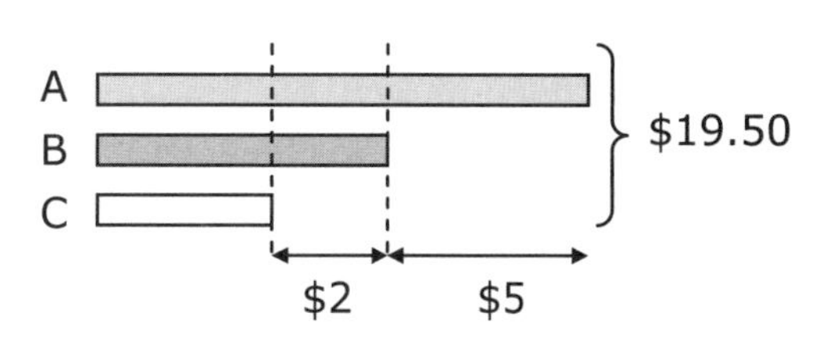

28. Total money spent Jan. – Mar. $= \$250 \times 3 = \$750$
Total money spent Apr. – May $= \$300 \times 2 = \$600$
Total money spent $= \$750 + \$600 = \$1350$
Average spent per month $= \$1350 \div 5 =$ **\$270**

29. Cost of one watch $= \$500 \div 20 = \$25$
Number of watches sold at \$40 $= \frac{3}{4} \times 20 = 15$
Number of watches sold at \$25 $= 20 - 15 = 5$
Total money $= (\$40 \times 15) + (\$25 \times 5) = \$600 + \$125 = \$725$
Money made $= \$725 - \$500 =$ **\$225**

30. 1 unit of water $= 4 - 2.6$
$= 1.4$ kg
Weight of bottle $= 2.6 - 1.4$
$=$ **1.2 kg**

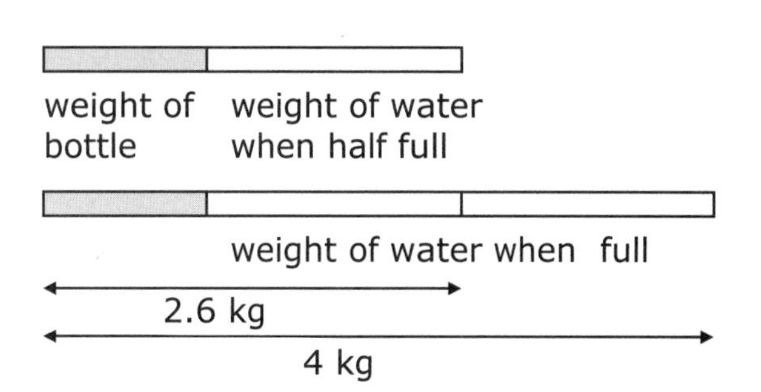

31. **5 : 8**

32. (**3d›** Brian → Gopal, Kevin → Rahim)
The number of Brian's books is 100%.
The number of Kevin's books is 130% of the number of Brian's books.
130% of Brian's books = 65
100% of Brian's books $= \frac{65}{130} \times 100 = 50$
Brian has **50** books.

33. Tarts sold Monday $= x$
Tarts sold Tuesday $= 3x$
Tarts sold Wednesday $= x + 36$
Total tarts sold $= x + 3x + x + 36 =$ **$5x + 36$**

34. Area of the rectangle $= 8 \times 9 = 72$ cm^2
Area of the square $= 72 \div 2 = 36$ cm^2
Length of side of the square $= 6$ cm $(6 \times 6 = 36)$
Perimeter of the square $= 4 \times 6 =$ **24 cm**

35. Base of the triangle $= 20 - 5 = 15$ cm Height of the triangle $= 10$ cm
Area $= \frac{1}{2} \times 10 \times 15 =$ **75 cm²**

36. Diameter of quarter circle $= 10 \times 2 = 20$ cm
Diameter of semicircle $= 10$ cm
Perimeter $= (\frac{1}{4} \times 3.14 \times 20) + (\frac{1}{2} \times 3.14 \times 10) + 10$
$= 15.7 + 15.7 + 10 =$ **41.4 cm**

37. Length of the side of the cube $= 4$ cm $(4 \times 4 = 16)$
Volume of one cube $= 16 \times 4 = 64$ cm³
Volume of the solid $= 3 \times 64 =$ **192 cm²**

38. Height water level fell $= \frac{4500}{30 \times 30} = 5$ cm
Fraction of container height that water fell by $= \frac{3}{4} - \frac{5}{8} = \frac{6}{8} - \frac{5}{8} = \frac{1}{8}$
$\frac{1}{8}$ of the height $= 5$ cm
Height of container $= 5 \times 8 =$ **40 cm**

39. $\angle DBC = (180° - 32°) \div 2 = 74°$ (isosceles Δ)
$\angle BAD = \angle ADB$, and $\angle DBC$ is an external angle of $\angle BAD$ and $\angle ADB$
$\angle BAD = 74° \div 2 =$ **37°**

40. $\angle ACB = 60°$ (ΔABC is equilateral)
$\angle DCB = 180° - 35° = 145°$ (adjacent $\angle$'s between // lines)
$\angle x = 145° - 60° =$ **85°**

41. **9** faces. 4 triangles, 4 rectangles around the side, 1 rectangle on the bottom.

42. (a) $\mathbf{\frac{1}{4}}$ of the people are boys. The 90° angle indicates $\frac{1}{4}$ of the circle.
(b) $\mathbf{\frac{1}{8}}$ of the people were women.
(c) $\frac{1}{8}$ of the people $= 120$
All of the people $= 120 \times 8 =$ **960**

Workbook Review 5
Workbook Review 6
Workbook Review 7

US› Unit 6 3d› Unit 5
More Challenging Word Problems

Part 1 – Whole Numbers and Decimals (US› pp. 83-87, 3d› pp. 67-71)

➢ Solve challenging word problems involving whole numbers and decimals.

This unit is optional. For all of these sections, encourage your student to solve the problems in different ways when possible. You can have your student solve the learning task problems without seeing the text solution, and then compare his or her method to the method given in the text. Guide your student in drawing models where necessary.

Answers to learning tasks are given in the text, but additional explanations or alternate methods will be given in this guide.

Learning Tasks 1-4, US› pp. 83-86, 3d pp. 67-70

1. For this problem, you can also use an additional diagram that, instead of separating the "before" and "after" situation, has a dashed line through Gopal's unit to make 2 parts out of it. Label the second part $10, which is what he spent. Extend the line up to Raju's bar, dividing it into two parts, and label the second part $60. By superimposing the diagrams for the two situations, it can sometimes be easier to see the relationship needed to set a certain number of units equal to a value.

2. Note that we can draw the comparison model to represent Ali's money and his brother's money in the after situation first, since we are given a ratio between their money. Then we draw the before situation, relating the lengths of the bars to the after situation.

   Alternate solutions:
   Since their mother gives each boy the same amount of money, the difference between their money remains unchanged.
   Difference = \$130 – \$45 = \$85
   1 unit = \$85
   Ali's money after = \$85 × 2 = \$170
   Amount of money given by mother = \$170 – \$130 = \$40.

3. We know the total difference in savings and the difference in savings per week. We use that to find the number of weeks.

US› Practice 6A, p. 87 3d› Practice 5A, p. 71

1.

blue 148 12

green 28 ?

Difference $= 148 - 28 + 12 = 132$
Or:
More green beads are added than blue beads. The difference in blue beads and green beads will be less by the amount of excess green beads added.
Excess green beads $= 28 - 12 = 16$
Difference $= 148 - 16 = 132$
There will be **132** more blue beads than green beads.

2. (**3d›** meatballs → fishballs, shrimps → prawns)
Cost of 40 meatballs $= \$1.50 \times 4 = \$6$
Cost of 600 g shrimps $= \$18 - \$6 = \$12$
Cost of 100 g shrimps $= \$12 \div 6 = \$2$
Cost of 1000 g shrimps $= \$2 \times 10 = \$20$
1 kg of shrimps cost **$20**.

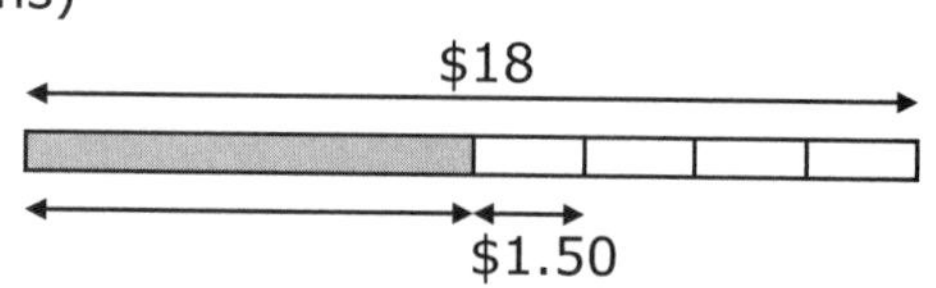

3. Number of mangoes sold $= 100 - 16 = 84$
3 mangoes $\longrightarrow \$4$
1 mango $\longrightarrow \$\frac{4}{3}$
84 mangoes $\longrightarrow \$\frac{4}{3} \times 84 = \$112$
Amount of money she made $= \$112 - \$90 =$ **$22**

4. 1 unit = cost of the racket
5 units $= \$13.75 + (4 \times \$5.50) = \$35.75$
1 unit $= \$35.75 \div 5 = \$7.15$
The racket costs $7.15
OR
1 unit = cost of birdie (**3d›** shuttlecock)
5 units = $13.75 - $5.50 = $8.25
1 unit = $8.25 ÷ 5 = $1.65
Cost of the racket = $1.65 + $5.50 = $7.15

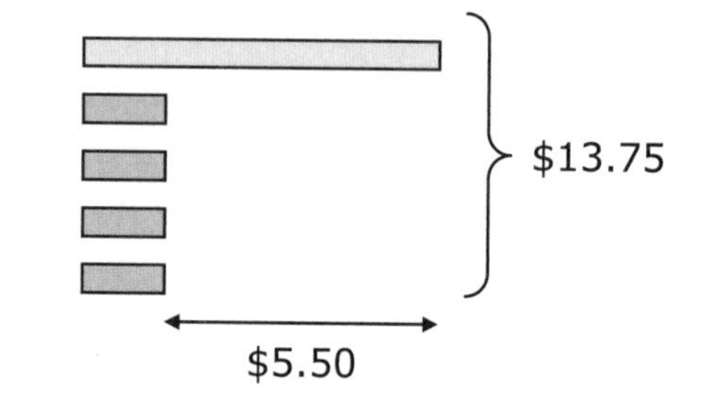

5. 1 unit = Brett's money
3 units = Rachel's money
2 units $= \$5 + \$9 = \$14$
1 unit $= \$14 \div 2 = \$7$
3 units $= \$7 \times 3 = \$21$
She had **$21** at first.

US› Before: **3d›**
Rachel Rosnah
Brett Minah
After:
Rachel Rosnah
Brett Minah
$5 $9

6.

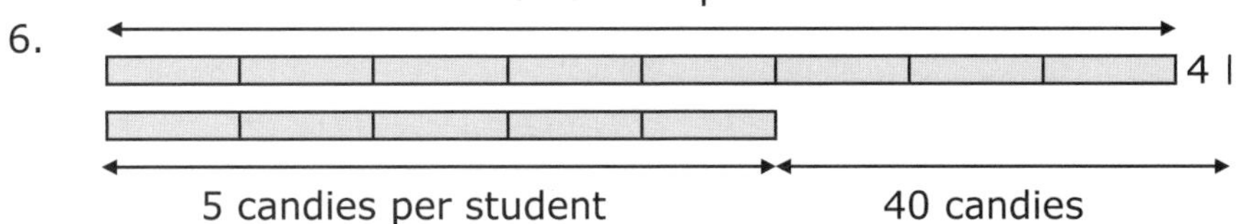

The unit in this diagram is equal to each student getting one candy; the first unit is all the students getting one candy, the second all the students getting a second candy, and so on. So the value of 1 unit is the number of students in the class.

1 unit = the number of students in her class.
3 units = 40 – 4 = 36
1 unit = 36 ÷ 3 = 12
There are **12** students in her class.

7. **US›** After: **3d›**
Jordan Fuming
Ricardo Minghua

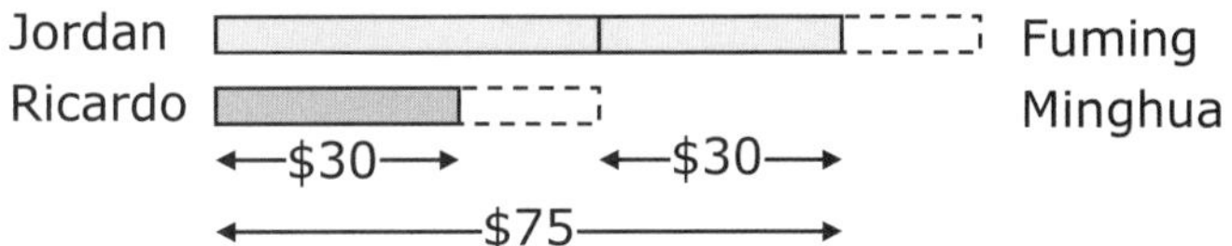

Amount given = $75 – (2 × $30) = **$15**
Or:
Difference remains the same.
Difference before = $75 – $30 = $45
1 unit = $45
Amount of money given = $45 – $30 = $15

8. 1 unit = 35 + (2 × 15) = 65
3 units = 65 × 3 = 195
They have **195** stickers altogether.
Or:

After:

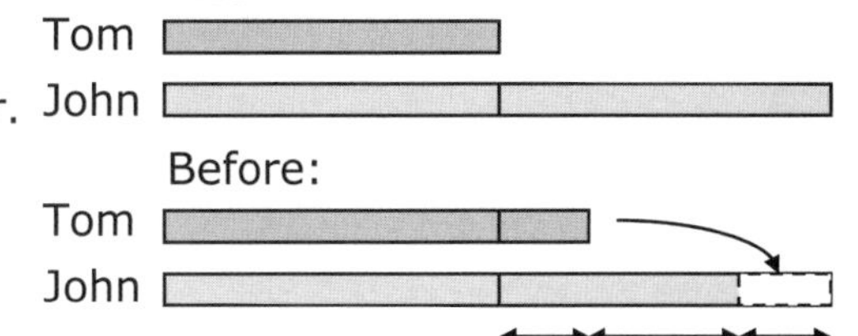

9. (**3d›** Damon → Rahim, Eddie → Ahmad)
$24 – $18 = $6
Each day Damon spent $6 less than Eddie.
Find how many days it takes for Damon to spend $120 less than Eddie.
$120 ÷ $6 = 20
It takes 20 days for Damon to spend $120 less than Eddie, which is when Eddie had no money left. Eddie spent all his money in 20 days.
$24 × 20 = $480
They each had **$480**.

10.

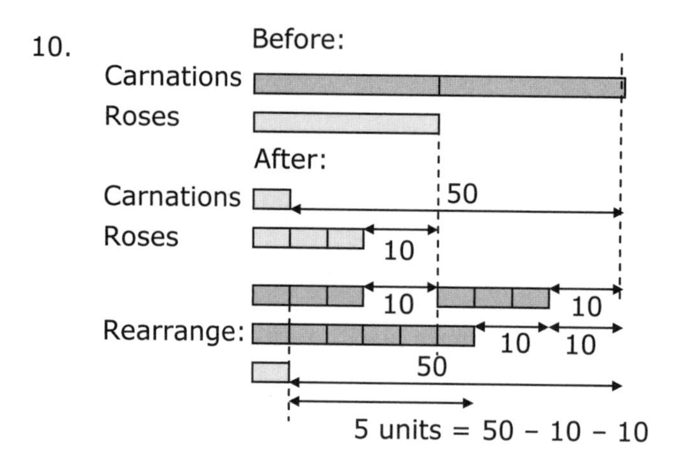

1 unit = carnations, after
Roses, before = 3 units + 10
Half of the carnations, before, also equal 3 units + 10.
You can rearrange the units to show that:
5 units = 50 – 10 – 10 = 30
1 unit = 30 ÷ 5 = 6
3 units = 6 × 3 = 18
Number of roses at first = 18 + 10 = 28

Part 2 – Fractions (US> pp. 88-93, 3d> pp. 72-77)

➢ Solve challenging word problems involving fractions.

US> Learning Tasks 1-4, pp. 88-91
3d> Learning Tasks 1-5, pp. 72-75

1. The number of red beads is half that of yellow beads. So, if the yellow beads are 3 units, then the red beads are $1\frac{1}{2}$ units, leaving $\frac{1}{2}$ unit for blue beads. Since there are 30 more red beads than blue beads, and 1 more unit of red beads than blue beads, 1 unit $= 30$. Alternatively, the $\frac{1}{5}$ unit can be divided into half, so 2 units $= 30$.

US> 4. **3d>** 5.

Since an equal number of cups is left, and $\frac{2}{3}$ of the blue cups and $\frac{1}{2}$ of the blue cups are left, then $\frac{2}{3}$ of the blue cups $= \frac{1}{2}$ of the red cups.

US> Practice 6B, p. 92 **3d> Practice 5B, p. 76**

1.

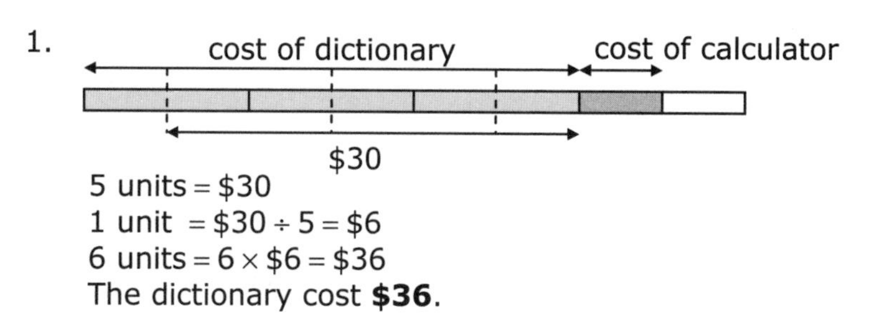

5 units $= \$30$
1 unit $= \$30 \div 5 = \$6$
6 units $= 6 \times \$6 = \$36$
The dictionary cost **$36**.

2.

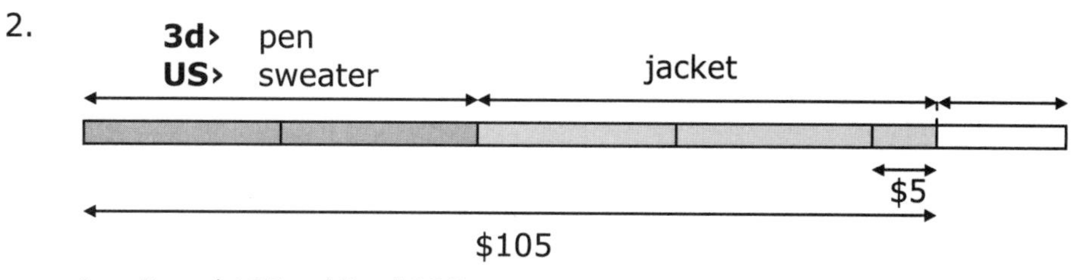

4 units $= \$105 - \$5 = \$100$
1 unit $= \$100 \div 4 = \$25$
Money left $= \$25 - \$5 =$ **$20**

3. **US›**, 2005 printing:

She can buy 12 pots with $\frac{2}{5}$ of her money, so 6 pots cost $\frac{1}{5}$ of her money.

Therefore, the 8 plants were bought with $\frac{2}{5}$ of her money.

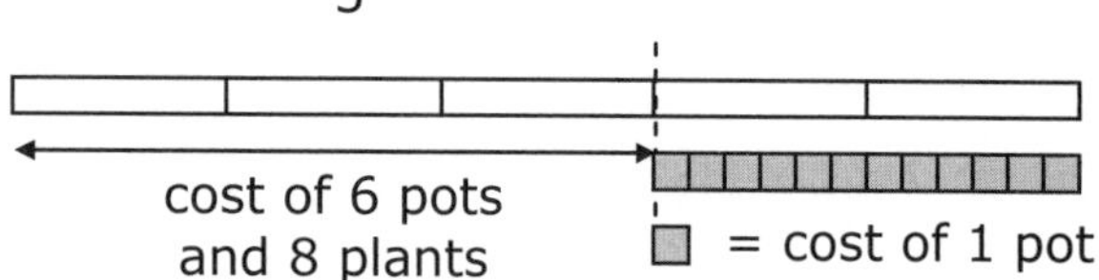

$\frac{2}{5} \longrightarrow 8$ plants

$\frac{1}{5} \longrightarrow \frac{8}{2} = 4$ plants

$1 \longrightarrow 4 \times 5 = 20$ plants.

She could buy **20** plants.

3d› and **US›** printing prior to 2005

She can buy 6 bowls with $\frac{2}{5}$ of her money, so 3 bowls cost $\frac{1}{5}$ of her money. Therefore, the 8 plates were bought with $\frac{2}{5}$ of her money.

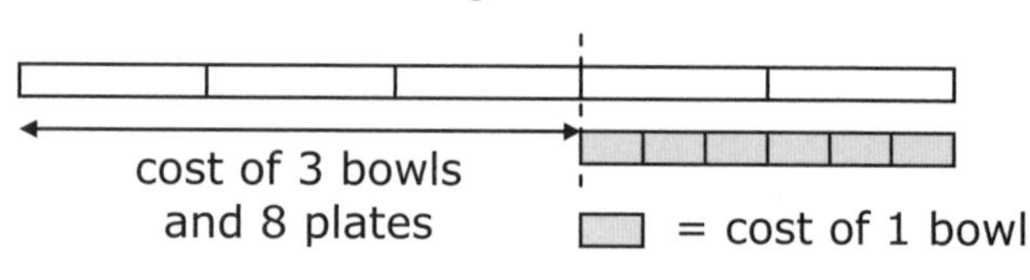

$\frac{2}{5} \longrightarrow 8$ plates

$\frac{1}{5} \longrightarrow \frac{8}{2} = 4$ plates

$1 \longrightarrow 4 \times 5 = 20$ plates.

She could buy **20** plates.

4.

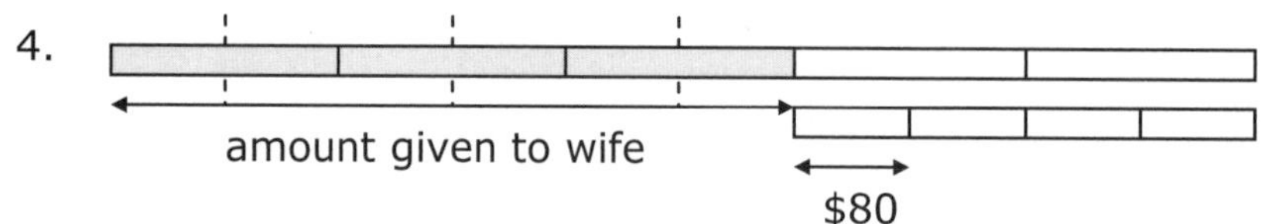

1 unit = \$80

6 units = \$80 × 6 = \$480

Or: $\frac{1}{4}$ of $\frac{2}{5} \longrightarrow \$80$

$\frac{1}{10} \longrightarrow \$80$ $\qquad \frac{3}{5} = \frac{6}{10}$

$\frac{6}{10} \longrightarrow \$80 \times 6 = \$480$

His wife received **\$480**.

5. Fraction of towels that are pink $= \frac{2}{5} = \frac{8}{20}$

Fraction of towels that are blue $= \frac{1}{4} = \frac{5}{20}$

Fraction of towels that are white $= 1 - \frac{8}{20} - \frac{5}{20} = \frac{7}{20}$

Fraction more pink than blue $\frac{8}{20} - \frac{5}{20} = \frac{3}{20}$

$\frac{7}{20} \longrightarrow 28$

$\frac{1}{20} \longrightarrow \frac{28}{7} = 4$

$\frac{3}{20} \longrightarrow 4 \times 3 = 12$

There are **12** more pink towels than blue towels.

6. Fraction spent both weeks $= \frac{1}{3} + \frac{1}{5} = \frac{5}{15} + \frac{3}{15} = \frac{8}{15}$

$\frac{8}{15}$ of his money $= \$160$

$\frac{1}{15}$ of his money $= \$160 \div 8 = \$20$

All of his money $= \$20 \times 15 = \$300$

He had **$300** at first.

7. 3 units $= \$18$

1 unit $= \$18 \div 3 = \$6$

5 units $= \$6 \times 5 = \$30$

He spent **$30**.

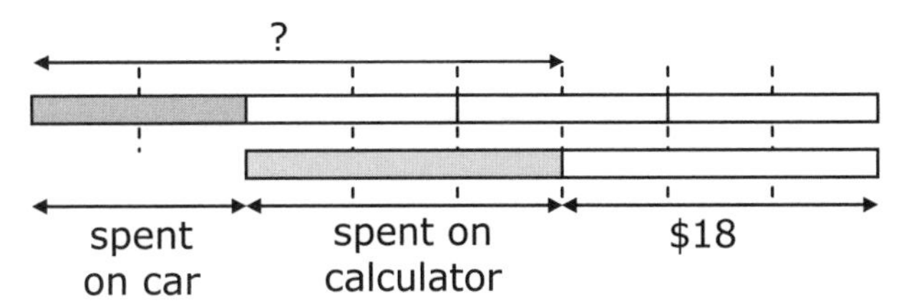

8. Cost of 1 mango = cost of 3 apples

Cost of 3 mangoes = cost of $3 \times 3 = 9$ apples.

Cost of 3 mangoes + 6 apples = cost of 9 apples + 6 apples = 15 apples

$\frac{3}{4}$ of his money $\longrightarrow$ 15 apples

$\frac{1}{4}$ of his money $\longrightarrow 15 \div 3 = 5$ apples

He could buy **5** more apples.

US> Practice 6C, p. 93 3d> Practice 5B, p. 77

1. Fraction remaining $= 1 - \frac{1}{3} - \frac{1}{9} = 1 - \frac{3}{9} - \frac{1}{9} = \frac{5}{9}$

   Fraction of white beads $= \frac{1}{5}$ of the remainder $\frac{1}{5} \times \frac{5}{9} = \frac{1}{9}$

   $\frac{1}{9} \longrightarrow 25$ beads

   $\frac{9}{9} \longrightarrow 25 \times 9 = 225$

   There were **225** beads altogether.

2. Fraction of total spent on calculator $= \frac{1}{4} \times \frac{2}{5} = \frac{1}{10}$

   Fraction spent on watch $= \frac{3}{5} = \frac{6}{10}$

   Difference $= \frac{6}{10} - \frac{1}{10} = \frac{5}{10} = \frac{1}{2}$

   $\frac{1}{2}$ of his money $= \$28$

   His total money $= 2 \times \$28 =$ **$56**

3. 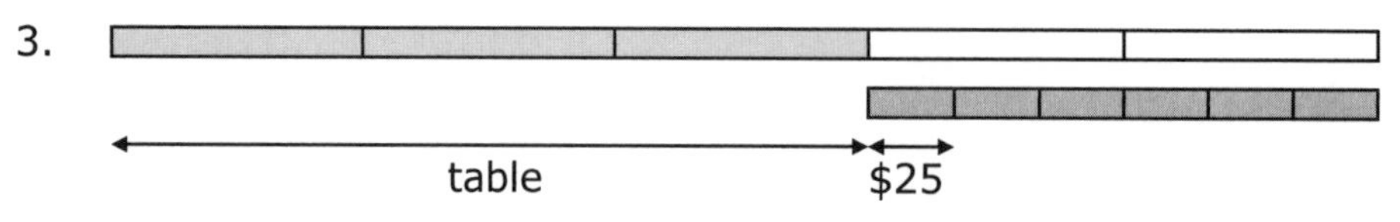

   Cost of 3 chairs $= \frac{1}{5}$ of his money $= 3 \times \$25 = \$75$

   $\frac{3}{5}$ of his money $= \$75 \times 3 = \$225$

   He spent **$225** on the table.

4. 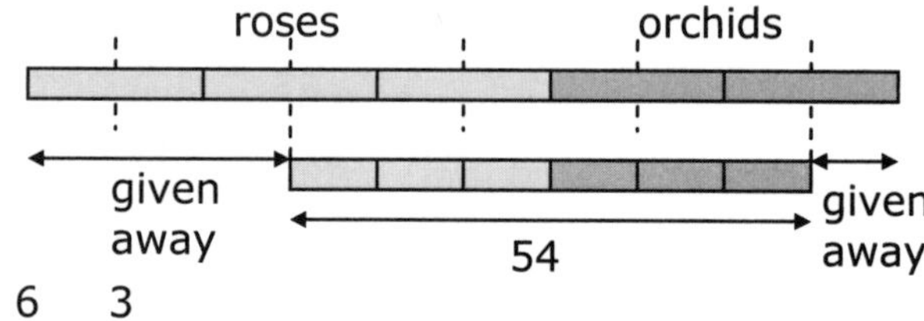

   6 units = 54
   1 unit $= 54 \div 6 = 9$
   10 units $= 9 \times 10 = 90$
   OR:

   $1 - \left(\frac{1}{2} \times \frac{3}{5}\right) - \left(\frac{1}{4} \times \frac{2}{5}\right) = 1 - \frac{3}{10} - \frac{1}{10} = \frac{6}{10} = \frac{3}{5}$

   $\frac{3}{5}$ of the flowers $= 54$

   $\frac{1}{5}$ of the flowers $= 54 \div 3 = 18$

   All of the flowers $= 18 \times 5 = 90$
   She had **90** flowers at first.

5. (**3d›** lb → kg)
3 units of oil = 3.3 – 1.5 = 1.8 lb
1 unit of oil = 1.8 ÷ 3 = 0.6 lb
Weight of bottle = 1.5 – 0.6 = **0.9 lb**

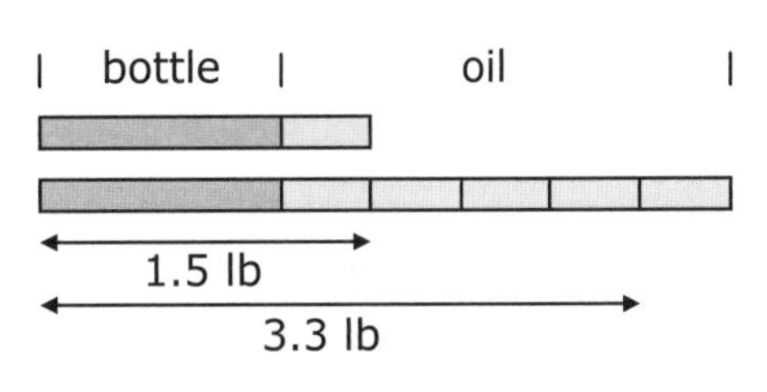

6. **US›** Juanita, Brett **3d›** Meiling, Fumin

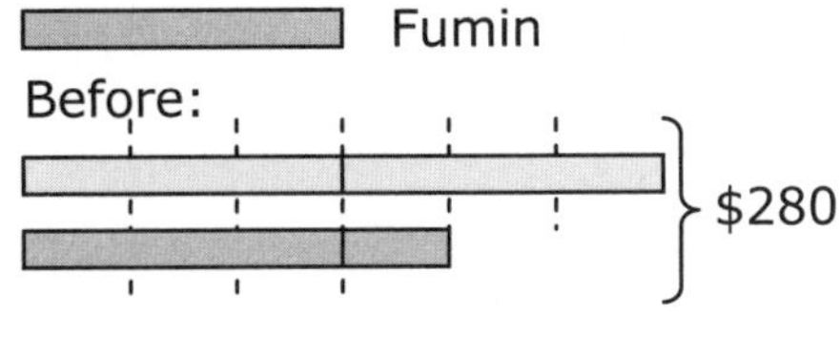

10 units = $280
1 unit = $28
6 units = $28 × 6 = $168
Juanita had **$168** at first.

7. 1 unit = cost of 1 magazine
3 units = cost of 1 book
4 units = $\frac{2}{5}$ of his money
6 units = $\frac{3}{5}$ of his money = $24
1 unit = $24 ÷ 6 = $4
3 units = $4 × 3 = $12
The book costs **$12**.

8.

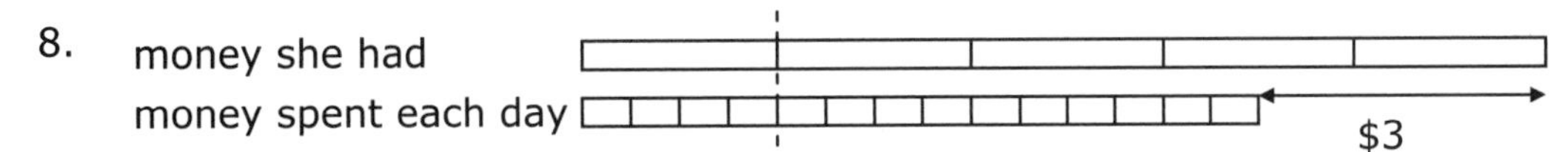

$\frac{1}{5}$ of her money = amount spent in 4 days
Divide each fifth in 4.
6 units = $30
1 unit = $30 ÷ 6 = $5
20 units = $5 × 20 = $100
She had **$100** at first.

Part 3 – Ratio (US› pp. 94-98, 3d› pp. 78-82)

➤ Solve challenging word problems involving ratio.

Some of the problems in this section involve one quantity given as a fraction of another. Students learned that they could interpret this as a ratio. For example, if A is $\frac{2}{5}$ of B, then the ratio of A to B is 2 : 5. Many of the strategies used to solve fraction problems by drawing bars and showing the fraction as a unit can be applied to problems involving ratio.

Learning Tasks 1-3, US› pp. 94-96, 3d pp. 78-80

US› Practice 6D, p. 97 3d› Practice 5D, p. 81

1. (**3d›** Emma → Suhua)
   Amount of money Jane had = \$50 + \$10 = \$60
   Emma's money : Jane's money = 50 : 60 = **5 : 6**

2. 3 units = 18
   1 unit = 18 ÷ 3 = 6
   8 units = 6 × 8 = 48
   There are **48** children altogether.

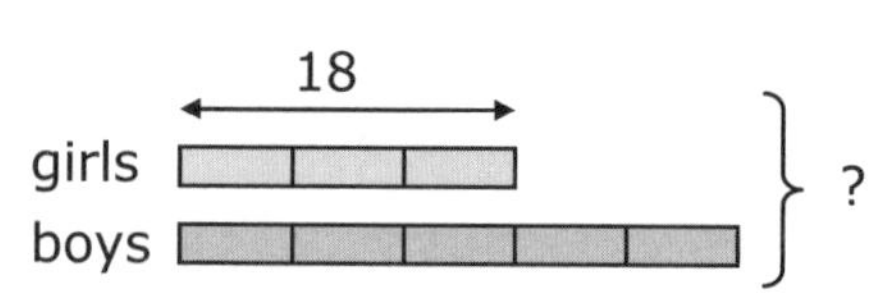

3. 12 units = 360
   1 unit = 360 ÷ 12 = 30
   2 units = 30 × 2 = 60
   Peter has **60** more stamps than Salim.

Peter
Salim
360
?

4. 5 units = 420 g
   1 unit = 420 ÷ 5 = 84 g
   14 units = 84 × 14 = 1176 g
   The three packages weigh **1176 g**.

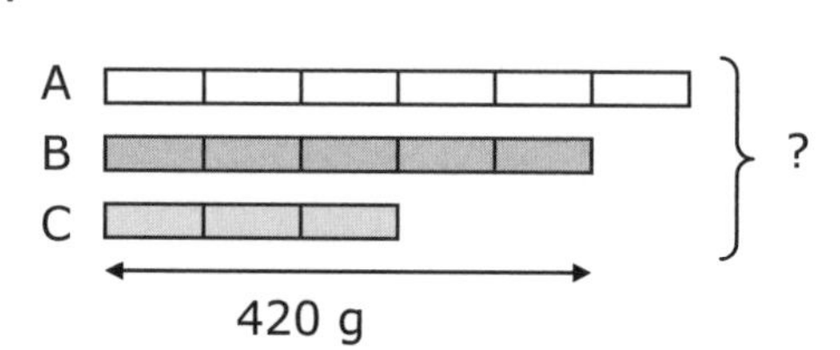

5. 12 units = 60 cm
   1 unit = 60 ÷ 12 = 5 cm
   3 units = 5 × 3 = 15 cm
   The shortest side is **15 cm** long.

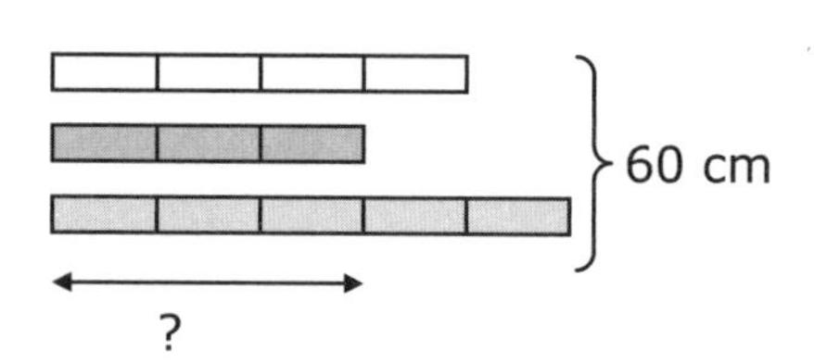

6. 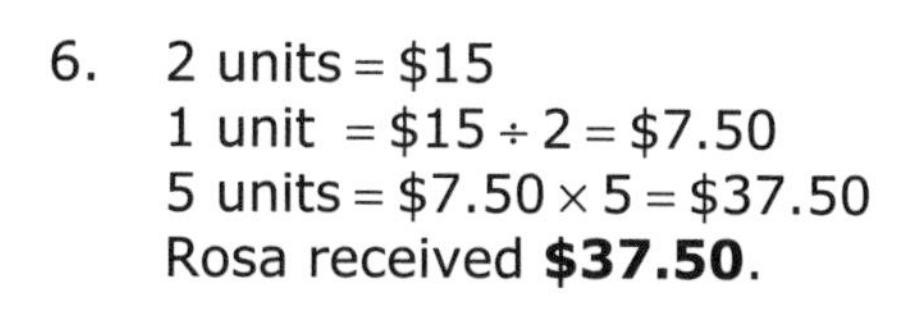
2 units = $15
1 unit = $15 ÷ 2 = $7.50
5 units = $7.50 × 5 = $37.50
Rosa received **$37.50**.

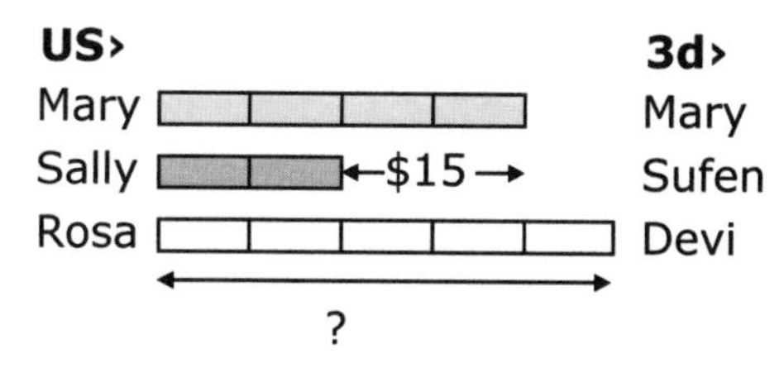

7. 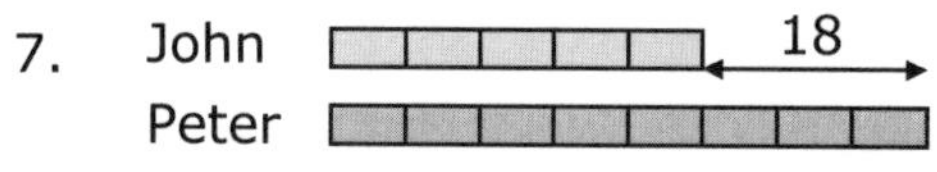

3 units = 18
1 unit = 18 ÷ 3 = 6

Number of John's stamps = 5 units = 5 × 6 = 30
Number of Peter's stamps = 8 units = 8 × 6 = 48
Peter gives 22 stamps to John.
New number of John's stamps = 30 + 22 = 52
New number of Peter's stamps = 48 – 22 = 26
New ratio = 52 : 26 = **2 : 1**

8. 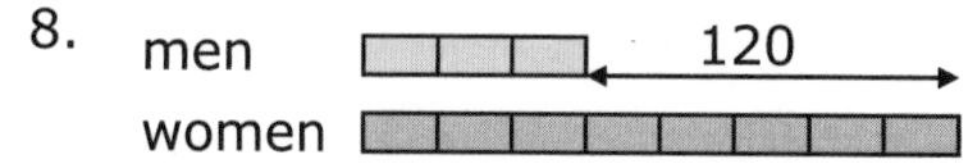

5 units = 120
1 unit = 120 ÷ 5 = 24

Number of men = 3 units = 24 × 3 = 72
Number of women = 8 units = 24 × 8 = 192
New number of men = 72 + 3 = 75
New number of women = 192 – 12 = 180
New ratio = 75 : 180 = **5 : 12**

9. 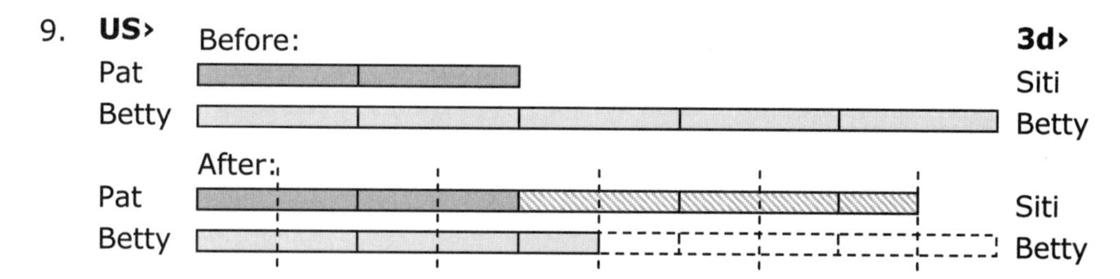

Ratio after = **9 : 5**

10. 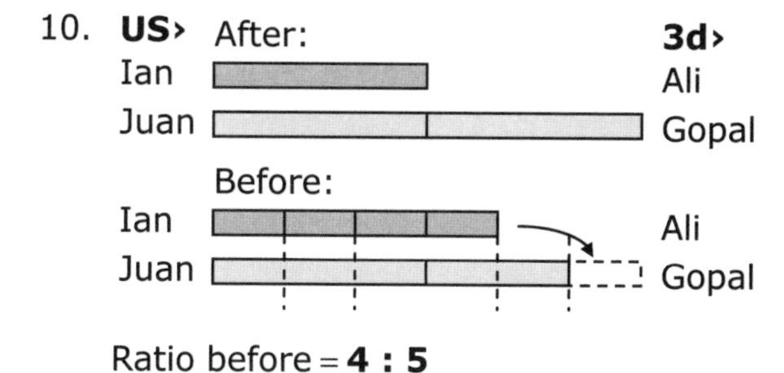

Ratio before = **4 : 5**

US› Practice 6E, p. 98 3d› Practice 5E, p. 82

1. Carol
   Mary

   Ratio = **6 : 1**

2. **US›** Kara, Holly **3d›** Devi, Gopal

   Ratio = **8 : 5**

3. 7 units = \$28
   1 unit = \$28 ÷ 7 = \$4
   12 units = \$4 × 12 = \$48
   John has **\$48**.

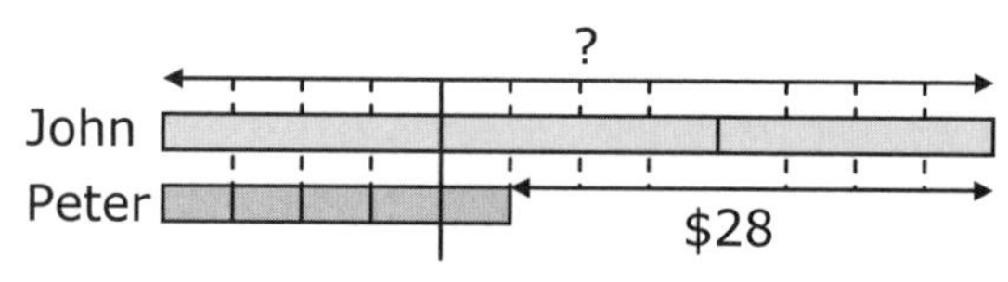

4. 4 units = 48
   1 unit = 48 ÷ 4 = 12
   10 units = 12 × 10 = 120
   There are **120** students in the choir.

   boys
   girls
   48
   ?

5. 3 units = \$30
   1 unit = \$10
   14 units = \$10 × 14 = \$140
   They have **\$140** altogether.

   US› Before: **3d›**
   Andrew Kassim
   Paul Paul
   After:
   Andrew Kassim
   Paul Paul
   \$30
   ?

6.

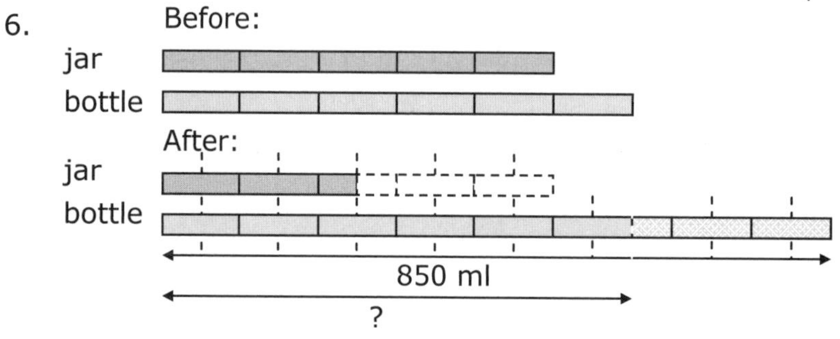

17 small units = 850 ml
1 small unit = 850 ÷ 17 = 50 ml
There were 12 units in the bottle originally.
12 units = 50 ml × 12 = 600 ml
The bottle had **600 ml** of water at first.

7.

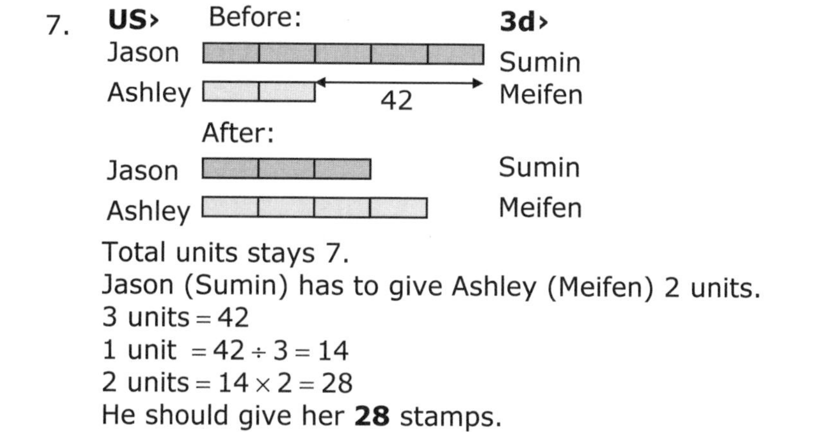

Total units stays 7.
Jason (Sumin) has to give Ashley (Meifen) 2 units.
3 units = 42
1 unit = 42 ÷ 3 = 14
2 units = 14 × 2 = 28
He should give her **28** stamps.

8.

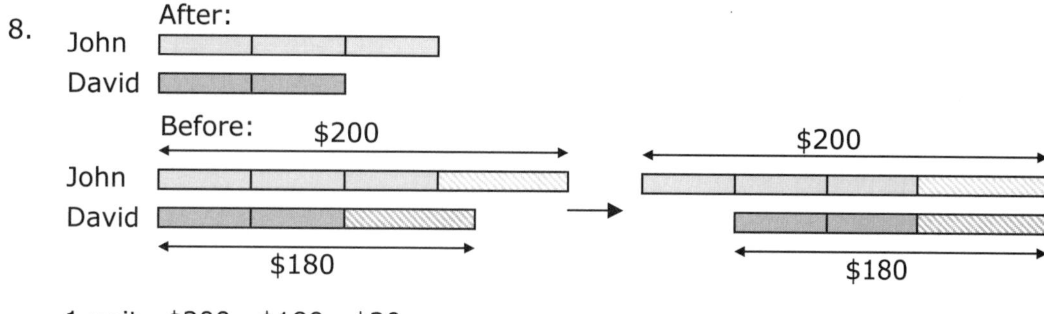

1 unit = \$200 – \$180 = \$20
2 units = \$20 × 2 = \$40
David spent \$180 – \$40 = \$140
Each spent **\$140**.

9.

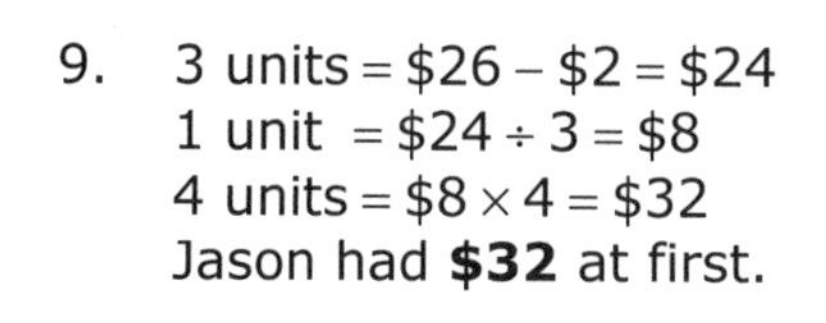

3 units = \$26 – \$2 = \$24
1 unit = \$24 ÷ 3 = \$8
4 units = \$8 × 4 = \$32
Jason had **\$32** at first.

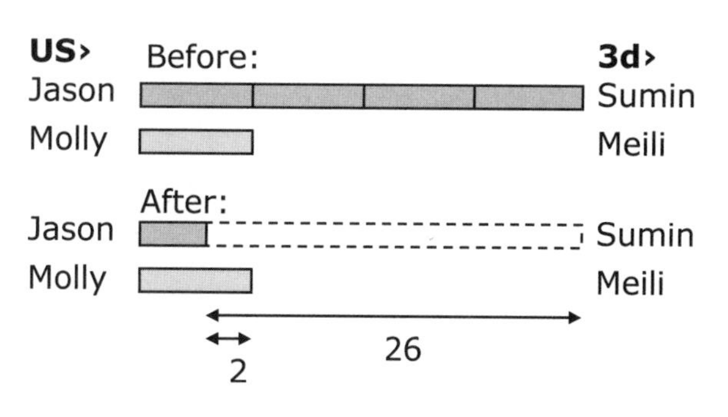

Part 4 – Percentage (US> pp. 99-101, 3d> pp. 83-85)

- Solve challenging word problems involving percentage.

Learning Tasks 1-2, US> pp. 99-100, 3d pp. 83-84

In all of these problems, it is important to establish the value to be sued as the base, or 100%. In task 1 it is the cost price, and in task 2 it is the total club members.

US> Practice 6F, p. 101 3d> Practice 5F, p. 85

1. The number of participants is 100%. If 60% are male, then 40% are female.

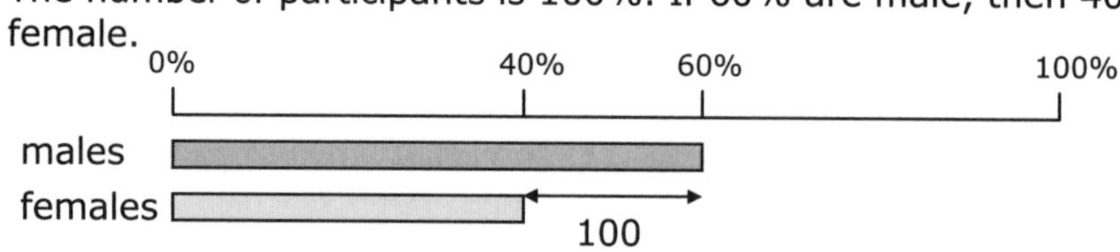

20% of the participants $= 100$

$20\% \longrightarrow 100$

$100\% \longrightarrow 100 \times 5 = 500$

There were **500** participants.

2.

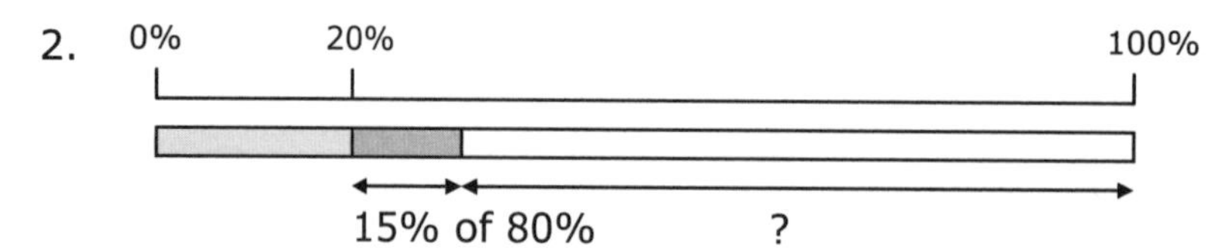

Percentage left $= 85\%$ of $80\% = \frac{85}{100} \times 80\% = \mathbf{68\%}$

3. The number of girls is 100%.

0% 100% 105%

girls

boys

Total number of children $= 205\%$ of the girls

5% of the girls is 2.

$5\% \longrightarrow 2$

$1\% \longrightarrow \frac{2}{5}$

$205\% \longrightarrow \frac{2}{5} \times 205 = 82$

There are **82** children.

4. Amount more that she gave away $= 240 - 160 = 80$
   Percent more she gave away this year than last year
   $= \frac{80}{160} \times 100\% = \mathbf{50\%}$

5. Amount of stamps that Betty bought $= 72 - 27 = 45$
   Percent more Anne bought than Betty $= \frac{27}{45} \times 100\% = \mathbf{60\%}$

6. (**3d>** U.S. stamps → Malaysian stamps)
   Number of Singapore stamps $= 420 - 150 = 270$
   Amount more Singapore than U.S. stamps $= 270 - 150 = 120$
   Per cent more Singapore stamps than U.S stamps $= \frac{120}{150} \times 100\% = \mathbf{80\%}$

7. 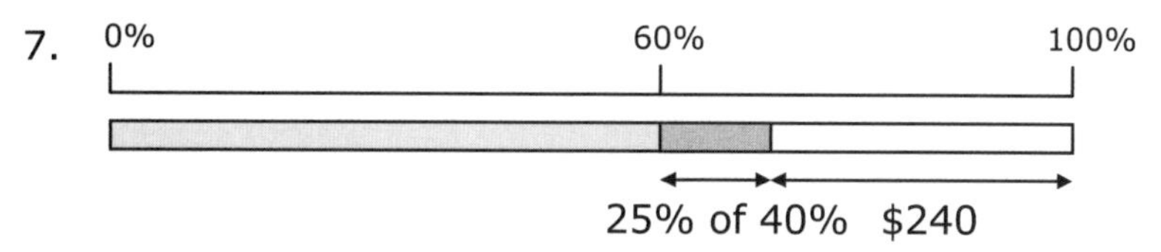

   Percentage left $= 75\%$ of $40\% = \frac{3}{4} \times 40\% = 30\%$
   $30\% \longrightarrow \$240$
   $1\% \longrightarrow \$240 \div 30 = \$8$
   $100\% \longrightarrow \$8 \times 100 = \$800$
   The sum of money was **$800**.

8. Marvin's money is 100%.

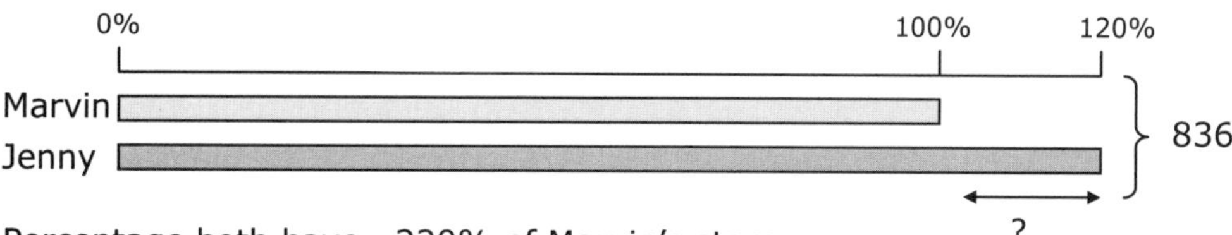

   Percentage both have $= 220\%$ of Marvin's stamps
   $220\% \longrightarrow 836$
   $1\% \longrightarrow \frac{836}{220}$
   $20\% \longrightarrow \frac{836}{220} \times 20 = 76$
   Jenny has **76** more stamps than Marvin.

9.

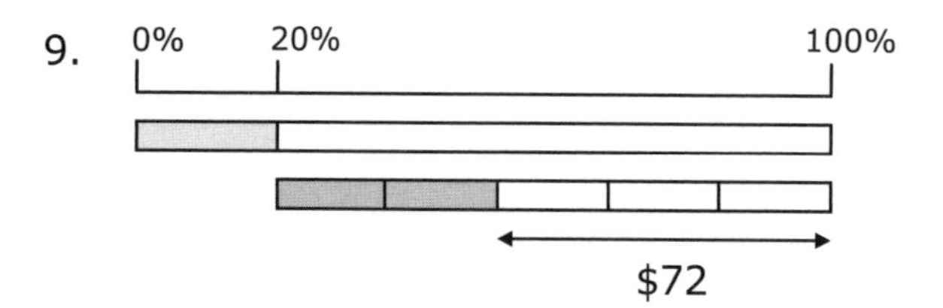

After buying the dress, he remainder is 80%.

$\frac{3}{5}$ of $80\% = 48\%$

$48\% \longrightarrow \$72$

$1\% \longrightarrow \$\frac{72}{48}$

$100\% \longrightarrow \$\frac{72}{48} \times 100 = \$150$

She had **$150** at first.

10.

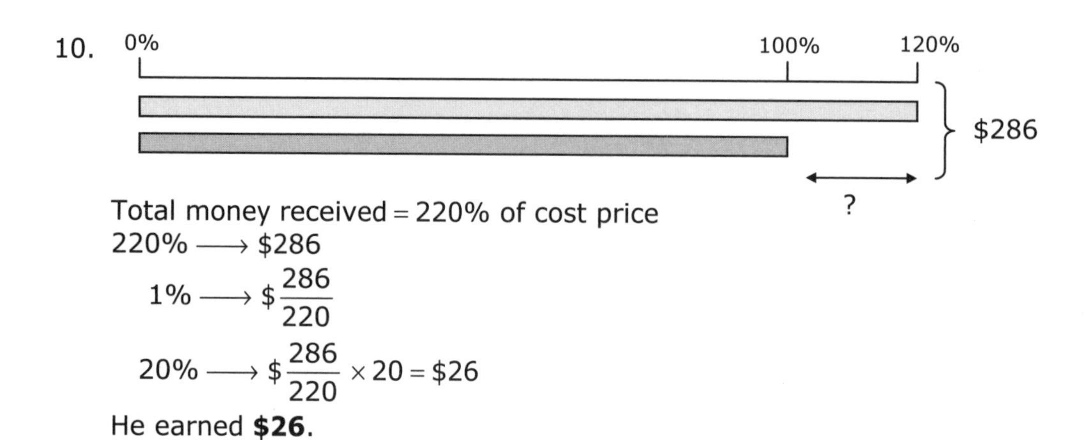

Total money received = 220% of cost price

$220\% \longrightarrow \$286$

$1\% \longrightarrow \$\frac{286}{220}$

$20\% \longrightarrow \$\frac{286}{220} \times 20 = \$26$

He earned **$26**.

Part 5 – Speed (US> pp. 102-105, 3d> pp. 86-89)

- Solve challenging word problems involving speed.

In these problems, we are dealing with 3 quantities, speed, time and distance. We can get the third quantity from the other two:

$$\text{Distance} = \text{Speed} \times \text{Time}$$

$$\text{Speed} = \frac{\text{Distance}}{\text{Time}}$$

$$\text{Time} = \frac{\text{Distance}}{\text{Speed}}$$

Your student should draw diagrams for these problems, using a line between two points to represent a trip or a part of it, and indicating all the given data. If they have two pieces of data for any part, they can find the third using the above formulae. Using the part of the trip for which they have two pieces of data to find the third is usually the first step in solving these problems.

To find the average speed for the whole distance, when a trip is divided into two parts, we need to find the total distance and the total time.

Learning Tasks 1-3, US> pp. 102-104, 3d pp. 86-88

1. Lead your student to see that to find the first driver's average speed, we need to find a time. We can get a time for the second driver (we have speed and distance for him), and use that to get the time for the first driver.

2. Since we have two pieces of data for the first part (speed and time) we can find the distance for the first part. Since we have the total distance, we can now find the distance for the second part by subtraction. Now we have two pieces of data for the second part (speed and distance) and so can find the time for the second part.

3. Since we have two pieces of data for the first part (speed and time), we can find the distance for the first part. From that, we can find the distance for the second part, and now we have two pieces of data for the second part (speed and distance) and can find the time.

 **US› Practice 6G, p. 105 3d› Practice 5G, p. 89**

1. 2 h, 70 km/h
P Q
80 km/h 3:00 p.m.

Distance = 70 km/h × 2 h = 140 km

Time for return = $\frac{140 \text{ km}}{80 \text{ km/h}} = \frac{7}{4}$ h = $1\frac{3}{4}$ h

$1\frac{3}{4}$ h after 3:00 p.m. is 4:45 p.m.

She reaches Town P at **4:45 p.m.**

2. Time for van = $\frac{190 \text{ km}}{60 \text{ km/h}} = 3\frac{1}{6}$ h = 3 h 10 min.

If the car leaves 50 minutes after the van and arrives 20 minutes earlier, its travel time is 70 minutes less. 70 min = 1 h 10 min
Time for car = 3 h 10 min − 1 h 10 min = 2 h

Speed of car = $\frac{190 \text{ km}}{2 \text{ h}}$ = **95 km/h**

3. Time for trip from P to Q = $\frac{120 \text{ km}}{40 \text{ km/h}}$ = 3 h

Time for return trip = $\frac{120 \text{ km}}{60 \text{ km/h}}$ = 2 h

Total time = 3 h + 2 h = 5 h
Total distance = 2 × 120 km = 240 km

Average speed = $\frac{240 \text{ km}}{5 \text{ h}}$ = **48 km/h**

4. 9:00 a.m. 250 km 1:30 p.m.
A B
60 km/h

Distance for 1st part = $\frac{3}{5}$ × 250 km = 150 km

Distance for 2nd part = 250 km − 150 km = 100 km
(or: Total distance = 5 units = 250 km; 1 unit = 50 km, 3 units = 150 km, and 2 units = 100 km)

Time for 1st part = $\frac{150 \text{ km}}{60 \text{ km/h}} = 2\frac{1}{2}$ h = 2 h 30 min

Total time = 4 h 30 min
Time for 2nd part = 4 h 30 min − 2 h 30 min = 2 h

Speed for 2nd part = $\frac{100 \text{ km}}{2 \text{ h}}$ = **50 km/h**

5.

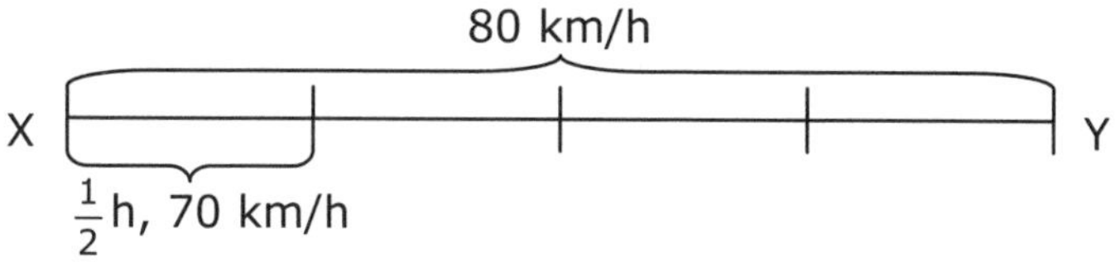

80 km/h

X Y

$\frac{1}{2}$h, 70 km/h

Distance for 1st part $= 70$ km/h $\times \frac{1}{2}$ h $= 35$ km

Distance for whole trip $= 35$ km $\times 4 = 140$ km

Time for whole trip $= \frac{140 \text{ km}}{80 \text{ km/h}} = 1\frac{3}{4}$ h

Time for 2nd part $= 1\frac{3}{4}$ h $- \frac{1}{2}$ h $=$ **$1\frac{1}{4}$ h**

6.

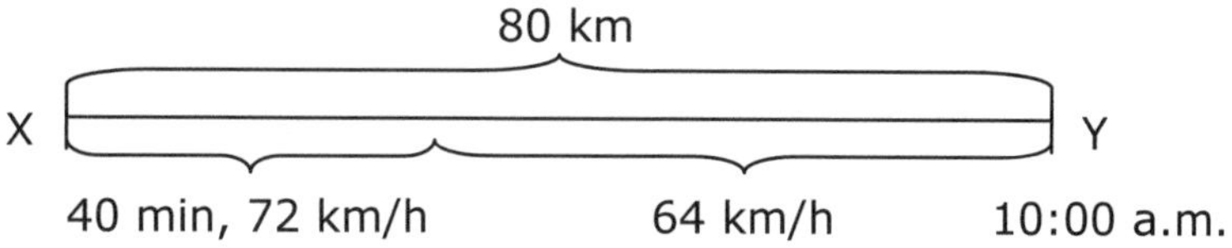

80 km

X Y

40 min, 72 km/h 64 km/h 10:00 a.m.

40 min $= \frac{40}{60}$ h $= \frac{2}{3}$ h

Distance for 1st part $= 72$ km/h $\times \frac{2}{3}$ h $= 48$ km

Distance for 2nd part $= 80$ km $- 48$ km $= 32$ km

Time for 2nd part $= \frac{32 \text{ km}}{64 \text{ km/h}} = \frac{1}{2}$ h $= 30$ min

Total time $= 40$ min $+ 30$ min $= 70$ min $= 1$ h 10 min
1 h 10 min before 10:00 a.m. is 8:50 a.m.
He left Town X at **8:50 a.m.**

7.

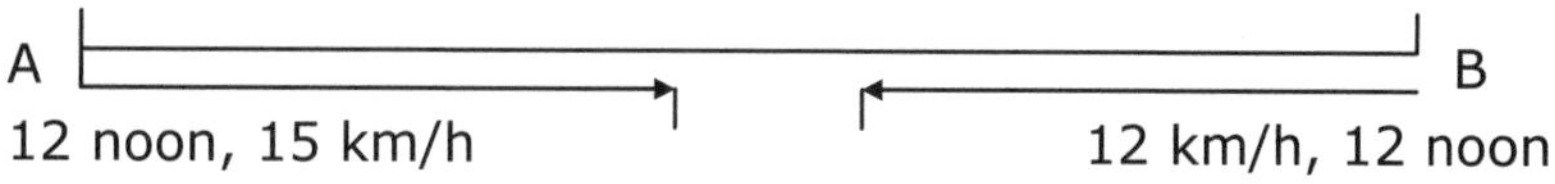

A B

12 noon, 15 km/h 12 km/h, 12 noon

Time for both $= \frac{2}{3}$ h

Distance for Peter $= 15$ km/h $\times \frac{2}{3}$ h $= 10$ km

Distance for Henry $= 12$ km/h $\times \frac{2}{3}$ h $= 8$ km

Distance between them $= 20 - 10 - 8 =$ **2 km**

Review (US> pp. 106-130, 3d> pp. 90-100)

Review F, US> pp. 106-110, 3d> pp. 90-94

1. (a) **356,000** (b) **4.3**
2. **0.103**
3. $\frac{2}{5}$ is smaller than $\frac{1}{2}$. The fractions in the list smaller than $\frac{1}{2}$ (where the numerator is less than half the denominator) are $\frac{4}{9}$ and $\frac{3}{8}$. $\frac{4}{9}$ is closer to $\frac{1}{2}$ than $\frac{3}{8}$, so $\frac{3}{8}$ is the most likely answer. Check: $\frac{3}{8}=\frac{15}{40}$; $\frac{2}{5}=\frac{16}{40}$ (or $\frac{4}{9}=\frac{32}{72}$ and $\frac{3}{8}=\frac{24}{72}$). $\mathbf{\frac{3}{8}}$ is the smallest fraction.
4. $0.045=\frac{45}{1000}=\mathbf{\frac{9}{200}}$
5. $\frac{2}{5}\times 60=\mathbf{24}$
6. **US>**

$$\frac{5}{8}-\frac{2}{3}\div\left(6\div\frac{3}{4}\right)=\frac{5}{8}-\frac{2}{3}\div\underline{\left(6\times\frac{4}{3}\right)}$$
$$=\frac{5}{8}-\underline{\frac{2}{3}\div 8}$$
$$=\frac{5}{8}-\underline{\frac{\not{2}^{1}}{3}\times\frac{1}{\not{8}_{4}}}$$
$$=\frac{5}{8}-\frac{1}{12}$$
$$=\mathbf{\frac{13}{24}}$$

3d>

$$7-2\frac{5}{6}=5-\frac{5}{6}$$
$$=\mathbf{4\frac{1}{6}}$$

7. (a)
$$20-(\underline{12-4})\div 4\times 2$$
$$=20-\underline{8\div 4}\times 2$$
$$=20-\underline{2\times 2}$$
$$=\underline{20-4}$$
$$=\mathbf{16}$$

(b)
$$2\frac{3}{4}-1\frac{4}{5}=1\frac{3}{4}-\frac{4}{5}$$
$$=1\frac{15}{20}-\frac{16}{20}$$
$$=\mathbf{\frac{19}{20}}$$

8. (a) **1000** (b) **1000**

9. 3% of $25 = $\frac{3}{100} \times \$25 =$ **$0.75**

10. Number of students that passed = 200 – 7 = 193

Percentage of the students that passed = $\frac{193}{200} \times 100\% =$ **96.5%**

11. (a) **4 : 5** (b) $\frac{4}{5} \times 100\% =$ **80%**

12. (a) The sum of money is 8 units. Fraction John received = $\mathbf{\frac{3}{8}}$

(b) $\mathbf{\frac{5}{3}}$

13. 4 units = $70
1 unit = $70 ÷ 4 = $17.50
3 units = $17.50 × 3 = $52.50
The watch cost **$52.50**.

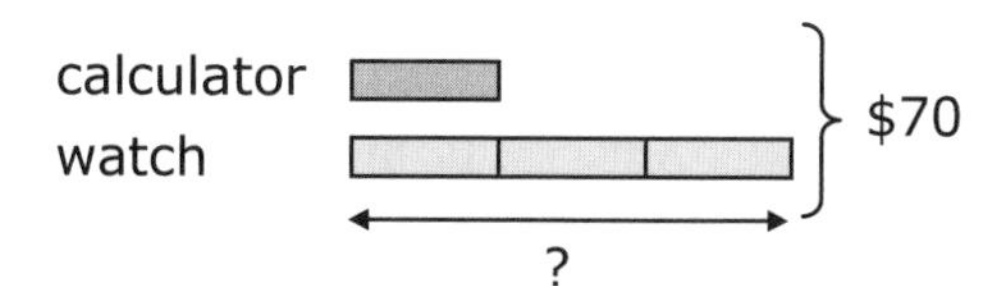

14. Together, they donated units of $9.
$1800 ÷ $9 = 200
Amount Matthew (**3d›** Mr. Wang) donated = 200 × $4 = **$800**

15. 3 pages → 45 min

24 pages → 45 × 8 = 360 min = $\frac{360}{60}$ h = **6 h** (3 × 8 = 24)

16. 100 g = $\frac{1}{10}$ kg $\frac{1}{2}$ kg = $\frac{5}{10}$ kg

$\frac{1}{10}$ kg → $3.20

$\frac{1}{2}$ kg → $3.20 × 5 = **$16**

17. The sum of the two numbers is 56 × 2 = 112
1 unit = the larger number
2 units = 112 + 10 = 122
1 unit = 122 ÷ 2 = 61
The larger number is **61**.

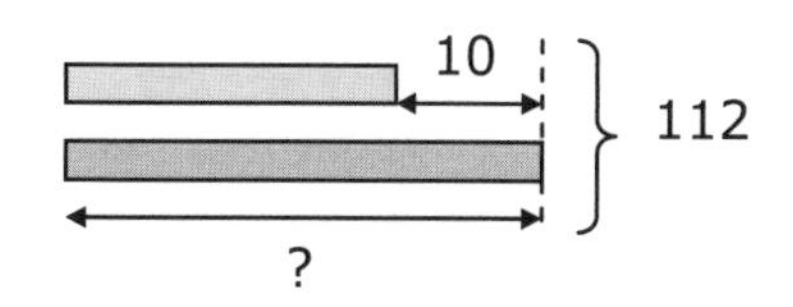

18.

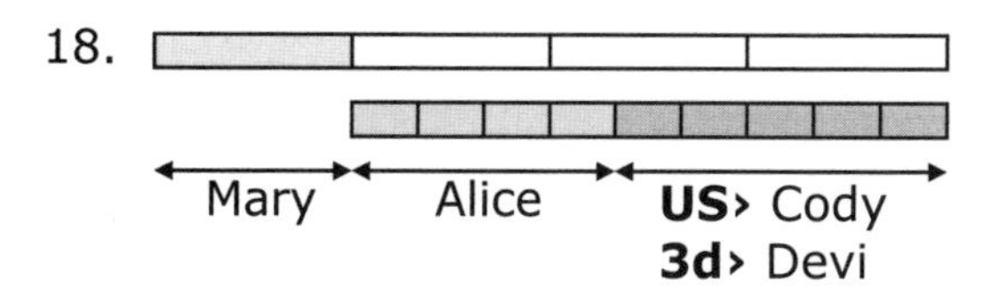

Fraction Cody (Devi) received

$= \frac{5}{9} \times \frac{3}{4} = \mathbf{\frac{5}{12}}$

19. Total weight $= 34 \text{ kg} \times 2 = 68 \text{ kg}$
8 units $= 68$ kg
1 unit $= 68 \div 8 = 8.5$ kg
5 units $= 8.5 \times 5 = 42.5$ kg
Kyle (Raju) weighs **42.5 kg**

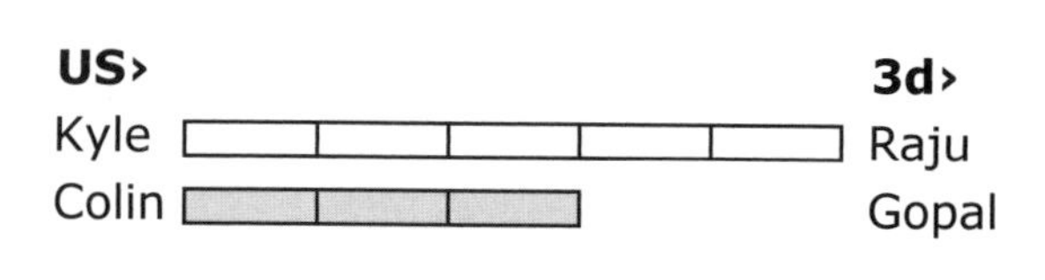

20. Fraction of the children with glasses

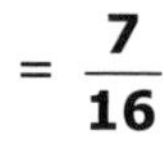

$= \mathbf{\frac{7}{16}}$

boys
girls
= with glasses

Or:

$\left(\frac{1}{3} \times \frac{3}{8}\right) + \left(\frac{1}{2} \times \frac{5}{8}\right) = \frac{1}{8} + \frac{5}{16} = \frac{2}{16} + \frac{5}{16} = \frac{7}{16}$

21. Fraction of his money left $= 1 - \frac{2}{5} = \frac{3}{5}$

Percentage of his money left $= \frac{3}{5} \times 100\% =$ **60%**

22. Amount of reduction $= \$40 - \$24 = \$16$

Percentage of reduction $= \frac{16}{40} \times 100\% =$ **40%**

23.

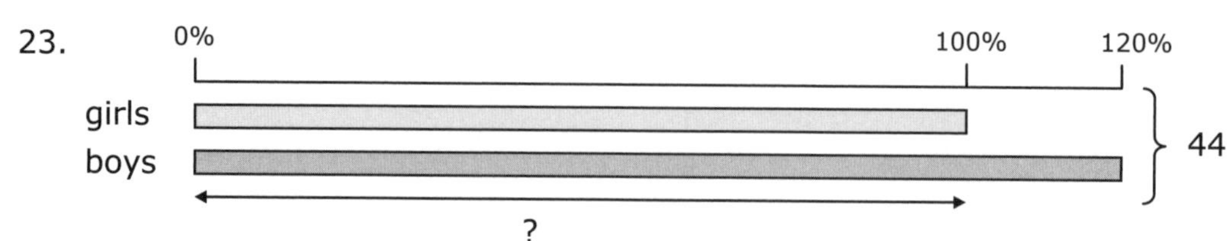

Number of girls is 100%.
Total number of students is 220% of the number of girls.
$220\% \longrightarrow 44$

$1\% \longrightarrow \frac{44}{220}$

$100\% \longrightarrow \frac{44}{220} \times 100 = 20$

There are **20** girls.

24. A ——— B

3 h, 12 km/h

Distance for first $\frac{2}{3} = 12 \text{ km/h} \times 3 \text{ h} = 36 \text{ km}$

Distance for $\frac{1}{3}$ of the trip $= 36 \div 2 = 18$ km

Total distance $= 36 + 18 =$ **54 km**

25.
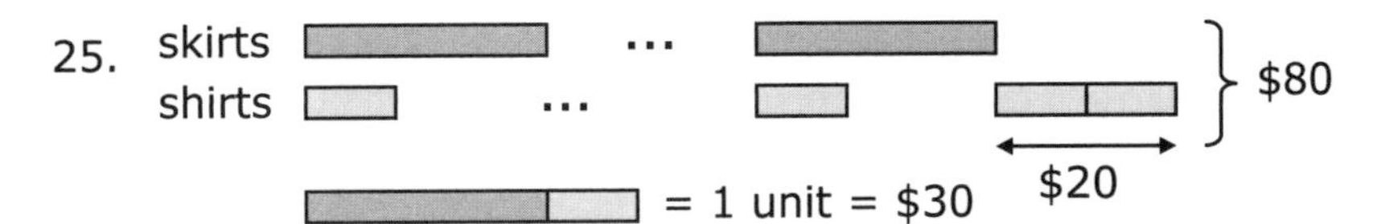

Number of $30 units = ($80 − $20) ÷ $30 = $60 ÷ $30 = 2
She bought 2 units of shirt and skirt plus 2 more shirts.
She bought a total of **4** shirts.

26. 7 units = $175
1 unit = $175 ÷ 7 = $25
Each chair cost **$25**.

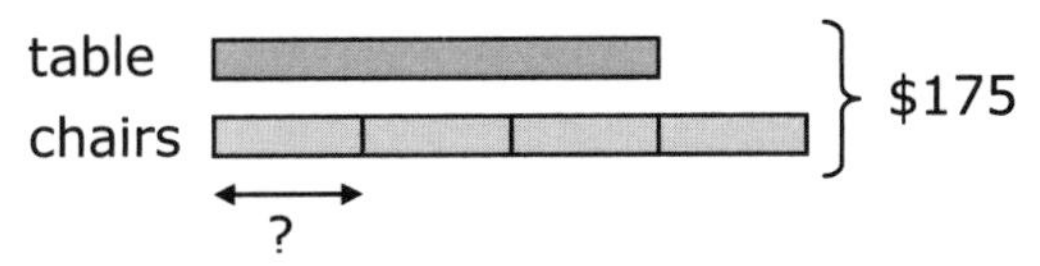

27. 11 units = $220
1 unit = $220 ÷ 11 = 20
6 units = $20 × 6 = $120
Joe has **$120**.

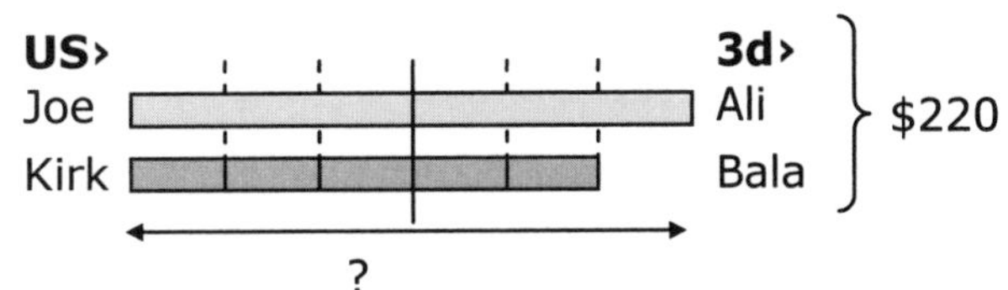

28. red
green

New ratio = **3 : 4**

29. Before 2 : 3
After 3 : 4
Emily's (Suhua's) total before and after remains the same.
Find equivalent ratio.
Before 6 : 9
After 6 : 8
1 unit = $30
9 units = $30 × 9 = $270
Alyssa (Meilin) had **$270** at first.

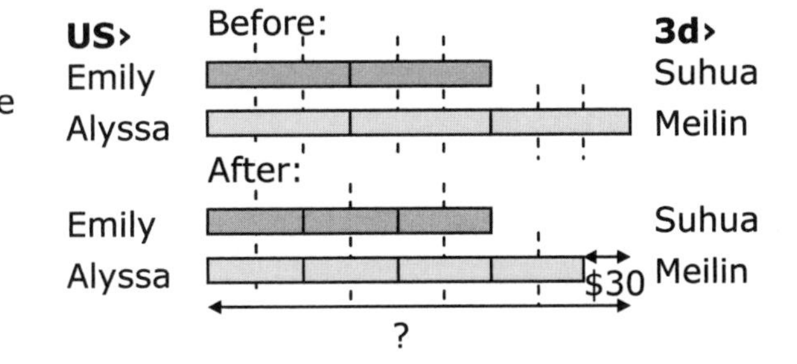

30.
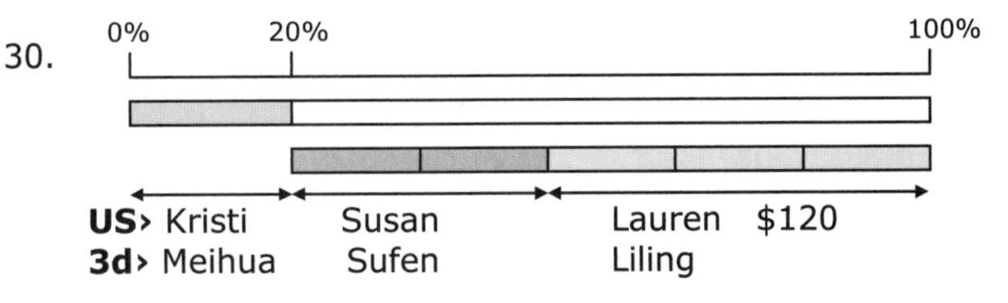

80% of the money, or was divided between was divided between Susan and Lauren in the ratio of 2 : 3
3 units = $120
1 unit = $120 ÷ 3 = $40
5 units = $40 × 5 = $200
80% → $200
10% → $200 ÷ 8 = $25
20% → $25 × 2 = $50
Kristi (Meihua) received **$50**.

31. Distance is the same in both cases.
Distance $= 60$ km/h $\times 2$ h $= 120$ km
Time for case 2 $= \frac{120 \text{ km}}{80 \text{ km/h}} = \mathbf{1\frac{1}{2}\ h}$

32. The distance between the two towns is the sum of the distances traveled by Henry and Paul.
Time for Henry = 12:00 noon to 12:30 p.m. $= \frac{1}{2}$ h
Distance for Henry $= 15$ km/h $\times \frac{1}{2}$ h $= 7\frac{1}{2}$ km $= 7.5$ km
Time for Paul = 12:10 p.m. to 12:30 p.m. = 20 min $= \frac{20}{60}$ h $= \frac{1}{3}$ h
Distance for Paul $= 12$ km/h $\times \frac{1}{3}$ h $= 4$ km
Distance between the towns = 7.5 km + 4 km = **11.5 km**

33. $\frac{2x-7}{3} = \frac{(2\times 8)-7}{3} = \frac{16-7}{3} = \frac{9}{3} = \mathbf{3}$

34. $\$10m$

$\$2m$?

3 photo albums cost $3 \times \$2m = \$6m$
2 T-shirts cost $\$10m - \$6m = \$4m$
1 T-shirt costs $\$4m \div 2 = \mathbf{\$2m}$

35. The sum of the angles at a point of intersection is 360°.
$\angle x = 360° - 90° - 200° = \mathbf{70°}$

36. $\angle PRQ = 180° - (2 \times 40°) = 100°$ (ΔPRQ is isosceles)
$\angle TRS = \angle PRQ = 100°$ (vertically opposite $\angle$'s)
$\angle UTR = \angle TRS + \angle RST$ (external angle of ΔTRS)
$= 100° + 20° = \mathbf{120°}$

37. $\angle CED = (180° - 30°) \div 2 = 75°$ (ΔCDE is isosceles)
$\angle AEC = 180° - \angle CED$ ($\angle$AEC and $\angle$CED are on a st. line)
$= 180° - 75° = 105°$
$\angle m = \angle AEC = \mathbf{105°}$ (opp. $\angle$'s of a parallelogram are =)

38. Side of Q = 5 cm $(5 \times 5 = 25)$
Side of P = 9 cm $(9 \times 9 = 81)$
Base of R = 5 cm
Height of R = 9 − 5 = 4 cm
Area of R $= \frac{1}{2} \times 5 \times 4 = \mathbf{10\ cm^2}$

39. The length of the rectangle is the diameter of the semicircle, and the width is the radius of the circle. So the width is twice the length. If the width is 1 unit, the length is 2 units.
Perimeter $= (2 \times 2$ units$) + (2 \times 1$ unit$) = 6$ units $= 30$ cm
Radius $= 1$ unit
Radius $= 30$ cm $\div 6 = 5$ cm
Diameter $= 2 \times 5$ cm $= 10$ cm
Perimeter $= (\frac{1}{2} \times 3.14 \times 10$ cm$) + 10$ cm $= 15.7$ cm $+ 10$ cm $=$ **25.7 cm**

40. Height $= \frac{\text{Volume}}{\text{base area}} = \frac{288}{6 \times 6} =$ **8 cm**

41. Volume of water $= 20 \times 15 \times 4 = 1{,}200$ cm^3
Volume of water and stone $= 1{,}200 + 1{,}200 = 2{,}400$ cm^3
Water level $= \frac{2{,}400}{20 \times 15} = 8$ cm
(Or, since the volume of the stone is the same as that of the water, the water will rise the same amount it was before, and the new water level will be
$4 + 4 = 8$ cm)
$\frac{4}{5}$ of the height $= 8$ cm
$\frac{1}{5}$ of the height $= 8 \div 4 = 2$ cm
All of the height $= 2 \times 5 =$ **10 cm**

42. (a) **36** students in 6A passed.
(b) The number that failed $= 40 - 28 = 12$
The percentage that failed $= \frac{12}{40} \times 100 =$ **30%**
(c) Total number of students who failed $= 4 + 16 + 12 + 10 = 42$
Average number of students who failed $= \frac{42}{4} =$ **10.5**

Review G, US pp. 111-116, 3d> pp. 95-100

1. (a) **10,027** (b) **2,012,000**
2. Multiples of 5 = 5, 10, 15, 20, 25
   Multiples of 4 = 4, 8, 12, 16, 20, 24, 28
   The number is **20**.
3. **107,802**
4. $\frac{150}{500} \times 100\% = \mathbf{30\%}$
5. There are 5 divisions between 250 and 500, so each division is 50.
   The weight of the papaya is **450 g**.
6. $2\frac{1}{6} \approx \mathbf{2.17}$
7. $\frac{3}{10}$ is smaller than $\frac{3}{8}$; the numerators are the same but $\frac{3}{10}$ has a larger denominator.
   $\frac{1}{3} = \frac{8}{24}$ and $\frac{3}{8} = \frac{9}{24}$, so $\frac{1}{3}$ is smaller.
   $\frac{2}{5} = \frac{16}{40}$ and $\frac{3}{8} = \frac{15}{40}$, so $\mathbf{\frac{2}{5}}$ is greater than $\frac{3}{8}$.
8. (a) **12** (b) **3**
9. **7:45 a.m.**
10. (a) $\frac{1}{4}$ h $= \frac{1}{4} \times 60$ min
    $= 15$ min
    $1\frac{1}{4}$ h = **1 h 15 min**

    (b) 0.3 km = 0.3 × 1000 m
    = 300 m
    2.3 km = **2 km 300 m**
11. (a) 0.8 km = 0.8 × 1000 m
    = **800** m

    (b) $\frac{3}{5}\,\ell = \frac{3}{5} \times 1000$ ml
    = **600** ml

    (c) 1.35 kg = 1.35 × 1000 g
    = **1350** g

    (d) 0.8 m = 0.8 × 100 cm
    = 80 cm
    4.8 m = **4** m **80** cm

US› 12. $\$1 \rightarrow 4$ quarters
$\$5 \rightarrow 5 \times 4 =$ **20** quarters
or: Number of quarters $= 5 \div \frac{1}{4} = 5 \times 4 = 20$

3d› 12. $\$1 \rightarrow 5$ twenty-cent coins
$\$5 \rightarrow 5 \times 5 =$ **25** twenty-cent coins

13. $\$12 \rightarrow 5$ jars (bottles)
$\$36 \rightarrow 5 \times 3 =$ **15** jars (bottles)

14. 100 g $\rightarrow \$0.95$
800 g $\rightarrow \$0.95 \times 8 =$ **$7.60**

15. Total age $= 30 \times 2 = 60$ years
1 unit = Mary's age
2 units $= 60 + 6 = 66$
1 unit $= 66 \div 2 = 33$
Mary is **33** years old.

Peter 6
Mary
60

16. Total postage $= (3 \times 30¢) + (5 \times 50¢) = 90¢ + 250¢ = 340¢ =$ **$3.40**

17. She had $\frac{2}{5}$ of her money left.

$\frac{3}{5}$ of her money $= \$48$

$\frac{1}{5}$ of her money $= \$\frac{48}{3} = \$16$

$\frac{2}{5}$ of her money $= \$16 \times 2 =$ **$32**

18.
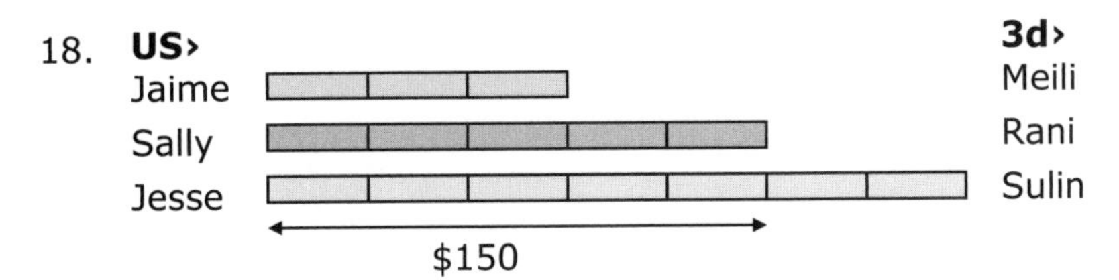

(a) Total units = 15
Fraction of the sum Sally (Rani) received $= \frac{5}{15} = \mathbf{\frac{1}{3}}$

(b) 5 units = $150
15 units $= \$150 \times 3 = \$450$
The girls shared **$450**.

19. 12% of $\$2{,}800 = \frac{12}{100} \times \$2{,}800 = 12 \times \$28 =$ **$336**

20. The cost price is 100%. With a 20% discount, the selling price is 80% of the cost price.
$20\% \rightarrow \$3$
$10\% \rightarrow \$\frac{3}{2}$
$80\% \rightarrow \$\frac{3}{2} \times 8 = \$12$
The selling price is **$12**.

21. Usual price is 100%. With a 10% discount, the selling price is 90% of the usual price.
$90\% \rightarrow \$28.80$
$10\% \rightarrow \$28.80 \div 9 = \$3.2$
$100\% \rightarrow \$3.2 \times 10 = \mathbf{\$32}$

22. $25 \text{ min} = \frac{25}{60} = \frac{5}{12} \text{ h}$
$\text{Distance} = 12 \text{ km/h} \times \frac{5}{12} \text{ h} = \mathbf{5 \text{ km}}$

23. Cost of 1 orange = $1.00 ÷ 5 = $0.20
Cost of 1 apple = $1.00 ÷ 4 = $0.25
He bought an equal number of each.
He paid $0.05 more for an apple than for an orange.
He paid $1.00 more for all apples than for all oranges.
$1.00 = 20 x $0.25, so he bought 20 sets of 1 apple and 1orange.
He ought **20** apples.

24. 1 unit = Peter's stamps at first.
After, half of Peter's bar is equal to John's bar, which is 2 units + 15.
You can rearrange the units to show that 3 units + 2 parts of 15 = 60 stamps.
$3 \text{ units} = 60 - (2 \times 15)$
$= 60 - 30$
$= 30$
$1 \text{ unit} = 30 \div 3$
$= 10$
Peter had **10** stamps at first.

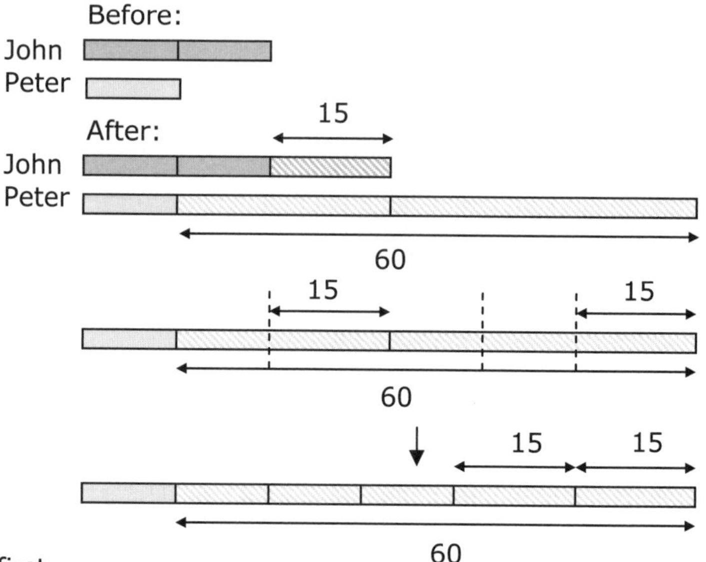

25. Number of boys $= \frac{1}{4} \times 40 = 10$

Number of boys after 8 more join $= 10 + 8 = 18$
Total number of members after 8 boys join $= 40 + 8 = 48$

Fraction of members that are boys $= \frac{18}{48} = \mathbf{\frac{3}{8}}$

26. Since the skirt cost twice as much, it is $\frac{2}{3}$ of what she spent.

She spent $\frac{2}{3}$ of $\frac{2}{3}$ of her money on the skirt.

$\frac{2}{3} \times \frac{2}{3} = \frac{4}{9}$

She spent $\mathbf{\frac{4}{9}}$ of her money on the skirt.

27.
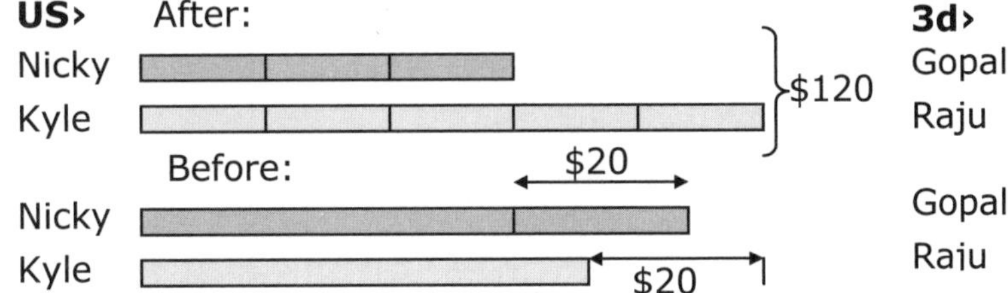

8 units $= \$120$
1 unit $= \$120 \div 8 = \$15$
3 units $= \$15 \times 3 = \$45$
Amount Nicky originally had $= \$45 + \$20 =$ **$65**

28.
Before:
Betty
David
After:
Betty $42
David $18

1 unit $= \$42 - \$18 = \$24$
2 units $= \$24 \times 2 = \$48$
Amount Betty had $= \$48 + \$42 = \$90$
Each of them had **$90**.

29. **US›** **3d›**

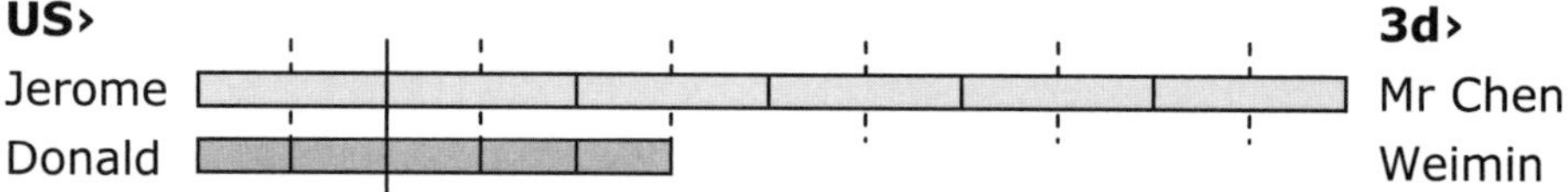

Ratio = 12 : 5
Or:

$\frac{1}{6}$ of Jerome's weight = $\frac{2}{5}$ of Donald's weight

All of Jerome's weight = $\frac{2}{5} \times 6 = \frac{12}{5}$ of Donald's weight.

Jerome's weight : Donald's weight = **12 : 5**

30. **US›** **3d›**

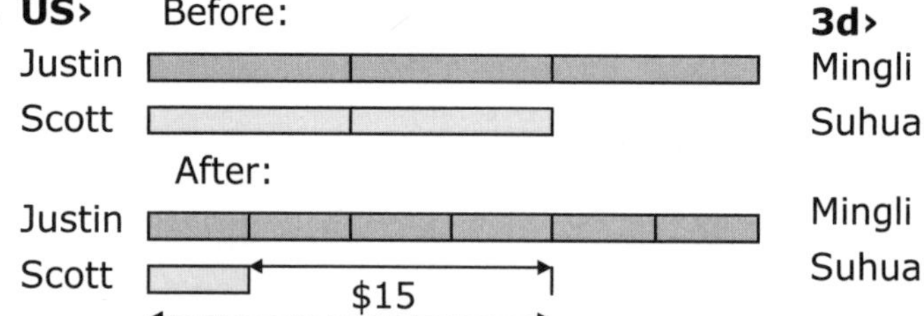

Before 3 : 2
After 6 : 1
Justin's (Mingli's) money stays the same. Find equivalent ratios where the number of Justin's (Mingli's) units is the same.
Before 6 : 4
After 6 : 1
3 units = $15
1 unit = $15 ÷ 3 = $5
4 units = $5 × 4 = $20
Scott (Suhua) had **$20**.

31. Peter and Mary begin with the same amount of money. The final ratio of Peter's money to Mary's money is 5 : 4, so Mary ends up with 4 units. If she spent $\frac{1}{3}$ of her money then $\frac{2}{3}$ of her money is 4 units, $\frac{1}{3}$ of her money is 2 units, and $\frac{3}{3}$ of her money, what she started with, is 6 units.

Peter must have started with 6 units and spent 1 unit to end up with 5 units.
1 unit = $50
5 units = $50 × 5 = $250
Peter had **$250** left.

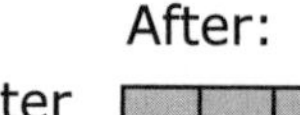

Peter
Mary
Before: $50
Peter
Mary

32. 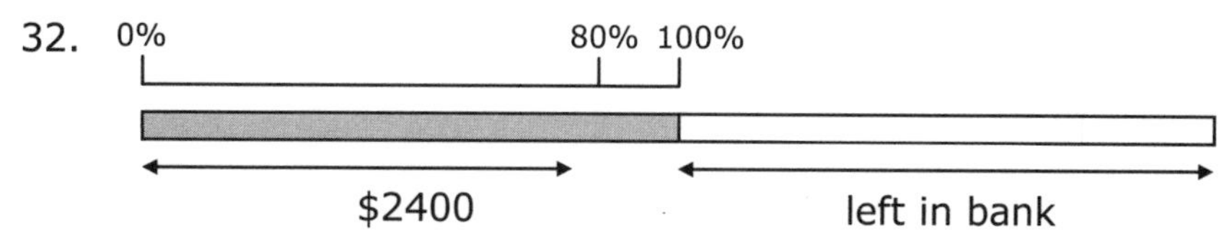

The money he took out of the bank is 100%. So the money in the bank is 200% of his withdrawal. 80% of his withdrawal is $2400.

$80\% \rightarrow \$2{,}400$

$10\% \rightarrow \$2{,}400 \div 8 = \$300$

$200\% \rightarrow \$300 \times 20 = \$6000$

He had **$6000** in the bank.

33. (a) $3r + \frac{r-3}{5} = (3 \text{ x } 8) + \frac{8-3}{5}$

$= 24 + \frac{5}{5}$

$= 24 + 1$

$= \mathbf{25}$

(b) $2r - \frac{r}{2} = (2 \text{ x } 8) - \frac{8}{2}$

$= 16 - 4$

$= \mathbf{12}$

34. The distance traveled in both cases is the same.

Distance $= 45$ km/h $\times$ 2 h $= 90$ km

Speed for case 2 $= 45$ km/h $+ 5$ km/h $= 50$ km/h

Time for case 2 $= \frac{90 \text{ km}}{50 \text{ km/h}} = 1\frac{4}{5}$ h

$\frac{4}{5}$ h $= \frac{4}{5} \times 60$ min $= 4 \times 12$ min $= 48$ min

He would take **1 h 48 min**.

35. 180 km, 3 h   55 km/h, 2 h

Distance for 2nd part $= 55$ km/h $\times$ 2 h $= 110$ km

Total distance $= 180$ km $+ 110$ km $= 290$ km

Total time $= 3$ h $+ 2$ h $= 5$ h

Average speed $= \frac{290 \text{ km}}{5 \text{ h}} =$ **58 km/h**

36. (**3d›** Chris → Ahmad, Chad → Daud)

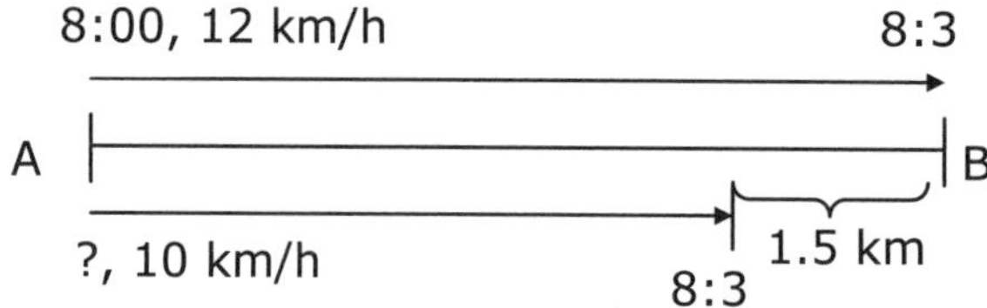

Time for Chris = 8:00 a.m. to 8:30 a.m. = $\frac{1}{2}$ h

Distance between the towns = 12 km/h × $\frac{1}{2}$ h = 6 km

Distance for Chad = 6 km – 1.5 km = 4.5 km

Time for Chad = $\frac{4.5 \text{ km}}{10 \text{ km/h}}$ = 0.45 h = 0.45 × 60 min = 27 min

27 min before 8:30 a.m. is 8:03 a.m.
Chad left Town A at **8:03 a.m.**

37.

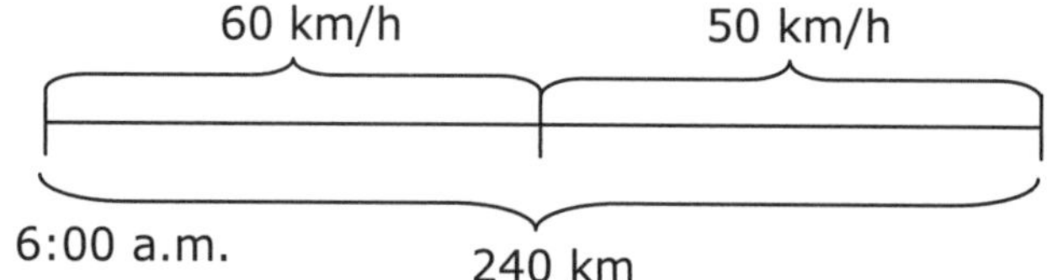

Distance for each part = 240 ÷ 2 = 120

Time for 1st part = $\frac{120 \text{ km}}{60 \text{ km/h}}$ = 2 h

Time for 2nd part = $\frac{120 \text{ km}}{50 \text{ km/h}}$ = $2\frac{2}{5}$ h

$\frac{2}{5}$ h = $\frac{2}{5}$ × 60 min = 24 min

Total time = 2 h + 2 h 24 min = 4 h 24 min
4 h 24 min after 6:00 a.m. = **10:24 a.m.**

38. Distance for John = 6 km/h × 3 h
= 18 km
Distance for Peter = 27 km – 18 km
= 9 km
6:00 a.m.
Speed for Peter = $\frac{9 \text{ km}}{3 \text{ h}}$ = **3 km/h**

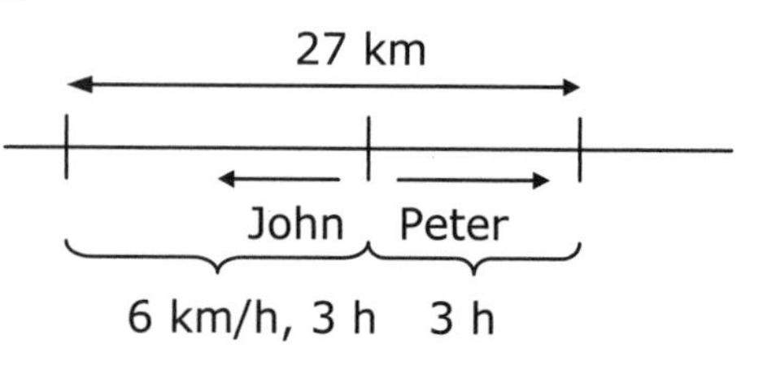

39. The two semicircles make a circle with diameter 10 cm.
Circumference = 3.14 × 10 cm = 31.4 cm
Perimeter = 31.4 cm + 5 cm + 5 cm = **41.4 cm**

40. The four quarter circles make a whole circle with radius 7 cm.
Shaded area = area of square − area of circle
$= (14\text{ cm} \times 14\text{ cm}) - (\frac{22}{7} \times 7\text{ cm} \times 7\text{ cm}) = 196\text{ cm}^2 - 154\text{ cm}^2 = \mathbf{42\text{ cm}^2}$

41. (**3d› in. → cm**)
The area of the shaded part is the area of both squares minus the area of the two larger unshaded triangles, one of which traverses both squares.
Shaded area
$= (6\text{ in.} \times 6\text{ in.}) + (4\text{ in.} \times 4\text{ in.}) - (\frac{1}{2} \times 10\text{ in.} \times 4\text{ in.}) - (\frac{1}{2} \times 6\text{ in.} \times 6\text{ in.})$
$= 36\text{ in.}^2 + 16\text{ in.}^2 - 20\text{ in.}^2 - 18\text{ in.}^2 = \mathbf{14\text{ in.}^2}$

42. Height of triangle = 14 cm
Area = area of triangle + area of semicircle
$= (\frac{1}{2} \times 18\text{ cm} \times 14\text{ cm}) + (\frac{1}{2} \times \frac{22}{7} \times 7\text{ cm} \times 7\text{ cm})$
$= 126\text{ cm}^2 + 77\text{ cm}^2 = \mathbf{203\text{ cm}^2}$

43. Volume of water and stone $= 3000\text{ cm}^3 + 33{,}000\text{ cm}^3 = 36{,}000\text{ cm}^3$
Height of water $= \frac{36{,}000}{50 \times 40} = 18$ cm
$\frac{2}{3}$ of the height of the tank = 18 cm
$\frac{1}{3}$ of the height of the tank $= 18 \div 2 = 9$ cm
The height of the tank $= 9 \times 3 =$ **27 cm**

44. $\angle PRT = (180° - 36°) \div 2 = 72°$ (ΔQRT is isosceles)
$\angle PST = \angle RPS + \angle PRS$ (∠PST is an external angle of ΔPRS)
$\angle RPS = \angle PST - \angle PRT$
$= 90° - 72° = \mathbf{18°}$

45. $\angle BCA = 180° - 100° - 40° = 40°$ (∠ sum of a Δ)
$\angle BCE = 40° + 15° = 55°$
$\angle AEC = 180° - 55° = 125°$ (The sum of a pair of ∠s between the parallel sides of an trapezoid is 180°)
$\angle CED = 180° - 125° = 55°$
$\angle x = \angle CED = \mathbf{55°}$ (ΔEDC is isosceles)

46. (a) **22** computers were sold in February.
(b) Increase = 18 − 10 = **8**
(c) Average $= \frac{18 + 22 + 10 + 18 + 14 + 20}{6} = \frac{102}{6} = \mathbf{17}$

US› Review H, pp. 117-120

1. (a) $\frac{1}{8} \div \frac{1}{2} = \frac{1}{8} \times 2 = \mathbf{\frac{1}{4}}$

   (b) $\frac{3}{4} \div \frac{2}{3} = \frac{3}{4} \times \frac{3}{2} = \frac{9}{8} = \mathbf{1\frac{1}{8}}$

   (c) $7 \div \frac{5}{8} = 7 \times \frac{8}{5} = \frac{56}{5} = \mathbf{11\frac{1}{5}}$

2. Number of $\frac{1}{5}$'s in $10 = 10 \div \frac{1}{5} = 10 \times 5 = \mathbf{50}$

3. (b) 1 m

4. (a) $\left(\frac{5}{6} - \frac{2}{3}\right) \div 4 = \left(\frac{5}{6} - \frac{4}{6}\right) \times \frac{1}{4}$

   $= \frac{1}{6} \times \frac{1}{4}$

   $= \mathbf{\frac{1}{24}}$

   (b) $\frac{1}{9} \div \left(\frac{2}{3} + \frac{1}{4}\right) = \frac{1}{9} \div \left(\frac{8}{12} + \frac{3}{12}\right)$

   $= \frac{1}{9} \div \frac{11}{12}$

   $= \frac{1}{9} \times \frac{12}{11}$

   $= \mathbf{\frac{4}{33}}$

   (c) $\frac{5}{7} + \underline{\frac{3}{8} \div \frac{1}{4}} = \frac{5}{7} + \underline{\frac{3}{8} \times 4}$

   $= \frac{5}{7} + \frac{3}{2}$

   $= \frac{10}{14} + \frac{21}{14}$

   $= \frac{31}{14} = \mathbf{2\frac{3}{14}}$

5. (a) 17 yd 1 ft ÷ 4 = (16 yd + 3 ft + 1 ft) ÷ 4
   = (16 yd ÷ 4) + (4 ft ÷ 4)
   = **4 yd 1 ft**

   (b) 19 qt 2 c ÷ 3 = (18 qt + 4 c + 2 c) ÷ 3
   = (18 qt ÷ 3) + (6 c ÷ 3)
   = **6 qt 2 c**

   (c) 15 lb 5 oz ÷ 7 = (14 lb + 16 oz + 5 oz) ÷ 7
   = (14 lb ÷ 7) + (21 lb ÷ 7)
   = **2 lb 3 oz**

(d) $11 \text{ ft } 3 \text{ in.} \div 9 = (9 \text{ ft} + 24 \text{ in.} + 3 \text{ in.}) \div 9$
$= (9 \text{ ft} \div 9) + (27 \text{ in.} \div 9)$
$=$ **1 ft 3 in.**

6. Area of rectangle $= 16 \times 7$
Both triangles have the same height, so bases can be added to find the total area of both triangles.
Area of triangles $= \frac{1}{2} \times 8 \times 7 = 4 \times 7$
Fraction shaded $= \frac{4 \times 7}{16 \times 7} = \mathbf{\frac{1}{4}}$

7. Remainder $= \frac{3}{5}$
Fraction spent on DVD's $= \frac{2}{5} \times \frac{3}{5} = \frac{6}{25}$
Amount spent on DVD's $= \frac{6}{25} \times \$1300 =$ **\$312**

8. (a) $\frac{3}{5} \div \left(\frac{1}{10} + \frac{2}{5}\right) = \frac{3}{5} \div \left(\frac{1}{10} + \frac{4}{10}\right)$
$= \frac{3}{5} \div \frac{1}{2}$
$= \frac{3}{5} \times 2$
$= \frac{6}{5} = \mathbf{1\frac{1}{5}}$

(b) $\frac{4}{7} \div 2 = \frac{4}{7} \times \frac{1}{2}$
$= \mathbf{\frac{2}{7}}$

9. $2 \text{ yd} = 2 \times 36 \text{ in.} = 72 \text{ in.}$
Percentage $= \frac{9}{72} \times 100\% = \frac{1}{8} \times 100\% =$ **12.5%**

10. (a) $7\frac{1}{3} \text{ yd} = 7\frac{1}{3} \times 36 \text{ in.} = 252 \text{ in.} + 12 \text{ in.} =$ **264 in.**
(b) $5\frac{3}{4} \text{ lb} = 5\frac{3}{4} \times 16 \text{ oz} = 80 \text{ oz} + 12 \text{ oz} =$ **92 oz**
(c) $3\frac{3}{4} \text{ gal} = 3\frac{3}{4} \times 16 \text{ c} = 48 \text{ c} + 12 \text{ c} =$ **60 c**

11. (a) $\frac{3}{5} \times \frac{5}{6} \div \frac{1}{2} = \frac{\cancel{3}^1}{\cancel{5}_1} \times \frac{\cancel{5}^1}{\cancel{6}_2} \times 2$
$= \mathbf{1}$

(b) $\frac{1}{8} \div \frac{1}{4} \times \frac{2}{5} = \frac{1}{\cancel{8}_{\cancel{2}_1}} \times \cancel{4}^1 \times \frac{\cancel{2}}{5}$
$= \mathbf{\frac{1}{5}}$

12. (a) **5 lb 4 oz** (b) **2 ft 10 in.** (c) **3 qt 1 pt**

13. $2 \times \$3.60 = \$7.20$

$12 \text{ oz} = \frac{3}{4} \text{ lb}; \ \frac{3}{4} \times \$3.60 = \$2.70$

$\$7.20 + \$2.70 = \mathbf{\$9.90}$

14. Weight of cooking oil = 2.5 lb − 11 oz
= $(2.5 \times 16 \text{ oz}) - 11 \text{ oz}$
= 40 oz − 11 oz
= **29 oz**

15. $2 \text{ gal} = 16 \text{ pt}$. Percentage $= \frac{12}{16} \times 100\% = \frac{3}{4} \times 100\% = \mathbf{75\%}$

16. If 1 pt of water from A to B results in the same amount of water in both, A must have 2 more pints than B.

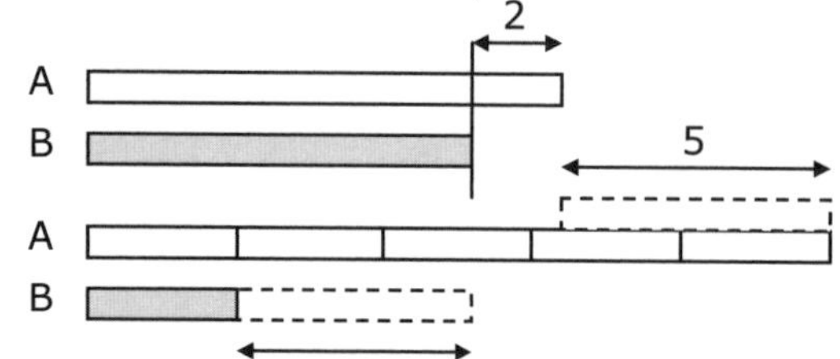

$4 \text{ units} = 5 + 2 + 5 = 12 \text{ pt}$
$1 \text{ unit} = 12 \text{ pt} \div 4 = 3 \text{ pt}$.
Total water = 6 units
$6 \text{ units} = 3 \text{ pt} \times 6 = \mathbf{18 \text{ pt}}$

17. $12 \text{ in.} \times 12 \text{ in.} \times 12 \text{ in.} = \mathbf{1728} \text{ in.}^3$ in 1 ft^3

18. $17\frac{3}{4} < 6$ yd (18 ft). $6 \text{ yd} = 216$ in. So **6.75** yd is longest.

19. $1.25 \text{ gal} = 20 \text{ c}$; $6 \text{ pt} = 12 \text{ c}$, $4\frac{1}{4} \text{ qt} = 17 \text{ c}$.

(a) **Taylor** (b) **Morgan** (c) **20 c**

20. (a) $6 \div \frac{1}{3} = 6 \times 3 = \mathbf{18}$

(b) $\frac{3}{5} \div \frac{2}{5} = \frac{3}{5} \times \frac{5}{2} = \frac{3}{2} = \mathbf{1\frac{1}{2}}$

(c) $\frac{3}{7} \div \frac{2}{9} = \frac{3}{7} \times \frac{9}{2} = \frac{27}{14} = \mathbf{1\frac{13}{14}}$

(d) $\frac{7}{10} \div \frac{2}{5} \div \frac{2}{3} = \frac{7}{10} \times \frac{5}{2} \times \frac{3}{2} = \frac{21}{8} = \mathbf{2\frac{3}{8}}$

(e) $1 \div \frac{7}{8} \div \frac{2}{7} = 1 \times \frac{8}{7} \times \frac{7}{2} = \mathbf{4}$

(f) $3 \div \frac{3}{4} \div 5 = 3 \times \frac{4}{3} \times \frac{1}{5} = \mathbf{\frac{4}{5}}$

21. Average speed $= 6325 \div 11\frac{1}{2} = 6325 \div \frac{23}{2} = 6325 \times \frac{2}{23} = \mathbf{550\ mi/h}$

22. Half was left.
4.5 ft = 4 ft 6 in
4 ft 6 in. ÷ 2 = **2 ft 3 in.**

23. Fraction for family $= \frac{3}{4}$

Fraction for each member $= \frac{3}{4} \div 6 = \frac{3}{4} \times \frac{1}{6} = \mathbf{\frac{1}{8}}$

24. (a) **1 cm** (b) **1 ft**

25.

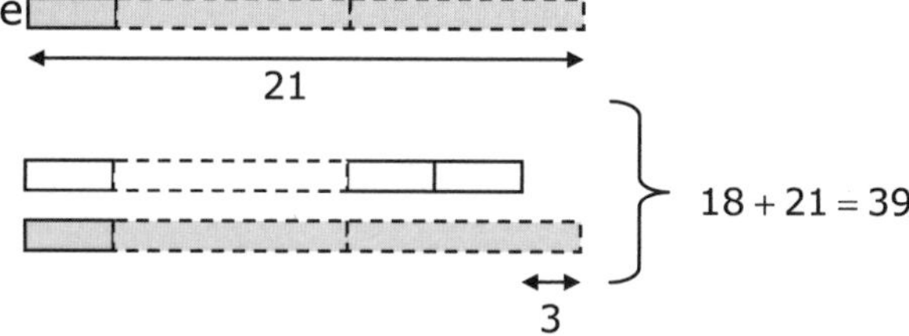

One long unit (unit given away) is 3 more than 2 short units.
Make each long unit into 2 short units + 3

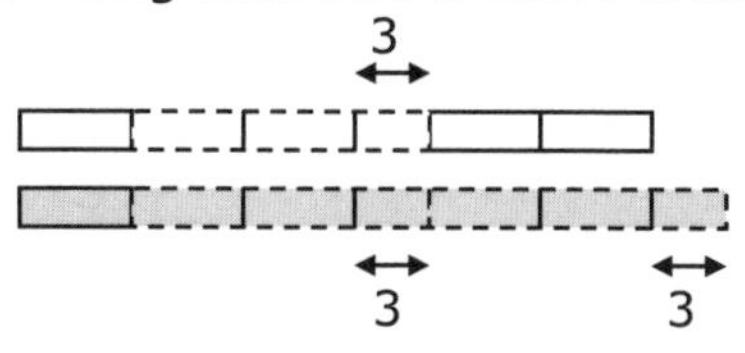

10 units = 39 − (3 × 3) = 30
1 unit = 3
Justin gave away 18 − (3 × 3) = 18 − 9 = **9**

26. 1.25 ft = 1.25 × 12 in. = 15 in.

Number of bars $= 15 \div \frac{3}{4} = 15 \times \frac{4}{3} = \mathbf{20}$

27. The ratio of their speeds is $\frac{65}{55} = \frac{13}{11}$.

So the car travels 13 units at the same time the truck travels 11 units.
They both travel a total of 24 units. Divide the distance into 24 units.
360 ÷ 24 = 15
Each unit is 15 mi.
Distance car travels in one unit = 13 × 15 mi = 195 mi
Distance truck travels in one unit = 11 × 15 = 165 mi
Time for car = Distance ÷ Speed = 195 mi ÷ 65 mi/h = 3 h
They pass after 3 h.
3 h after 10:30 a.m. is **1:30 p.m.**

28. Time to destination $= 150$ mi $\div 50$ mi/h $= 3$ h
Time spent so far $= 3$ h 30 min, time is now 3:30 p.m.

Time for return to get back by 6:00 p.m. is $2\frac{1}{2}$ h.

Speed at which he must travel $= 150 \text{ mi} \div 2\frac{1}{2} \text{ h}$

$= 150 \div \frac{5}{2}$

$= 150 \times \frac{2}{5}$

$= \mathbf{60\ mi/h}$

29. 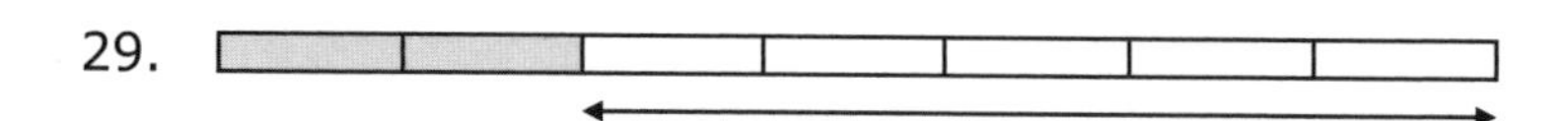

5 units $= 3.5$ gal
1 unit $= 3.5 \div 5 = 0.7$ gal
If 2.1 gal were added, 3 units would be added, and 5 out of 7 units would be filled.

The fraction of the tank filled would be $\mathbf{\frac{5}{7}}$.

Solutions to Workbook Exercises and Reviews

Exercise 1

1. (a) **12; 12** (b) **5; 10; 10** (c) **2; 8; 8** (d) **6; 18; 18**

2. (a) **6** (b) **5; 15**
(c) **12** (d) **16**
(e) **25** (f) **18**
(b) **8** (h) **42**

Exercise 2

1. (a) $\mathbf{\frac{1}{9}}$

(b) $\mathbf{\frac{1}{6}}$; $\mathbf{\frac{1}{12}}$

(c) $\frac{1}{6} \div 4 = \frac{1}{6} \times \frac{1}{4}$
$= \mathbf{\frac{1}{24}}$

(d) $\frac{4}{5} \div 2 = \frac{\cancel{4}^2}{5} \times \frac{1}{\cancel{2}_1}$
$= \mathbf{\frac{2}{5}}$

(e) $\frac{2}{5} \div 4 = \frac{\cancel{2}^1}{5} \times \frac{1}{\cancel{4}_2}$
$= \mathbf{\frac{1}{10}}$

(f) $\frac{8}{9} \div 4 = \frac{\cancel{8}^2}{9} \times \frac{1}{\cancel{4}_1}$
$= \mathbf{\frac{2}{9}}$

(g) $\frac{3}{4} \div 2 = \frac{3}{4} \times \frac{1}{2}$
$= \mathbf{\frac{3}{8}}$

(h) $\frac{2}{3} \div 6 = \frac{\cancel{2}^1}{3} \times \frac{1}{\cancel{6}_3}$
$= \mathbf{\frac{1}{9}}$

Exercise 3

1. (a) $\frac{1}{2} \div \frac{1}{3} = \frac{1}{2} \times 3$
$= \mathbf{\frac{3}{2}}$ or $\mathbf{1\frac{1}{2}}$

(b) $\frac{1}{3} \div \frac{1}{6} = \frac{1}{\cancel{3}_1} \times \cancel{6}^2$
$= \mathbf{2}$

(c) $\frac{4}{5} \div \frac{1}{5} = \frac{4}{\cancel{5}_1} \times \cancel{5}^1 = \mathbf{4}$

(d) $\frac{5}{8} \div \frac{1}{4} = \frac{5}{\cancel{8}_2} \times \cancel{4}^1 = \frac{5}{2} = \mathbf{2\frac{1}{2}}$

(e) $4 \div \frac{4}{5} = \cancel{4}^1 \times \frac{5}{\cancel{4}_1} = \mathbf{5}$

(f) $6 \div \frac{3}{4} = \cancel{6}^2 \text{ x } \frac{4}{\cancel{3}_1} = \mathbf{8}$

(g) $\frac{1}{8} \div \frac{3}{4} = \frac{1}{\cancel{8}_2} \text{ x } \frac{\cancel{4}^1}{3} = \mathbf{\frac{1}{6}}$

(h) $\frac{4}{9} \div \frac{2}{3} = \frac{\cancel{4}^2}{\cancel{9}_3} \times \frac{\cancel{3}^1}{\cancel{2}_1} = \mathbf{\frac{2}{3}}$

Exercise 4

1. (a) $\frac{3}{4} - \frac{3}{8} + \frac{1}{2} = \frac{6}{8} - \frac{3}{8} + \frac{4}{8} = \mathbf{\frac{7}{8}}$

(b) $\frac{3}{8} + \frac{2}{3} - \frac{1}{4} = \frac{9}{24} + \frac{16}{24} - \frac{6}{24} = \mathbf{\frac{19}{24}}$

(c) $\frac{\cancel{2}^1}{\cancel{3}_1} \times \frac{\cancel{3}^1}{\cancel{8}\,\cancel{4}_2} \times \cancel{2}^1 = \mathbf{\frac{1}{2}}$

(d) $\frac{4}{9} \div 2 \div \frac{1}{6} = \frac{\cancel{4}^2}{\cancel{9}_3} \times \frac{1}{\cancel{2}_1} \times \cancel{6}^2 = \frac{4}{3} = \mathbf{1\frac{1}{3}}$

(e) $7 \div 2 \times \frac{2}{7} = \cancel{7}^1 \times \frac{1}{\cancel{2}_1} \times \frac{\cancel{2}^1}{\cancel{7}_1} = \mathbf{1}$

(f) $\frac{5}{6} \times \frac{4}{5} \div 4 = \frac{\cancel{5}^1}{6} \times \frac{\cancel{4}^1}{\cancel{5}_1} \times \frac{1}{\cancel{4}_1} = \mathbf{\frac{1}{6}}$

(g) $\frac{3}{5} \times \frac{2}{9} \div \frac{3}{10} = \frac{\cancel{3}^1}{\cancel{5}_1} \times \frac{2}{9} \times \frac{\cancel{10}^2}{\cancel{3}_1} = \mathbf{\frac{4}{9}}$

(h) $\frac{3}{8} \div \frac{3}{4} \times \frac{2}{5} = \frac{\cancel{3}^1}{\cancel{8}\,\cancel{2}_1} \times \frac{\cancel{4}^1}{\cancel{3}_1} \times \frac{\cancel{2}^1}{5} = \mathbf{\frac{1}{5}}$

Exercise 5

1. (a) $\frac{\cancel{4}^2}{\cancel{5}_1} \times \frac{\cancel{5}^1}{\cancel{6}_3} - \frac{2}{3} = \frac{2}{3} - \frac{2}{3}$
$= \mathbf{0}$

(b) $\frac{3}{4} \div \frac{9}{10} - \frac{1}{2} = \frac{\cancel{3}^1}{\cancel{4}_2} \times \frac{\cancel{10}^5}{\cancel{9}_3} - \frac{1}{2}$
$= \frac{5}{6} - \frac{1}{2}$
$= \mathbf{\frac{1}{3}}$

(c) $3 + \cancel{4}^1 \times \frac{5}{\cancel{8}_2} = 3 + \frac{5}{2}$
$= \mathbf{5\frac{1}{2}}$

(d) $5 - \frac{2}{3} \div \frac{1}{6} = 5 - \frac{2}{\cancel{3}_1} \times \cancel{6}^2$
$= 5 - 4$
$= \mathbf{1}$

(e) $\frac{5}{6} - \frac{\cancel{2}^1}{\cancel{3}_1} \times \frac{\cancel{3}^1}{\cancel{8}_4} = \frac{5}{6} - \frac{1}{4}$
$= \frac{10}{12} - \frac{3}{12}$
$= \mathbf{\frac{7}{12}}$

(f) $\frac{3}{4} + \frac{2}{5} \div \frac{3}{10} = \frac{3}{4} + \frac{2}{\cancel{5}_1} \times \frac{\cancel{10}^2}{3}$
$= \frac{3}{4} + \frac{4}{3}$
$= \frac{9}{12} + \frac{16}{12}$
$= \mathbf{2\frac{1}{12}}$

(g) $\frac{1}{2} + 3 \times \frac{1}{4} \div \frac{3}{8} = \frac{1}{2} + \frac{\cancel{3}^1}{\cancel{4}_1} \times \frac{\cancel{8}^2}{\cancel{3}_1}$
$= \frac{1}{2} + 2$
$= \mathbf{2\frac{1}{2}}$

(h) $\frac{1}{2} + \frac{\cancel{5}^1}{\cancel{6}_2} \times \frac{\cancel{9}^3}{\cancel{10}_2} - \frac{1}{3} = \frac{1}{2} + \frac{3}{4} - \frac{1}{3}$
$= \frac{6}{12} + \frac{9}{12} - \frac{4}{12}$
$= \mathbf{\frac{11}{12}}$

2. (a) $\frac{7}{8} - \frac{3}{4} + \frac{1}{2}$
$= \frac{7}{8} - \frac{6}{8} + \frac{4}{8}$
$= \mathbf{\frac{5}{8}}$

(b) $\frac{1}{3} + \frac{5}{6} - \frac{1}{2}$
$= \frac{2}{6} + \frac{5}{6} - \frac{3}{6}$
$= \frac{4}{6}$
$= \mathbf{\frac{2}{3}}$

(c) $\frac{2}{3} \times \frac{1}{8} \div \frac{1}{2}$
$= \frac{\cancel{2}^1}{3} \times \frac{1}{\cancel{8}\ \cancel{4}_2} \times \cancel{2}^1$
$= \mathbf{\frac{1}{6}}$

(d) $\frac{4}{5}-\underline{\frac{\cancel{3}^1}{5}\times\frac{1}{\cancel{6}_2}}$

$=\frac{4}{5}-\frac{1}{10}$

$=\frac{8}{10}-\frac{1}{10}$

$=\mathbf{\frac{7}{10}}$

(e) $\frac{1}{2}+\underline{8\div\frac{4}{9}}$

$=\frac{1}{2}+\cancel{8}^2\times\frac{9}{\cancel{4}_1}$

$=\frac{1}{2}+18$

$=\mathbf{18\frac{1}{2}}$

(f) $\frac{4}{5}\div\frac{3}{5}\times\frac{1}{3}$

$=\frac{4}{\cancel{5}_1}\times\frac{\cancel{5}^1}{3}\times\frac{1}{3}$

$=\mathbf{\frac{4}{9}}$

Exercise 6

1. (a) $\left(\frac{3}{5}-\frac{1}{3}\right)\times\frac{5}{8}=\left(\frac{9}{15}-\frac{5}{15}\right)\times\frac{5}{8}$

$=\frac{\cancel{4}^1}{15_3}\times\frac{\cancel{5}^1}{\cancel{8}_2}$

$=\mathbf{\frac{1}{6}}$

(b) $\frac{3}{4}\div\left(\frac{1}{6}+\frac{\cancel{2}^4}{\cancel{3}_6}\right)=\frac{3}{4}\div\frac{5}{6}$

$=\frac{3}{\cancel{4}_2}\times\frac{\cancel{6}^3}{5}$

$=\mathbf{\frac{9}{10}}$

(c) $\frac{2}{5}+(5-3)\div\frac{4}{5}=\frac{2}{5}+\cancel{2}^1\times\frac{5}{\cancel{4}_2}$

$=\frac{2}{5}+\frac{5}{2}$

$=\frac{4}{10}+\frac{25}{10}$

$=\frac{29}{10}=\mathbf{2\frac{9}{10}}$

(d) $\frac{4}{5}-\left(1-\frac{2}{5}\right)\div 3=\frac{4}{5}-\frac{\cancel{3}^1}{5}\times\frac{1}{\cancel{3}_1}$

$=\frac{4}{5}-\frac{1}{5}$

$=\mathbf{\frac{3}{5}}$

(e) $\frac{6}{7}\times\left(\frac{1}{4}+\frac{1}{3}\right)-\frac{1}{3}$

$=\frac{6}{7}\times\left(\frac{3}{12}+\frac{4}{12}\right)-\frac{1}{3}$

$=\frac{\cancel{6}^1}{\cancel{7}_1}\times\frac{\cancel{7}^1}{\cancel{12}_2}-\frac{1}{3}$

$=\frac{1}{2}-\frac{1}{3}$

$=\mathbf{\frac{1}{6}}$

(f) $\frac{3}{4}+\left(\frac{\cancel{1}^2}{\cancel{4}_8}+\frac{3}{8}\right)\div\frac{5}{6}=\frac{3}{4}+\underline{\frac{5}{8}\div\frac{5}{6}}$

$=\frac{3}{4}+\underline{\frac{\cancel{5}^1}{\cancel{8}_4}\times\frac{\cancel{6}^3}{\cancel{5}_1}}$

$=\frac{3}{4}+\frac{3}{4}$

$=\frac{3}{2}=\mathbf{1\frac{1}{2}}$

(g) $\left(1-\frac{3}{8}\right)\div\left(\frac{1}{3}\times\frac{1}{2}\right)=\frac{5}{8}\div\frac{1}{6}$

$=\frac{5}{\cancel{8}_4}\times\cancel{6}^3$

$=\mathbf{\frac{15}{4}}$ or $\mathbf{3\frac{3}{4}}$

(h) $4\div\left(\frac{1}{5}+\frac{1}{4}\right)\times\frac{3}{10}=4\div\left(\frac{4}{20}+\frac{5}{20}\right)\times\frac{3}{10}$

$=4\div\frac{9}{20}\times\frac{3}{10}$

$=4\times\frac{\cancel{20}^2}{\cancel{9}_3}\times\frac{\cancel{3}^1}{\cancel{10}_1}$

$=\frac{8}{3}=\mathbf{2\frac{2}{3}}$

2. (a) $\frac{1}{2}+\frac{1}{2}\times\frac{1}{4}-\frac{3}{8}=\frac{1}{2}+\frac{1}{8}-\frac{3}{8}$

$=\frac{4}{8}+\frac{1}{8}-\frac{3}{8}$

$=\frac{2}{8}$

$=\mathbf{\frac{1}{4}}$

(b) $\frac{2}{5}\times(5-3)\div\frac{7}{10}=\frac{2}{5}\times 2\div\frac{7}{10}$

$=\frac{2}{\cancel{5}_1}\times 2\times\frac{\cancel{10}^2}{7}$

$=\frac{8}{7}=\mathbf{1\frac{1}{7}}$

(c) $\frac{2}{3}\div 4\times\frac{3}{4}=\frac{\cancel{2}^1}{3_1}\times\frac{1}{\cancel{4}_2}\times\frac{\cancel{3}^1}{4}$

$=\mathbf{\frac{1}{8}}$

(d) $2\div\left(\frac{1}{2}+\frac{1}{4}\right)\times\frac{3}{8}=2\div\left(\frac{2}{4}+\frac{1}{4}\right)\times\frac{3}{8}$

$=\cancel{2}^1\times\frac{\cancel{4}^1}{\cancel{3}_1}\times\frac{\cancel{3}^1}{\cancel{8}_1}$

$=\mathbf{1}$

(e) $\left(1-\frac{3}{8}\right)\div\left(\frac{1}{2}+\frac{1}{3}\right)=\frac{5}{8}\div\left(\frac{2}{6}+\frac{3}{6}\right)$

$=\frac{\cancel{5}^1}{\cancel{8}_4}\times\frac{\cancel{6}^3}{\cancel{5}_1}$

$=\mathbf{\frac{3}{4}}$

(f) $\frac{1}{6}+\underline{\frac{5}{6}\div\frac{5}{6}}-\frac{2}{3}=\frac{1}{6}+\underline{\frac{5}{6}\times\frac{6}{5}}-\frac{2}{3}$

$=\frac{1}{6}+1-\frac{2}{3}$

$=\frac{1}{6}+\frac{6}{6}-\frac{4}{6}$

$=\frac{3}{6}$

$=\mathbf{\frac{1}{2}}$

ISOSCELES

Exercise 7

1. Remainder $= \frac{3}{5} \times 150 = 3 \times 90 = 90$ lb

   Weight in each bag $= 90$ lb $\div 5 =$ **18 lb**

2. Total stamps = 8 units
   US stamps = 5 units
   Amount given to friend = 1 unit
   Amount left = 3 units
   8 units = 400
   1 unit = 400 ÷ 8 = 50
   7 units = 50 × 7 = 350

   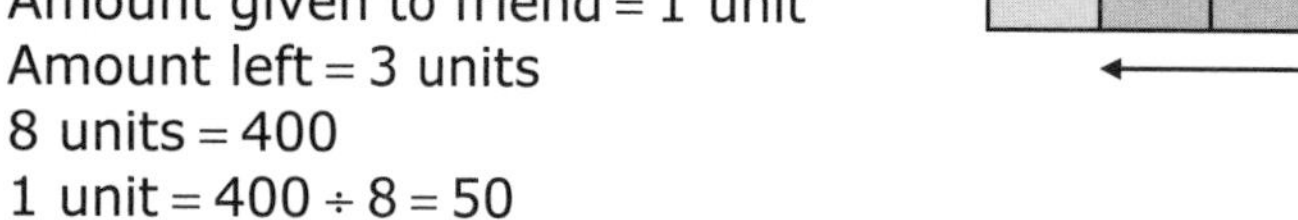

   He had **350** stamps left.

   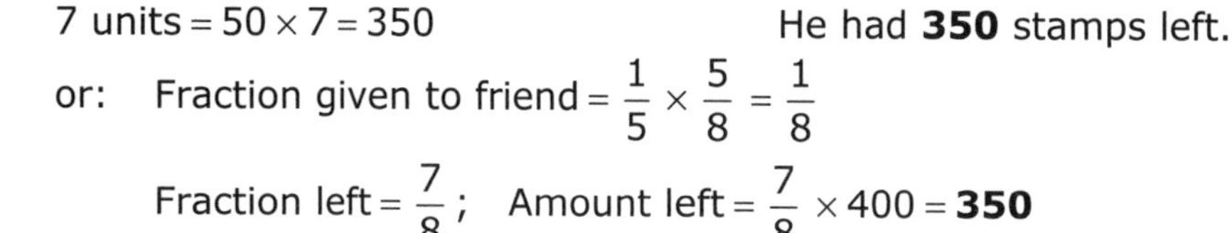

   or: Fraction given to friend $= \frac{1}{5} \times \frac{5}{8} = \frac{1}{8}$

   Fraction left $= \frac{7}{8}$; Amount left $= \frac{7}{8} \times 400 =$ **350**

3. Total money = 7 units
   Remainder = 5 units
   Amount spent = 3 units
   Amount left = 2 units
   2 units = \$300
   1 unit = \$300 ÷ 2 = \$150
   7 units = 7 × \$150 = \$1050

   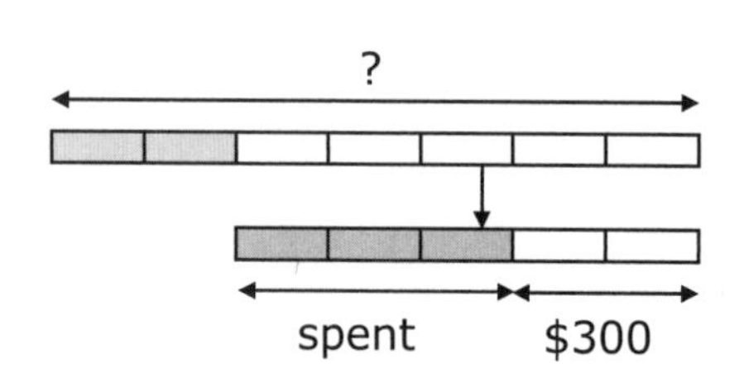

   or: Remainder $= \frac{5}{7}$; Fraction not spent $= \frac{2}{5} \times \frac{5}{7} = \frac{2}{7}$

   $\frac{2}{7} \rightarrow \$300$ $\quad \frac{1}{7} \rightarrow \$150$ $\quad \frac{7}{7} \rightarrow$ **\$1050**

4. Common denominator is 12. Draw bar with 12 units.

   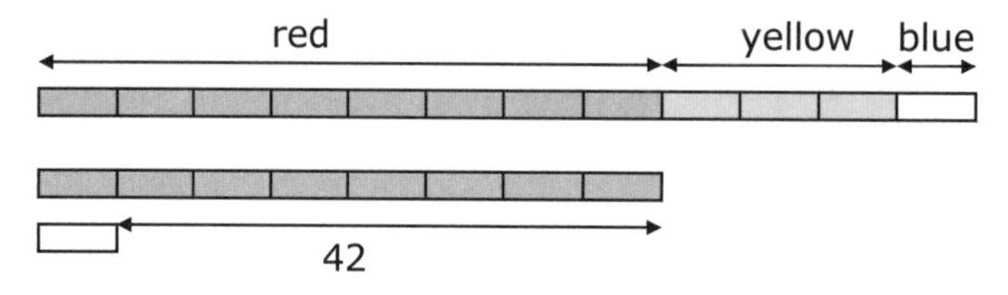

   Red beads = 8 units
   Blue beads = 1 unit
   7 units more red than blue beads
   7 units = 42

   12 units $= \frac{42}{7} \times 12 = 72$

   There are **72** beads total.

   or: Fraction blue beads
   $= 1 - \frac{2}{3} - \frac{1}{4} = \frac{1}{12}$

   Difference in red and blue beads
   $= \frac{2}{3} - \frac{1}{12} = \frac{7}{12}$

   $\frac{7}{12} \rightarrow 42$, $\frac{1}{12} \rightarrow 6$, $\frac{12}{12} \rightarrow$ **72**

Exercise 8

1. She has $\frac{2}{5}$ of her money left. Each unit is $\frac{1}{5}$. Since the handbag cost twice as much as the dress, divide the units in half to have 6 for the hand bag. Then the dress costs 3 units, and 1 unit is left for the belt. The dress is 2 units more than the belt. So 2 units is \$20. 2 units is the same as $\frac{1}{5}$ of her money.

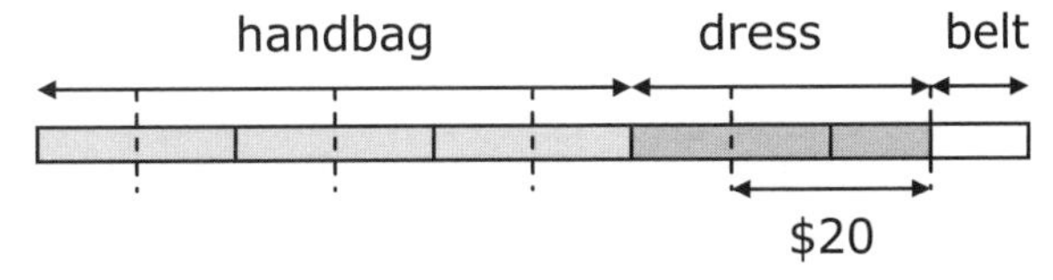

Total money $= \$20 \times 5 =$ **\$100**

2. $\frac{2}{3}$ of the remainder is $\frac{1}{2}$ of his money, so if 1 unit $= \frac{1}{3}$ of the remainder then 2 units is half his money, and all his money is 4 units.
1 unit $= \$48$
All his money $= \$48 \times 4 =$ **\$192**.

US› Exercise 9 **3d› Exercise 1**

5. (a) Radius = **2 cm**
Diameter = **4 cm**

(b) Radius = **6 cm**
Diameter = **12 cm**

US› Exercise 10 **3d› Exercise 2**

1. The actual circumference does not need to be calculated. Estimate the circumference as 3 times the diameter. Remember to use the diameter, not the radius.

31.4	**37.7**
125.6	**62.8**
18.8	**25.1**

2. (a) $\pi \times 5\text{ cm} = 3.14 \times 5\text{ cm}$
$=$ **15.7 cm**

(b) $\pi \times 14\text{ cm} = \frac{22}{7} \times 14\text{ cm}$
$=$ **44 cm**

(c) $\pi \times 8\text{ m} = 3.14 \times 8\text{ m}$
$=$ **25.12 m**

(d) $\pi \times 70\text{ m} = \frac{22}{7} \times 70\text{ m}$
$=$ **220 m**

3. (a) $\pi \times 2 \times 13\text{ cm} = 3.14 \times 26\text{ cm}$
$=$ **81.64 cm**

(b) $\pi \times 2 \times 15\text{ cm} = 3.14 \times 30\text{ cm}$
$=$ **94.2 cm**

(c) $\pi \times 2 \times 14 \text{ m} = \frac{22}{7} \times 2 \times 14 \text{ m}$
$= \mathbf{88 \text{ m}}$

(d) $\pi \times 2 \times 21 \text{ cm} = \frac{22}{7} \times 2 \times 21 \text{ cm}$
$= \mathbf{132 \text{ m}}$

US› Exercise 11 3d› Exercise 3

1. (a) Perimeter $= (\frac{1}{2} \times \pi \times \text{diameter}) + \text{diameter}$
$= (\frac{1}{2} \times \frac{22}{7} \times 28 \text{ cm}) + 28 \text{ cm} = 44 \text{ cm} + 28 \text{ cm} = \mathbf{72 \text{ cm}}$

(b) Perimeter $= (\frac{1}{2} \times \pi \times 2 \times \text{radius}) + (2 \times \text{radius})$
$= (\frac{1}{2} \times 3.14 \times 2 \times 10 \text{ m}) + (2 \times 10 \text{ m}) = 31.4 \text{ m} + 20 \text{ m} = \mathbf{51.4 \text{ m}}$

2. Perimeter $= (\frac{1}{4} \times \pi \times 2 \times \text{radius}) + (2 \times \text{radius})$
$= (\frac{1}{4} \times 3.14 \times 2 \times 5 \text{ cm}) + (2 \times 5 \text{ cm}) = 7.85 \text{ cm} + 10 \text{ cm} = \mathbf{17.85 \text{ cm}}$

3. The diameter is 10 cm.
Circumference $= 3.14 \times 10 \text{ cm} = \mathbf{31.4 \text{ cm}}$

4. Length $= \frac{1}{2}$ the circumference of a circle with diameter 12 m
$+ \frac{1}{2}$ the circumference of a circle with diameter 8 m
$= (\frac{1}{2} \times \pi \times 12 \text{ m}) + (\frac{1}{2} \times \pi \times 8 \text{ m}) = (6 \text{ m} \times \pi) + (4 \text{ m} \times \pi) = 10 \text{ m} \times \pi = \mathbf{10\pi \text{ m}}$

Note: π can be treated similarly to a variable. $6\pi + 4\pi = 10\pi$, just as $6p + 4p = 10p$ where p is a variable.

US› Exercise 12 3d› Exercise 4

1. (a) $\pi \times 9 \text{ cm} \times 9 \text{ cm} = 3.14 \times 81 \text{ cm}^2$
$= \mathbf{254.34 \text{ cm}^2}$

(b) $\pi \times 5 \text{ cm} \times 5 \text{ cm} = 3.14 \times 25 \text{ cm}^2$
$= \mathbf{78.5 \text{ m}^2}$

(c) Radius = 10 cm
$\pi \times 10 \text{ cm} \times 10 \text{ cm} = 3.14 \times 100 \text{ cm}^2$
$= \mathbf{314 \text{ cm}^2}$

(d) Radius = 6 m
$\pi \times 6 \text{ m} \times 6 \text{ m} = 3.14 \times 36 \text{ m}^2$
$= \mathbf{113.04 \text{ m}^2}$

2. (a) $\pi \times 7 \text{ cm} \times 7 \text{ cm} = \frac{22}{7} \times 7 \text{ cm} \times 7 \text{ cm}$
$= \mathbf{154 \text{ cm}^2}$

(b) $\pi \times 14 \text{ m} \times 14 \text{ m} = \frac{22}{7} \times 14 \text{ m} \times 14 \text{ m}$
$= \mathbf{616 \text{ m}^2}$

(c) Radius = 7 cm

$\pi \times 7 \text{ cm} \times 7 \text{ cm} = \frac{22}{7} \times 7 \text{ cm} \times 7 \text{ cm}$

$= \mathbf{154\ cm^2}$

(d) Radius = 35 m

$\pi \times 35 \text{ m} \times 35 \text{ m} = \frac{22}{7} \times 35 \text{ m} \times 35 \text{ m}$

$= \mathbf{3850\ m^2}$

US› Exercise 13 3d› Exercise 5

1. Radius = 10 cm
   Area $= \pi \times 10 \text{ cm} \times 10 \text{ cm} = 3.14 \times 100 \text{ cm}^2 = \mathbf{314\ cm^2}$

2. Area $= \frac{1}{4} \times \pi \times 10 \text{ cm} \times 10 \text{ cm} = \frac{1}{4} \times 3.14 \times 100 \text{ cm}^2 = \mathbf{78.5\ cm^2}$

3. (a) Area $= \frac{1}{2} \times \pi \times 7 \text{ cm} \times 7 \text{ cm} = \frac{1}{2} \times \frac{22}{7} \times 7 \text{ cm} \times 7 \text{ cm} = \mathbf{77\ cm^2}$

   (b) Radius = 14 cm
   Area $= \frac{1}{2} \times \pi \times 14 \text{ cm} \times 14 \text{ cm} = \frac{1}{2} \times \frac{22}{7} \times 14 \text{ cm} \times 14 \text{ cm} = \mathbf{308\ cm^2}$

US› Exercise 14 3d› Exercise 6

1. (a) The shaded area consists of 4 quarter circles, which together make one whole circle. The radius is 7 cm.
   Area $= \pi \times 7 \text{ cm} \times 7 \text{ cm} = \frac{22}{7} \times 7 \text{ cm} \times 7 \text{ cm} = \mathbf{154\ cm^2}$

   (b) The shaded area consists of a semicircle and a quarter circle, which together make $\frac{3}{4}$ of one whole circle. The radius is 7 cm.
   Area $= \frac{3}{4} \times \pi \times 7 \text{ cm} \times 7 \text{ cm} = \frac{3}{4} \times \frac{22}{7} \times 7 \text{ cm} \times 7 \text{ cm} = \mathbf{115.5\ cm^2}$

   (c) The shaded area consists of 2 semicircles and a quarter circle, which together make $\frac{5}{4}$ of one whole circle. The radius is 7 cm.
   Area $= \frac{5}{4} \times \pi \times 7 \text{ cm} \times 7 \text{ cm} = \frac{5}{4} \times \frac{22}{7} \times 7 \text{ cm} \times 7 \text{ cm} = \mathbf{192.5\ cm^2}$

2. (a) The shaded area consists of 1 semicircle of radius 4 cm and a smaller semicircle of radius 2 cm.
   Area $= (\frac{1}{2} \times \pi \times 4 \text{ cm} \times 4 \text{ cm}) + (\frac{1}{2} \times \pi \times 4 \text{ cm}^2)$

   $= (8 \text{ cm}^2 \times \pi) + (2 \text{ cm}^2 \times \pi) = \mathbf{10\pi\ cm^2}$

(b) The shaded area consists of 1 quarter circle of radius 10 cm and 2 smaller semicircles of radius 5 cm. The two semicircles make 1 whole circle.

$$\text{Area} = (\frac{1}{4} \times \pi \times 10 \text{ cm} \times 10 \text{ cm}) + (\pi \times 5 \text{ cm} \times 5 \text{ cm})$$

$$= (25 \text{ cm}^2 \times \pi) + (25 \text{ cm}^2 \times \pi) = \mathbf{50\pi\ cm^2}$$

(c) The shaded area consists of 4 quarter circles of radius 2, which together make a whole circle.
Area $= \pi \times 2 \text{ cm} \times 2 \text{ cm} = \mathbf{4\pi\ cm^2}$

3. The shaded area is the area of the square minus the area of the circle with radius 7 cm.
Area $= (14 \text{ cm} \times 14 \text{ cm}) - (\pi \times 7 \text{ cm} \times 7 \text{ cm})$

$$= 196 \text{ cm}^2 - (\frac{22}{7} \times 7 \text{ cm} \times 7 \text{ cm}) = 196 \text{ cm}^2 - 154 \text{ cm}^2 = \mathbf{42\ cm^2}$$

4. The shaded area is the area of the square of side 20 cm minus the area of the 4 quarter circles, which together make a whole circle of radius 10 cm.
Area $= (20 \text{ cm} \times 20 \text{ cm}) - (\pi \times 10 \text{ cm} \times 10 \text{ cm})$
$= 400 \text{ cm}^2 - (3.14 \times 100 \text{ cm}^2) = 400 \text{ cm}^2 - 314 \text{ cm}^2 = \mathbf{86\ cm^2}$

5. Since the area of the shaded semicircle is the same as the area of the unshaded semicircle, the shaded area is the area of the square.
Area $= 5 \text{ cm} \times 5 \text{ cm} = \mathbf{25\ cm^2}$

US› Exercise 15 **3d› Exercise 7**

1. (a) $\frac{1}{2} \times \frac{22}{7} \times 7 \text{ cm} \times 7 \text{ cm} = \mathbf{77\ cm^2}$
(b) $14 \text{ cm} \times 14 \text{ cm} = \mathbf{196\ cm^2}$
(c) $196 \text{ cm} + 77 \text{ cm} = \mathbf{273\ cm^2}$

2. (a) $3.14 \times 5 \text{ cm} \times 5 \text{ cm} = \mathbf{78.5\ cm^2}$
(b) $12 \text{ cm} \times 10 \text{ cm} = \mathbf{120\ cm^2}$
(c) $120 \text{ cm}^2 + 78.5 \text{ cm}^2 = \mathbf{198.5\ cm^2}$

3. (a) $\frac{1}{2} \times 3.14 \times 4\text{cm} \times 4\text{cm} = \mathbf{25.12\ cm^2}$
(b) $\frac{1}{2} \times 8 \text{ cm} \times 10 \text{ cm} = \mathbf{40\ cm^2}$
(c) $25.12 \text{ cm}^2 + 40 \text{ cm}^2 = \mathbf{65.12\ cm^2}$

4. (a) $11 \text{ m} \times 7 \text{ m} = \mathbf{77\ m^2}$
(b) $\frac{1}{2} \times \frac{22}{7} \times 3.5\text{m} \times 3.5\text{m} = \mathbf{19.25\ m^2}$
(c) $77 \text{ m}^2 - 19.25 \text{ m}^2 = \mathbf{57.75\ m^2}$

5. (a) $4 \text{ cm} \times 4 \text{ cm} = \mathbf{16\ cm^2}$
(b) $3.14 \times 1 \text{ cm} \times 1 \text{ cm} = \mathbf{3.14\ cm^2}$
(c) $16 \text{ cm}^2 - 3.14 \text{ cm}^2 = \mathbf{12.86\ cm^2}$

6. (a) $20 \text{ cm} \times 35 \text{ cm} = \mathbf{700\ cm^2}$ (b) $3.14 \times 10\text{cm} \times 10\text{cm} = \mathbf{314\ cm^2}$ (c) $700 \text{ cm}^2 - 314 \text{ cm}^2 = \mathbf{386\ cm^2}$

US› Exercise 16 **3d› Exercise 8**

1. Perimeter = half the circumference + 3 sides of the rectangle
$= (\frac{1}{2} \times 3.14 \times 10 \text{ m}) + 10 \text{ m} + 14 \text{ m} + 14 \text{ m} = 15.7 \text{ m} + 38 \text{ m} = \mathbf{53.7\ m}$

2. Area = area of the square + area of the semicircle + area of the triangle
$= (8 \text{ cm} \times 8 \text{ cm}) + (\frac{1}{2} \times 3.14 \times 4 \text{ cm} \times 4 \text{ cm}) + (\frac{1}{2} \times 8 \text{ cm} \times 5 \text{ cm})$
$= 64 \text{ cm}^2 + 25.12 \text{ cm}^2 + 20 \text{ cm}^2 = \mathbf{109.12\ cm^2}$

3. Area = area of 3 semicircles of radius 10 cm + area of the square
$= (3 \times \frac{1}{2} \times 3.14 \times 10 \text{ cm} \times 10 \text{ cm}) + (20 \text{ cm} \times 20 \text{ cm})$
$= 471 \text{ cm}^2 + 400 \text{ cm}^2 = \mathbf{871\ cm^2}$
Perimeter = (3 × half the circumference) + one side of the square
$= (3 \times \frac{1}{2} \times 3.14 \times 20 \text{ cm}) + 20 \text{ cm} = 94.2 \text{ cm} + 20 \text{ cm} = \mathbf{114.2\ cm}$

4. The semicircle and quarter circle together make $\frac{3}{4}$ of a circle with radius 10 cm.
Area = area of the square – area of $\frac{3}{4}$ of the circle
$= (20 \text{ cm} \times 20 \text{ cm}) - (\frac{3}{4} \times 3.14 \times 10 \text{ cm} \times 10 \text{ cm})$
$= 400 \text{ cm}^2 - 235.5 \text{ cm}^2 = \mathbf{164.5\ cm^2}$
Perimeter = 2 sides of the square + $\frac{3}{4}$ the circumference of the circle
$= 20 \text{ cm} + 20 \text{ cm} + (\frac{3}{4} \times 3.14 \times 20 \text{ cm}) = 40 \text{ cm} + 47.1 \text{ cm} = \mathbf{87.1\ cm}$

US› Exercise 17 **3d› Exercise 9**

1. (a) **16** (b) **12** (c) $16 + 12 + 4 + 8 = \mathbf{40}$
(d) $\frac{8}{40} = \mathbf{\frac{1}{5}}$ (e) $\frac{4}{40} = \mathbf{\frac{1}{10}}$

2. (a) **Cars** (b) **2000** (c) $3200 + 800 + 2000 + 4000 = \mathbf{10{,}000}$
(d) $\frac{800}{10{,}000} = \mathbf{\frac{2}{25}}$ (e) $\frac{3200}{10{,}000} = \mathbf{\frac{8}{25}}$

3. (a) $150 + 100 = \mathbf{250}$

   (b) Chicken + Egg = Tuna + Ham (‹**US**; **3d**› Sardine)
   Number of chicken sandwiches $= 250 - 50 = \mathbf{200}$

   (c) $150 + 200 + 50 + 100 = \mathbf{500}$

   (d) $\frac{100}{500} \times 100\% = \mathbf{20\%}$ (e) $\frac{150}{50} = \mathbf{3}$

4. (a) Entertainment (‹**US**; **3d**› Stationery)has a 90° angle, so is $\frac{1}{4}$ of his allowance. Transport and savings would then together be $\frac{1}{4}$. Each is the same, so Savings is $\mathbf{\frac{1}{8}}$ of his allowance.

   (b) $\frac{1}{8} \longrightarrow \$5$
   $1 \longrightarrow \$5 \times 8 = \mathbf{\$40}$

   (c) $\mathbf{\frac{1}{2}}$

   (d) $\frac{1}{4} = \mathbf{25\%}$

   (e) $\frac{1}{8} : \frac{1}{2} = \frac{1}{8} : \frac{4}{8} = \mathbf{1 : 4}$

US› Exercise 18 **3d› Exercise 10**

1. Total $= 40 + 80 + 50 + 30 = 200$

   Motorcycles $= \frac{40}{200} = \mathbf{\frac{1}{5}}$ Cars $= \frac{80}{200} = \mathbf{\frac{2}{5}}$

   Vans $= \frac{50}{200} = \mathbf{\frac{1}{4}}$ **US›** Trucks $= \frac{30}{200} = \mathbf{\frac{3}{20}}$ (**3d›** Lorries)

2. (a) $\mathbf{\frac{3}{8}}$ (b) $\mathbf{\frac{1}{4}}$ (90° angle)

   (c) $1 - \frac{1}{4} - \frac{1}{4} - \frac{3}{8} = \mathbf{\frac{1}{8}}$ (d) $\frac{3}{8} \times 400 = \mathbf{150}$

   (e) $\frac{1}{4} \times 400 = \mathbf{100}$

3. (a) $\mathbf{\frac{1}{2}}$ (b) $\frac{1}{2} - \frac{1}{6} - \frac{1}{9} = \frac{9}{18} - \frac{3}{18} - \frac{2}{18} = \frac{4}{18} = \mathbf{\frac{2}{9}}$

   (c) $\frac{1}{9} \times 180 = \mathbf{20}$ (d) $\frac{1}{6} \times 180 = \mathbf{30}$

   (e) $30 - 20 = \mathbf{10}$

4. (a) **Chocolate**

(b) $\frac{1}{2} - \frac{1}{10} = \frac{4}{10} = \mathbf{\frac{2}{5}}$

(c) $\frac{3}{10} = \mathbf{30\%}$

(d) $\frac{1}{2} - \frac{3}{10} = \frac{5}{10} - \frac{3}{10} = \frac{2}{10} = \frac{1}{5} = \mathbf{20\%}$

(e) $\frac{3}{10} \longrightarrow 48$ $\frac{10}{10} \longrightarrow \frac{48}{3} \times 10 = \mathbf{160}$

US› Exercise 19 **3d› Exercise 11**

1. Total $= \$100 + \$150 + \$400 + \$350 = \$1000$

Fan $= \frac{100}{1000} = \mathbf{10\%}$

Vacuum cleaner $= \frac{150}{1{,}000} = \mathbf{15\%}$

Television $= \frac{400}{1000} = \mathbf{40\%}$

Oven $= \frac{350}{1000} = \mathbf{35\%}$

2. (a) **15%**

(b) **25%**

(c) $100\% - 15\% - 20\% - 25\% = \mathbf{40\%}$

(d) $\frac{15}{100} \times 80 = \mathbf{12}$

(e) $\frac{20}{100} \times 80 = \mathbf{16}$

3. (a) **4**

(b) $50\% - 25\% - 15\% = \mathbf{10\%}$

(c) $\frac{15}{100}$ x 40 kg $= \mathbf{6\ kg}$

(d) $\frac{1}{2} \times 40$ kg $= \mathbf{20\ kg}$

(e) $\frac{1}{4} \times 40$ kg $= \mathbf{10\ kg}$

4. (a) $35\% = \frac{35}{100} = \mathbf{\frac{7}{20}}$

(b) **25%**

(c) $100\% - 35\% - 25\% - 25\% = \mathbf{15\%}$

(d) $25\% \rightarrow 30$

$100\% \rightarrow 30 \times 4 = \mathbf{120}$

(e) $\frac{35}{100} \times 120 = \mathbf{42}$

Review 1

1. **10,000**
2. **247,000**
3. **0.106** (divisions are 0.002)
4. **2.85**

5. (a) **3** (b) **9**

6. $\frac{25}{200} = \mathbf{\frac{1}{8}}$

7. $\frac{750}{2000} \times 100\% = \mathbf{37.5\%}$

8. **US›** (a) $\frac{2}{3} \div \frac{5}{6} = \frac{2}{\cancel{3}_1} \times \frac{\cancel{6}^2}{5} = \mathbf{\frac{4}{5}}$

(b) $\frac{5}{8} \times \left(\frac{3}{4} + \frac{2}{5}\right) = \frac{5}{8} \times \left(\frac{15}{20} + \frac{8}{20}\right) = \frac{\cancel{5}^1}{8} \times \frac{23}{\cancel{20}_4} = \mathbf{\frac{23}{32}}$

3d› **1 h 35 min**

9. Total height $= 1.65 \text{ m} \times 4 = 6.6 \text{ m}$
Height of 3 boys $= 6.6 \text{ m} - 1.68 \text{ m} = 4.92 \text{ m}$
Average height of 3 boys $\frac{4.92}{3} = \mathbf{1.64\ m}$

10. $\frac{7}{4+7+9} = \frac{7}{20} = \frac{35}{100} = \mathbf{35\%}$

11. Discount $= 15\%$ of $\$800 = \frac{15}{100} \times \$800 = \$120$
Selling price $=$ Usual Price $-$ Discount $= \$800 - \$120 = \mathbf{\$680}$

12. $200 \text{ m} \longrightarrow 1 \text{ min}$
$4000 \text{ m} \longrightarrow \frac{1}{200} \times 4000$
$= \mathbf{20\ min}$

Or: $\text{Time} = \frac{\text{Distance}}{\text{Speed}}$
$= \frac{4000}{200} = 20 \text{ min}$

13. 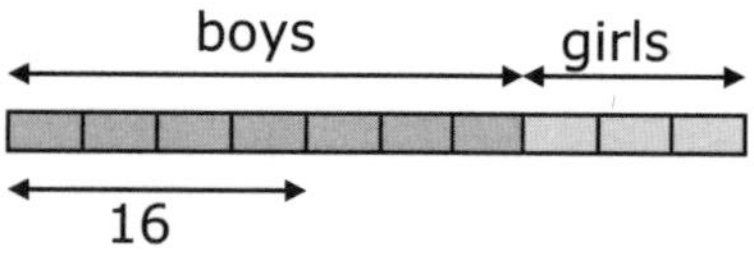

4 units $= 16$
1 unit $= \frac{16}{4}$
10 units $= \frac{16}{4} \times 10 = 40$
There are **40** students.

Or: $\frac{7}{10}$ of the students are boys.
$\frac{3}{10}$ of the students are girls.
$\frac{7}{10} - \frac{3}{10} = \frac{4}{10}$
$\frac{4}{10} \longrightarrow 16$
$\frac{10}{10} \longrightarrow \frac{16}{4} \times 10 = 40$

14. 11 units $= 132$

$3 \text{ units} = \frac{132}{11} \times 3 = 36$

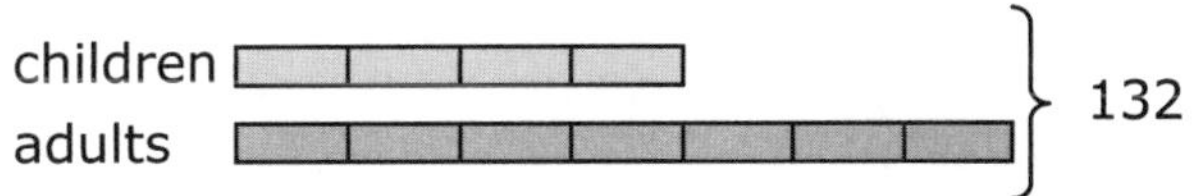

There are **36** more adults than children.

15. 225% of the girls is 450.

$225\% \longrightarrow 450$

$25\% \longrightarrow \frac{450}{225} \times 25 = 50$

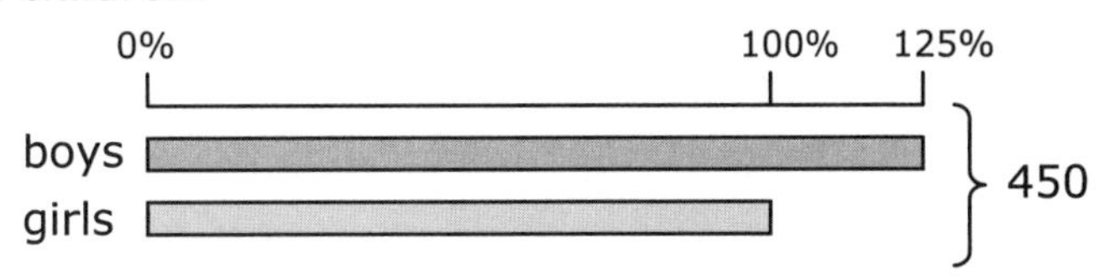

There are **50** more boys than girls.

16. 3:00 p.m. to 5:00 p.m. $= \$1.50 \times 2 = \$3.00$
5:00 p.m. to 6:10 p.m. $= \$1.00 \times 2 - \$2.00$
Total fee $= \$3.00 + \$2.00 =$ **\$5.00**

17. The figure can be split up various ways.

Area = area of 3 rectangles $= (5 \text{ cm} \times 8 \text{ cm}) + (9 \text{ cm} \times 4 \text{ cm}) + (5 \text{ cm} \times 8 \text{ cm})$
$= 40 \text{ cm}^2 + 36 \text{ cm}^2 + 40 \text{ cm}^2$
$= \mathbf{116 \text{ cm}^2}$

18. Bottom edges of triangles are 4 and 5 cm. The length of the top of rectangle not covered with the triangles is $14 \text{ cm} - 4 \text{ cm} - 5 \text{ cm} = 5 \text{ cm}$
Perimeter $= 6 + 4 + 4 + 5 + 5 + 5 + 6 + 14 =$ **49 cm**

19. Area = area of semicircle + area of rectangle + area of triangle
The semicircle has a radius of 10 cm.
The width of the rectangle and base of the triangle is $(2 \times 10) = 20$ cm.

$\text{Area} = (\frac{1}{2} \times 3.14 \times 10 \text{ cm} \times 10 \text{ cm}) + (30 \text{ cm} \times 20 \text{ cm}) + (\frac{1}{2} \times 20 \text{ cm} \times 20 \text{ cm})$
$= 157 \text{ cm}^2 + 600 \text{ cm}^2 + 200 \text{ cm}^2 = \mathbf{957 \text{ cm}^2}$

Circ π x diameter

20. Perimeter = half the circumference of a circle with diameter 12 cm
+ half the circumference of 3 circles with diameter 4 cm

$= (\frac{1}{2} \times \pi \times 12 \text{ cm}) + 3 \times (\frac{1}{2} \times \pi \times 4 \text{ cm}) = 6\pi \text{ cm} + 6\pi \text{ cm} = \mathbf{12\pi \text{ cm}}$

21.

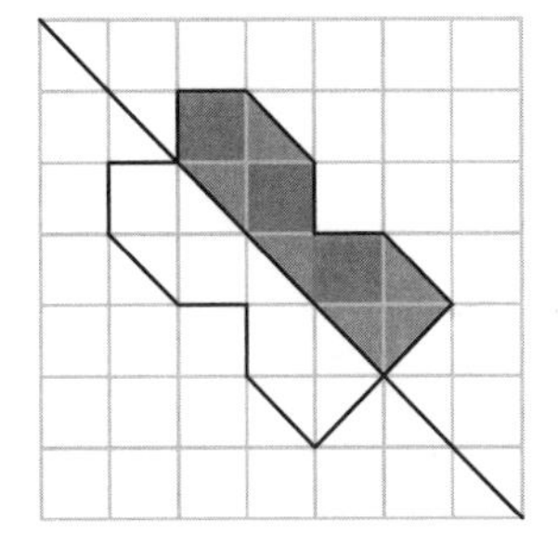

22. (a) $50 - 20 =$ **30 kg** (b) $40 : 25 =$ **8 : 5** (c) $\frac{30}{50} = \mathbf{\frac{3}{5}}$

23. Money from tarts $= 200 \times \$0.40 = \$80$
Money spent on plates $= \$80 - \$28.80 = \$51.20$
Cost of 1 plate $= \$51.20 \div 8 = \mathbf{\$6.40}$

24. $\frac{2}{5}$ of the boys $= \frac{2}{10}$ of the students
$\frac{1}{2}$ of the girls $= \frac{1}{4}$ of the students
Fraction of the pupils that go by (**US>** bus, **3d>** MRT)
$= \frac{2}{10} + \frac{1}{4} = \frac{4}{20} + \frac{5}{20} = \mathbf{\frac{9}{20}}$

25. Ben's share $= \$60 - \$15 = \$45$
Rajah's share $= \$45 \times 3 = \mathbf{\$135}$

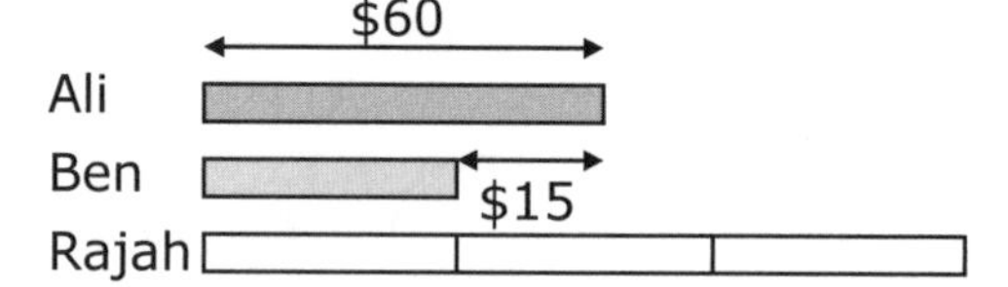

26. 10% of the children last year $= 11$
10% $\longrightarrow$ 11
100% $\longrightarrow$ 110
There were 110 members last year.
Number of boys last year $= \frac{1}{2}$ of the total members last year $= \frac{1}{2} \times 110 = \mathbf{55}$

Review 2

1. **5**

2. (a) **10** (b) **4**

3. (a) $27 + \underline{96 \div 12} \div 4$
$= 27 + \underline{8 \div 4}$
$= \underline{27 + 2}$
$= \mathbf{29}$

(b) $(\underline{45 + 27}) \div (\underline{17 - 8})$
$= 72 \div 9$
$= \mathbf{8}$

4. **150**

5. Half of the two middle fourths, and half of the last fourth is shaded.
$\frac{1}{2} \times \frac{2}{4} + \frac{1}{2} \times \frac{1}{4} = \frac{2}{8} + \frac{1}{8} = \mathbf{\frac{3}{8}}$

6. $\mathbf{\frac{4}{7}}$

7. **3.71**

8. **3**

9. Cost of shorts $= 1$ unit
Cost of T-shirt $= 1$ unit $+ \$5$
4 units $= \$54 - (3 \times \$5)$
$= \$54 - \$15$
$= \$39$
1 unit $= \$\frac{39}{4} = \$9.75$
The shorts cost **$9.75**.

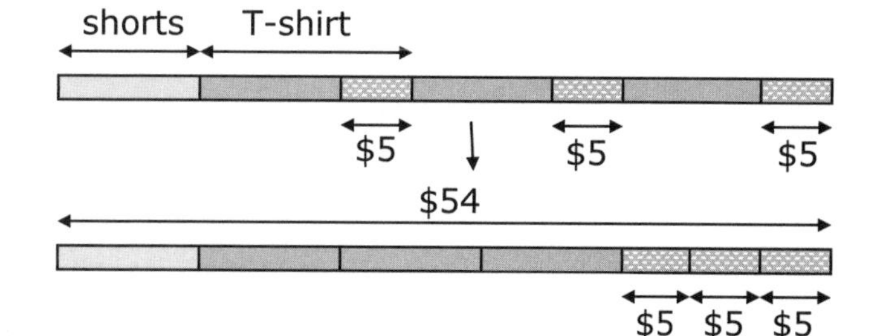

10. His remainder after giving away $\frac{2}{3} = \frac{1}{3}$ of the mangoes $= \frac{1}{3} \times 54 = 18$

Amount left after eating $\frac{1}{6}$ of remainder $= \frac{5}{6}$ of remainder $= \frac{5}{6} \times 18 =$ **15** mangoes.

OR:

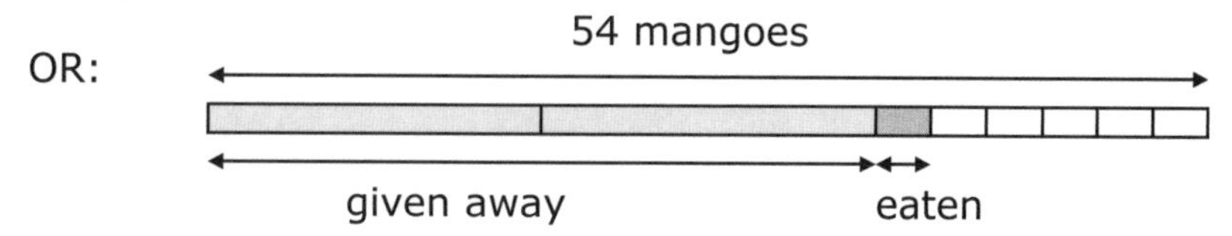

One third (the remainder) is divided into 6 small units to show the $\frac{1}{6}$ of the remainder that were eaten. 5 small units are left.
Divide the whole bar into small units, giving $3 \times 6 = 18$ units.
18 units = 54 mangoes
5 units $= \frac{54}{18} \times 5 = 15$
15 mangoes are left.

11. Fraction of total capacity poured out $= \frac{1}{2} - \frac{1}{3} = \frac{3}{6} - \frac{2}{6} = \frac{1}{6}$

$\frac{1}{6}$ of capacity $= 200$ ml

$\frac{6}{6}$ of capacity $= 200 \times 6 =$ **1200 ml**

12. There are 8 units total, so for each to have the same number A. gives H. 1 unit.
8 units $= 1{,}000$
1 unit $= 125$
A. gives Henry **125** stamps.

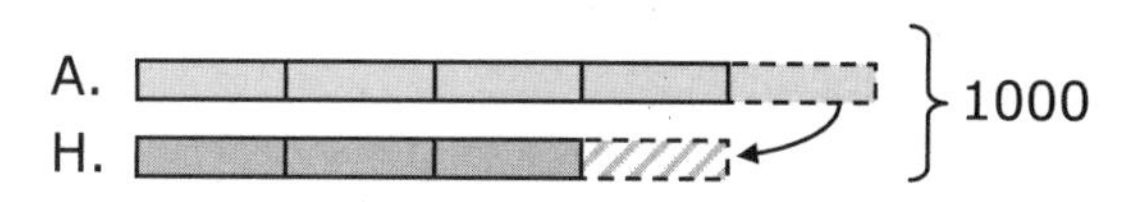

13. The original cost is 100%. Final cost is 110% of the original cost.
$110\% \longrightarrow \$2420$
$100\% \longrightarrow \$\frac{2420}{110} \times 100 = 2200$
The price before the increase was **$2200**.

14. 25% of Susan's savings is $200. Susan has 100% of Susan's savings, and Mary has 125% of Susan's savings. Together they have 225% of Susan's savings.
$25\% \longrightarrow \$200$
$225\% \longrightarrow \$\frac{200}{25} \times 225 = \$1800$
Their total savings is **$1800**.

15. $\text{Time} = \frac{\text{Distance}}{\text{Speed}} = \frac{800 \text{ m}}{50 \text{ m / min}} = \mathbf{16 \text{ min}}$

16. (a) $\frac{2a - 3}{4} = \frac{2 \text{ x } 3 - 3}{4} = \frac{6 - 3}{4} = \mathbf{\frac{3}{4}}$

(b) $40 - a^3 = 40 - 3 \times 3 \times 3 = 40 - 27 = \mathbf{13}$

17. Total weight of 3 girls $= 3x$
Total weight of 4 girls $= 30 \times 4 = 120$
Weight of 4th girl $= \mathbf{120 - 3x}$ **kg**.

18. The figure can be divided up into rectangles in various ways. One way is to draw vertical lines 2 m from the left edge and 2 m from the right edge. Another would be to draw a horizontal line up 2 m from the bottom. Area is the sum of the 3 rectangles formed. For the first way:
$\text{Area} = (2 \text{ m} \times 4 \text{ m}) + (3 \text{ m} \times 2 \text{ m}) + (2 \text{ m} \times 7 \text{ m}) = 8 \text{ m}^2 + 6 \text{ m}^2 + 14 \text{ m}^2 = \mathbf{28 \text{ m}^2}$

19. Base of triangle is $14 - 2 = 12$ cm. Height is 14 cm. Radius of circle is 7 cm.
Area = area of triangle + area of semicircle
$= (\frac{1}{2} \times 12 \text{ cm} \times 14 \text{ cm}) + (\frac{1}{2} \times \frac{22}{7} \times 7 \text{ cm} \times 7 \text{ cm})$
$= 84 \text{ cm}^2 + 77 \text{ cm}^2 = \mathbf{161 \text{ cm}^2}$

20. The sides of the triangle are all 20 cm. The diameter of the circle is 40 m.
Perimeter = One fourth the circumference of the circle + 3 sides
$= (\frac{1}{4} \times 3.14 \times 40 \text{ cm}) + (3 \times 20 \text{ cm}) = 31.4 \text{ cm} + 60 \text{ cm} = \mathbf{91.4 \text{ cm}}$

21. There are 16 sides in the perimeter.
$128 \text{ cm} \div 16 = 8 \text{ cm}$
Area $= 8 \text{ cm} \times 8 \text{ cm} =$ $\mathbf{64 \ cm^2}$

22. Answers can vary.

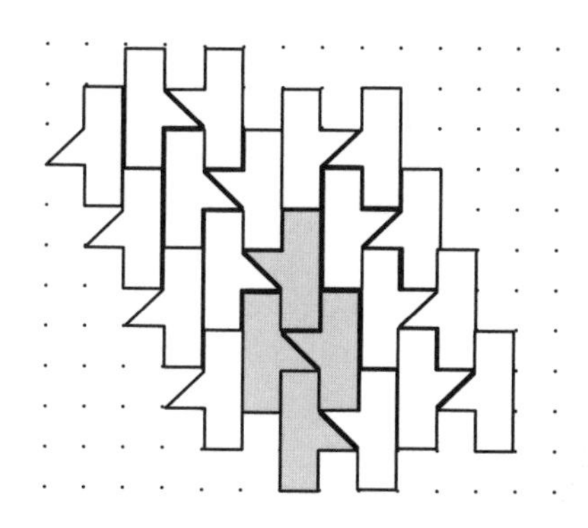

23. (a) $\$160 - \$90 =$ **$70**
(b) $\$90 + \$70 + \$160 + \$140 + \$150 =$ **$610**

24.

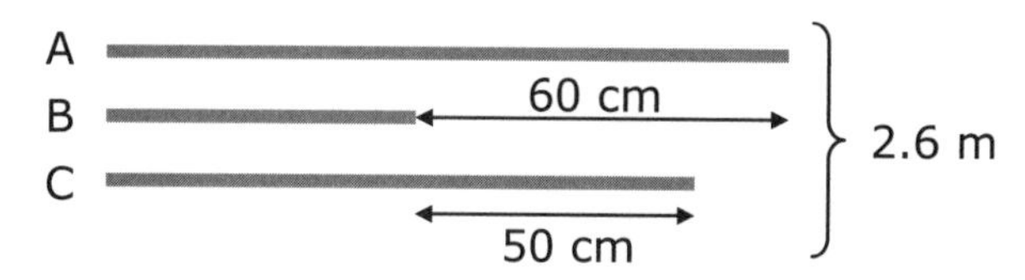

Let the length of A be 1 unit. If 60 cm is added, B would be 1 unit, and if 10 cm is added to C, C would be 1 unit. So 70 cm needs to be added to get 3 units.
3 units $= 260 + 70 = 330$ cm
1 unit $= 330 \div 3 = 110$ cm
Ribbon A is **110 cm** long (or 1.1 m).

25. Fraction sold on Tuesday $= 1 - \frac{3}{5} = \frac{2}{5}$

Fraction fewer sold on Tuesday $= \frac{3}{5} - \frac{2}{5} = \frac{1}{5}$

$\frac{1}{5}$ of the postcards $= 25$

$\frac{5}{5}$ of the postcards $= 25 \times 5 = 125$

He had **125** postcards.

26. $\frac{3}{4}$ of the beads are yellow and blue.

40% of $\frac{3}{4}$ of the beads are blue.

40% of $\frac{3}{4} = \frac{40}{100} \times \frac{3}{4} = \frac{3}{10}$

$\frac{3}{10}$ of the beads $= 48$

$\frac{10}{10}$ of the beads $= \frac{48}{3} \times 10 = 160$

There are **160** beads.

27. Time for car $= 1$ h

Distance for car $= 60$ km/h $\times 1$ h $= 60$ km

Time for van $= \frac{60 \text{ km}}{40 \text{ km/h}} = \frac{3}{2}$ h $= 1$ h 30 min

Time van arrived at B $= 2{:}20 + 1$ h 30 min

$=$ **3:50 p.m.**

40 km/h
2:20 →
A |———| B
3:30 ← 2:30
60 km/h

US› 28. (a) $\frac{1}{4} + \frac{3}{4} \times 8 - \frac{1}{8} = \frac{1}{4} + 6 - \frac{1}{8}$

$= 6\frac{1}{4} - \frac{1}{8}$

$= \mathbf{6\frac{1}{8}}$

(b) $\frac{3}{5} \times \left(\frac{2}{3} \div \frac{1}{8}\right) + \frac{1}{2} = \frac{\not{3}^1}{5} \times \frac{2}{\not{3}_1} \times 8 + \frac{1}{2}$

$= \frac{16}{5} + \frac{1}{2}$

$= 3\frac{1}{5} + \frac{1}{2}$

$= \mathbf{3\frac{7}{10}}$

US› Exercise 20 3d› Exercise 12

1. Volume of each cube $= 8$ cm^3

(a) 8×8 cm^3 $=$ **64 cm^3**
(b) 11×8 cm^3 $=$ **88 cm^3**
(c) 7×8 cm^3 $=$ **56 cm^3**
(d) 11×8 cm^3 $=$ **88 cm^3**

2. (a) $5 \times 3 \times 4 =$ **60**
(b) $6 \times 8 \times 5 =$ **240**

3. (a) **10 cm**
(b) Height $= \frac{720}{120} =$ **6 cm**

US› Exercise 21 3d› Exercise 13

1. (a) Volume $= 10 \times 16 \times 8 = 1280$ cm^3 = **1.28 ℓ**
   (b) Volume $= 10 \times 20 \times 12 = 2400$ cm^3 = **2.4 ℓ**
   (c) Volume $= 20 \times 20 \times 8 = 3200$ cm^3 = **3.2 ℓ**
   (d) Volume $= 8 \times 15 \times 4 = 480$ cm^3 = **0.48 ℓ**

2. Height of water $= \frac{2}{3} \times 12$ cm $= 8$ cm
   Volume $= 20 \times 15 \times 8 = 2400$ cm^3 = **2.4 ℓ**

3. Height by which water decreased $= 20 - 16 = 4$ cm
   Volume removed $= 40 \times 30 \times 4 = 4800$ cm^3 = **4.8 ℓ**

4. Height of water $= \frac{42{,}000}{60 \times 50} = 14$ cm
   Total height $= 14 \times 3 =$ **42 cm**

5. Height of water added $= \frac{24{,}000}{60 \times 50} = 8$ cm
   $\frac{1}{5}$ of the height of the tank $= 8$ cm
   Total height of the tank $= 8 \times 5 =$ **40 cm**

US› Exercise 22 3d› Exercise 14

1. Drop in water level = 15 cm − 9 cm = 6 cm
   Volume of stone = 40 cm × 30 cm × 6 cm = **7200 cm^3**

2. Capacity of tank = 30 cm × 25 cm × 15 cm = 11,250 cm^3
   Volume of cube = 10 cm × 10 cm × 10 cm = 1000 cm^3
   Volume of water needed = 11,250 cm^3 − 1000 cm^3 = 10,250 cm^3 = **10.25 ℓ**

3. Increase in height of water level = 16 cm − 12 cm = 4 cm
   Volume of 4 balls = 50 cm × 20 cm × 4 cm = 4000 cm^3
   Volume of 1 ball = 4000 cm^3 ÷ 4 = **1000 cm^3**

4. Volume of the 6 cubes = 6 × 10 cm × 10 cm × 10 cm = 6000 cm^3
   $\frac{1}{5}$ of the capacity of the tank = 6000 cm^3
   Total capacity of the tank = 6000 cm^3 × 5 = 30,000 cm^3
   Height of tank $= \frac{30{,}000}{50 \times 30} =$ **20 cm**

5. Height by which the water needs to be raised = 20 cm – 15 cm = 5 cm
Volume of cubes to be added = 30 cm × 15 cm × 5 cm = 2250 cm^3
Volume of 1 cube = 5 × 5 × 5 = 125 cm^3
Number of cubes needed = $\frac{2250}{125}$ = **18**

US› Exercise 23 3d› Exercise 15

1. Capacity of tank = 40 cm × 30 cm × 15 cm = 18,000 cm^3 = 18 ℓ
12 ℓ ⟶ 1 min
1 ℓ ⟶ $\frac{1}{12}$ min
18 ℓ ⟶ $\frac{1}{12} \times 18 = \frac{3}{2}$ min = $1\frac{1}{2}$ min = 1 min 30 s
It will take **1 min 30 s** to fill the tank.

2. Volume of water in tank = 80 cm × 50 cm × 60 cm = 240,000 cm^3 = 240 ℓ
15 ℓ ⟶ 1 min
1 ℓ ⟶ $\frac{1}{15}$ min
240 ℓ ⟶ $\frac{1}{15} \times 240$ min = 16 min
It will take **16 min** to empty the tank.

3. Volume of cubes = 2 × 10 cm × 10 cm × 10 cm = 2000 cm^3 = 2 ℓ
Volume of water + volume of cubes = 60 cm × 40 cm × 30 cm = 72,000 cm^3 = 72 ℓ
Volume of water = 72 ℓ – 2 ℓ = 70 ℓ
10 ℓ → 1 min
70 ℓ → 1 × 7 = 7 min
It will take **7 min** to empty the tank.

4. Volume of water added in 3 min = 10 ℓ × 3 = 30 ℓ
Volume of cubes = 2 × 10 × 10 × 10 = 2000 cm^3 = 2 ℓ
Capacity of tank = volume of water + volume of cubes = 30 ℓ + 2 ℓ = 32 ℓ
Height = $\frac{32,000}{40 \times 25}$ = 32 cm
The height of the tank is **32 cm**.

Review 3

1. **0.12**
2. **5.81**
3. (a) $2\frac{1}{4} - 1\frac{5}{8} = 1\frac{2}{8} - \frac{5}{8} = \frac{10}{8} - \frac{5}{8} = \mathbf{\frac{5}{8}}$

   US› (b) $\frac{1}{5} \div \frac{2}{3} \times \frac{3}{4} = \frac{1}{5} \times \frac{3}{2} \times \frac{3}{4} = \mathbf{\frac{9}{40}}$

   3d› (b) $\frac{\cancel{4}^{2}}{5} \times \frac{1}{\cancel{6}_{3}} = \mathbf{\frac{2}{15}}$

4. $2\frac{3}{4}$ h $= 2$ h $+ \frac{3}{4} \times 60$ min $=$ **2 h 45 min**
5. $\frac{1}{4} \longrightarrow 45$

   $\frac{1}{2} \longrightarrow 45 \times 2 = \mathbf{90}$
6. Number of girls $= 40 - 24 = 16$
   Number of girls : number of boys $= 16 : 24 =$ **2 : 3**
7. $0.045 \times 100\% =$ **4.5%**
8. 35% of 720 g $= \frac{35}{100} \times 720$ g $=$ **252 g**
9. **8:10 a.m.**
10. \$2.50 $\longrightarrow$ 3 chocolate bar
    \$5 $\longrightarrow$ 6 chocolate bars
    \$15 $\longrightarrow 6 \times 3 =$ **18** chocolate bars
11. Total height of 2 boys $= 1.65 \times 2 = 3.30$ m
    Height of shorter boy $= \frac{1}{2} \times (3.30 - 0.02) = \frac{1}{2} \times 3.28 =$ **1.64 m**
12. Remaining money $= \frac{3}{8}$

    Fraction of remaining money left $= \frac{5}{6}$

    Fraction of total money left $= \frac{5}{6} \times \frac{3}{8} = \mathbf{\frac{5}{16}}$

13. 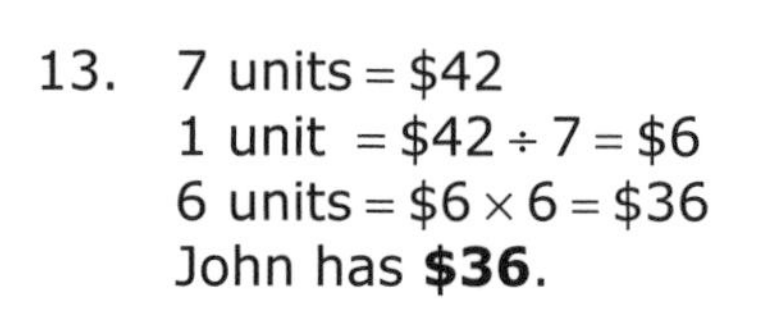
7 units = \$42
1 unit = $\$42 \div 7 = \$6$
6 units = $\$6 \times 6 = \$36$
John has **\$36**.

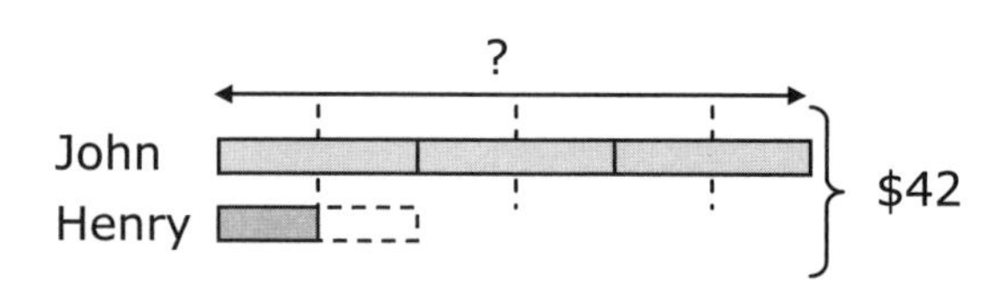

14. 3 units = 39
1 unit = $39 \div 3 = 13$
There are **13** more black beads.

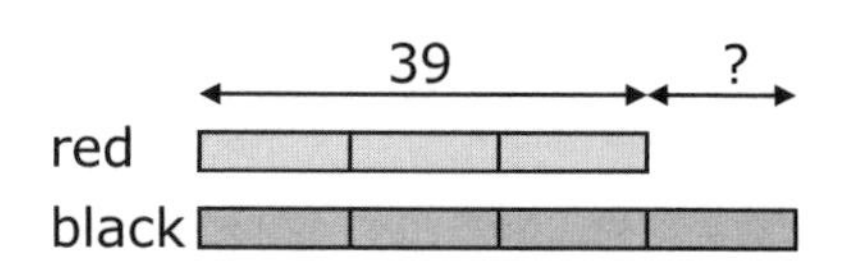

15. **US›** **3d›**
Dan Ali
Tommy Gopal

New ratio = **3 : 19**

16. New salary = 110% of old salary. Increase is 10% of old salary.
110% ⟶ \$1650

$$10\% \longrightarrow \$\frac{1650}{11} = \$150$$

The increase is **\$150**.

17. 160 bottles ⟶ 2 min

$$1 \text{ bottle} \longrightarrow \frac{2}{160} \text{ min}$$

$$400 \text{ bottles} \longrightarrow \frac{2}{160} \times 400 = 5 \text{ min}$$

It will take **5 min** to cap 400 bottles.

18. Distance = Speed × Time = 60 km/h × 4 h = 240 km

$$\text{New time at new speed} = \frac{\text{Distance}}{\text{Speed}} = \frac{240 \text{ km}}{80 \text{ km/h}} = \mathbf{3\ h}$$

19. **$\$(45x + 50)$**

20. Four semicircles = 2 whole circles

The radius is $\frac{1}{4}$ of 20 cm, or 5 cm.

Area of remaining cardboard = area of rectangle − area of 2 circles

$$= (20 \times 12) - (2 \times 3.14 \times 5 \times 5)$$
$$= 240 - 157$$
$$= \mathbf{83\ cm^2}$$

21. The quarter circle has a radius of 6 cm. The two semicircles make a whole circle with radius 3 cm.

$$\text{Perimeter} = (\frac{1}{4} \times \pi \times 2 \times 6) + (\pi \times 2 \times 3) = 3\pi + 6\pi = \mathbf{9\pi\ cm}$$

22. Height of water $= \frac{108{,}000}{90 \times 50} =$ **24 cm**

23. **(c)**

24. (a) **$450**

    (b) $\frac{200+600+450+150+100+250}{6} = \frac{1750}{6} \approx$ **$292**

25. Money from sale of 3 watches $= 3 \times \$110 = \$330$
    Money from sale of 2 watches $= \$490 - \$330 = \$160$
    Cost price of 1 watch $= \frac{1}{2} \times \$160 = \$80$
    Cost price of 5 watches $= \$80 \times 5 = \$400$
    Amount he made $= \$490 - \$400 =$ **$90**

26.

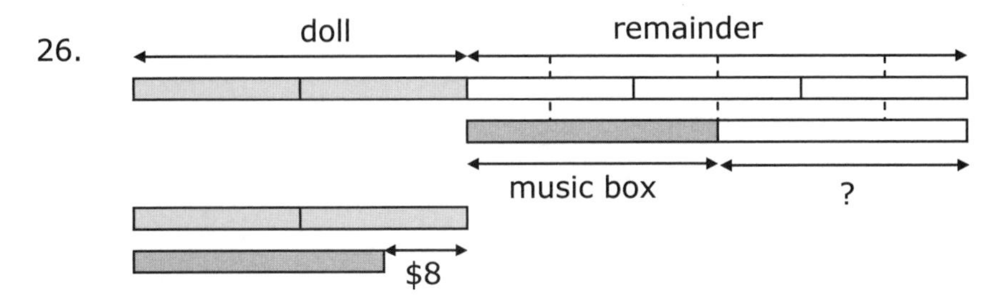

She spent half of a fifth, or one tenth of her money, more on the doll than on the box. Let $\frac{1}{10}$ of her money be 1 unit. She has 3 units left

1 unit $= \$8$
3 units $= \$8 \times 3 = \$24$
She had **$24** left.

Review 4

1. **507.904**
2. (a) **4** (b) **10**
3. (a) **8** (b) **7**
4. **1.7 ℓ**
5. 48 km $\longrightarrow$ 4 ℓ
   1 km $\longrightarrow \frac{4}{48}$ ℓ
   72 km $\longrightarrow \frac{4}{48} \times 72 =$ **6 ℓ**

6. $\frac{1}{2}$ of a number is 50% of the number.
   50% $\longrightarrow$ 15
   10% $\longrightarrow$ $15 \div 5 = 3$
   20% $\longrightarrow$ $3 \times 2 =$ **6**

7. Cost of 1 skirt = 1 unit
   4 units = \$46
   1 unit = $\$\frac{46}{4}$
   2 units = $\$\frac{46}{4} \times 2 = \$23$
   A shirt costs **\$23**.

   shirt
   skirts
   \$46

8. Total weight of 3 boys = $41.5 \times 3 = 124.5$ kg
   Total weight of 2 boys = $43.7 \times 2 = 87.4$
   Weight of 1 boy = $124.5 - 87.4 =$ **37.1 kg**

9. 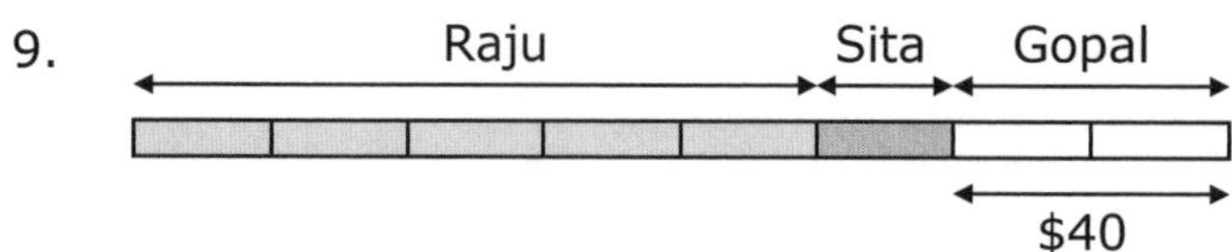

   2 units = \$40
   1 unit = \$20
   8 units = $\$20 \times 8 = \$160$
   They had **\$160** altogether.

10. John : Peter : Mary
    2 : 3
    = 4 : 6
    6 : 7
    4 : 6 : 7
    Mary : Peter : John = **7 : 6 : 4**

    John
    Peter
    Peter
    Mary

11. The remainder is 60%.
    He spent 10% of the remainder.
    10% of 60% = 6%
    Total spent = 40% + 6% = 46%
    Money left = 100% − 46% = 54%
    He spent \$92, so 46% of his money is \$92.
    46% → \$92
    1% → $\$92 \div 46 = \$2$
    54% → $\$2 \times 54 = \$108$.
    He had **\$108** left.

12. Area of shaded part = area of quarter circle – half the area of the square

$= (\frac{1}{4} \times 3.14 \times 10 \text{ cm} \times 10 \text{ cm}) - (\frac{1}{2} \times 10 \text{ cm} \times 10 \text{ cm})$

$= 78.5 \text{ cm}^2 - 50 \text{ cm}^2 = \mathbf{28.5 \text{ cm}^2}$

13. Perimeter = circumference of a circle of diameter 7 + two sides of the square

$= (\frac{22}{7} \times 7 \text{ cm}) + (2 \times 7 \text{ cm}) = 22 \text{ cm} + 14 \text{ cm} = \mathbf{36 \text{ cm}}$

14. There would be 5 cubes along the length, 3 along the breadth, and 3 along the height.
Number of cubes needed $= 5 \times 3 \times 3 =$ **45**

15. Volume of one cube $= \frac{108}{4} = 27 \text{ cm}^3$
Side of one cube = 3 cm
Area of one face of the cube $= 3 \text{ cm} \times 3 \text{ cm} = 9 \text{ cm}^2$
Area of shaded face $= 4 \text{ cm}^2 \times 9 \text{ cm}^2 = \mathbf{36 \text{ cm}^2}$

16. **C.** The net has 4 equilateral triangles.

17. (a) **25%** (The rent is a quarter circle.)
(b) 50% – 25% – 10% = **15%**
(c) 25% → \$200
50% → \$200 × 2 = **\$400**

18. 12 km/h → ; ← 16 km/h
A ——— 4 km ——— B

They both traveled a half-hour.

Distance for (**US›** Ryan, **3d›** Rajah) $= 12 \text{ km/h} \times \frac{1}{2} \text{ h} = 6 \text{ km}$

Distance for (**US›** Scott, **3d›** Gopal) $= 16 \text{ km/h} \times \frac{1}{2} \text{ h} = 8 \text{ km}$

Total distance between towns $= 6 + 4 + 8 =$ **18 km**

US› Exercise 24 3d› Exercise 16

1. $\angle XWY = 180 - 134° = 46°$ (∠'s on a st. line)
$\angle y = \angle WXY + \angle XWY = 90° + 46° = 136°$ (ext. ∠ of a Δ)
OR:
$\angle XWY = 180 - 134° = 46°$ (∠'s on a st. line)
$\angle WYX = 90° - 46° = 44°$ (right Δ)
$\angle y = 180° - 44° = 136°$ (∠'s on a st. line)

2. ΔBCD is isosceles. Find $\angle$DBC.
$\angle DBC = \angle EBA = 116^\circ$ (vert. opp. $\angle$'s)
$\angle d = (180^\circ - 116^\circ) \div 2 = \mathbf{32^\circ}$ ($\angle$ sum of a Δ, iso. Δ)

3. Find the angles around point B.
$\angle DBE = 90^\circ - 50^\circ = 40^\circ$ (right Δ)
$\angle b = 360^\circ - 90^\circ - 125^\circ - 40^\circ$ ($\angle$'s around a point)
$= \mathbf{105^\circ}$

4. $\angle BCD = 90^\circ - 38^\circ = 52^\circ$ (right Δ)
$\angle ADC = 180^\circ - \angle BCD$ (inside $\angle$'s)
$= 180^\circ - 52^\circ = 128^\circ$
$\angle x = 128^\circ - 90^\circ = \mathbf{38^\circ}$

5. $\angle PSR = 112^\circ$ (opp. $\angle$'s of //)
$\angle m = (180^\circ - 112^\circ) \div 2$ (ΔPRS is isosceles)
$= \mathbf{34^\circ}$

6. Since EFGH is a square, FG = GH, which makes FGH an isosceles triangle.
$\angle GHF = 45^\circ$ (ΔFGH is a right isosceles Δ)
$\angle m = 180^\circ - \angle GHF$ ($\angle$'s on a st. line)
$= 180^\circ - 45^\circ = \mathbf{135^\circ}$

7. $\angle PQR = 90^\circ - 20^\circ = 70^\circ$
$\angle x = 180^\circ - 70^\circ = \mathbf{110^\circ}$ (inside $\angle$'s)

8. $\angle PQR = 180^\circ - 118^\circ = 62^\circ$ (inside $\angle$'s)
$\angle y = 90^\circ - 62^\circ = \mathbf{28^\circ}$

9. $\angle TQR = 180^\circ - 60^\circ = 120^\circ$ ($\angle$'s on a st. line)
$\angle TSR = \angle TQR = 120^\circ$ (opp. $\angle$s of //)
$\angle x = 120^\circ - 50^\circ = \mathbf{70^\circ}$

10. $\angle ADC = 180^\circ - 104^\circ = 76^\circ$ ($\angle$'s on a st. line)
$\angle ABC = 76^\circ$ (opp. $\angle$'s of //)
$\angle a = (180 - 76) \div 2 = \mathbf{52^\circ}$ (ΔABC is iso. Δ)

11. $\angle QRS = 180^\circ - 112^\circ = 68^\circ$ ($\angle$s on a st. line)
$\angle QPS = 68^\circ$ (opp. $\angle$'s of //)
$\angle b = 180^\circ - 46^\circ - 68^\circ = \mathbf{66^\circ}$ ($\angle$ sum of a Δ)

12. $\angle CDE = 90^\circ - 35^\circ = 55^\circ$ (right Δ)
$\angle CBE = 55^\circ$ (opp. $\angle$'s of a //)
$\angle t = 180^\circ - 55^\circ = \mathbf{125^\circ}$ ($\angle$'s on a st. line)

US› Exercise 25 3d› Exercise 17

1. $\angle ADB = 18° + 26° = 44°$ (ext. ∠ of ΔBDC)
   $\angle d = (180° - 44°) \div 2 = 68°$ (iso. Δ)
   OR:
   $\angle BDC = 180° - 18° - 26° = 136°$ (∠ sum of a Δ)
   $\angle ADB = 180° - 136° = 44°$ (∠'s on a st. line)
   $\angle d = (180° - 44°) \div 2 = 68°$ (iso. Δ)

2. $\angle PRQ = (180° - 64°) \div 2 = 58°$ (iso. Δ)
   $\angle PRT = 180° - (2 \times 48°) = 84°$ (iso. Δ)
   $\angle t = 180° - 58° - 84° = \mathbf{38}°$ (∠s on a st. line)

3. $\angle ACB = 60°$ (equ. Δ)
   $\angle BCF = 60° + 50° = 110°$
   $\angle AFC = 180° - 110° = 70°$ (inside ∠s ≠)
   $\angle r = 180° - 70° = \mathbf{110°}$ (∠'s on a st. line)

4. $\angle PML = 180° - 116° = 64°$ (inside ∠s ≠)
   $\angle y = (180° - 64°) \div 2 = \mathbf{58°}$ (iso. Δ)

5. $\angle DCF = 60°$ (equ. Δ)
   $\angle p = 180° - 90° - 60° = \mathbf{30°}$ (∠'s on a st. line)

6. $\angle FEG = (180° - 38°) \div 2 = 71°$ (iso. Δ)
   $\angle DEF = 180° - 71° = 109°$ (∠'s on a st. line)
   $\angle x = \mathbf{109°}$ (opp. ∠s of //)

7. $\angle FAD = 180° - 120° = 60°$ (inside ∠'s)
   $\angle BAD = 180° - 110° = 70°$ (inside ∠'s)
   $\angle FAB = 60° + 70° = \mathbf{130°}$

8. $\angle ABF = 110°$ (opp. ∠'s of //)
   $\angle BAF = (180° - 110°) \div 2 = 35°$ (iso. ΔABF)
   $\angle DAB = 180° - 110° = 70°$ (inside ∠'s)
   $\angle DAE = 70° - 35° = \mathbf{35°}$

9. $\angle ADC = 32° + 90° = 122°$ (ext. ∠ of a Δ)
   $\angle DAB = 180° - 122° = \mathbf{58°}$ (inside ∠'s)

10. $\angle ABD = (180° - 40°) \div 2 = 70°$ (iso. ΔABD)
    $\angle EAB = 70° - 40° = \mathbf{30°}$ (ext. ∠ of a Δ, $\angle ABD = \angle EAB + \angle AEB$)

11. $\angle DAB = (180° - 28°) \div 2 = 76°$ (iso. Δ)
    $\angle DCB = \mathbf{76}°$ (opp. ∠'s of //)

12. $\angle DFB = 40°$ (opp. ∠'s of //)
    $\angle FBD = (180° - 40°) \div 2° = 70°$ (iso. ΔBDF)
    $\angle ABF = \angle ABD - \angle FBD$ (∠ABD is a right ∠)
    $= 90° - 70° = 20°$
    $\angle AFB = 90° - 20° = \mathbf{70}°$ (right Δ)

Review 5

1. (a) **70,000** (b) **10**

2. $500 \times 200 =$ **100,000**

3. $0.34 = 0.34 \times 100\% =$ **34%**

4. 25% of $\$9 = \frac{25}{100} \times \$9 = \$\frac{9}{4} = \$2\frac{1}{4} =$ **$2.25**

5. $\frac{15}{20} \times 100\% = \frac{3}{4} \times 100\% =$ **75%**

6. 6 pencils $\longrightarrow$ \$2.40
   2 pencils $\longrightarrow$ $\$2.40 \div 3 =$ **$0.80**

7. 6 min $\longrightarrow$ 300 pages
   1 min $\longrightarrow$ $\frac{300}{6}$ pages
   15 min $\longrightarrow$ $\frac{300}{6} \times 15 =$ **750** pages

8. Cost of 3 shirts $= \$50 - \$18.50 = \$31.50$
   Cost of 1 shirt $= \$31.50 \div 3 =$ **$10.50**

9. January to March = 3 months
   Total savings for Jan. – Mar. $= 3 \times \$120 = \$360$
   January to April = 4 months
   Total savings for Jan. – Apr. $= 4 \times \$150 = \$600$
   Savings in April $= \$600 - \$360 =$ **$240**

10. Remainder $= \frac{7}{8}$
    Amount left $= \frac{2}{3}$ of the remainder $= \frac{2}{3} \times \frac{7}{8} = \frac{7}{12}$
    Number of oranges left $= \frac{7}{12} \times 168 =$ **98**

11. Money spent on camera $= \frac{1}{4} \times \$400 = \$100$
    Money spent on both $= \$100 + \$160 = \$260$
    Amount saved $= \$400 - \$260 = \$140$
    Percentage saved $= \frac{140}{400} \times 100\% =$ **35%**

12. 1 unit = \$800 ÷ 8 = \$100
David's money = 3 × \$100 = \$300
John's money = 5 × \$100 = \$500
David's money after giving John \$50 = \$300 – \$50 = \$250
John's money after receiving \$50 = \$500 + \$50 = \$550
New ratio = 250 : 550 = **5 : 11**

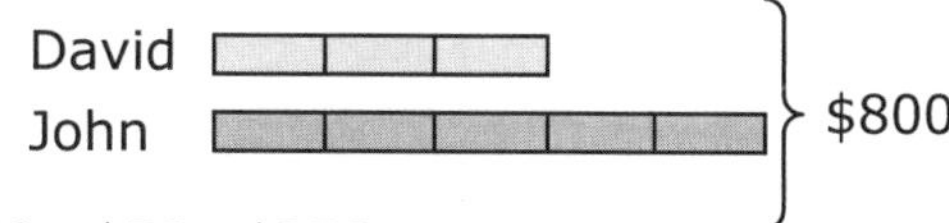

13. 3 units = 60
1 unit = 60 ÷ 3 = 20
Total = 10 units = 20 × 10
= **200**

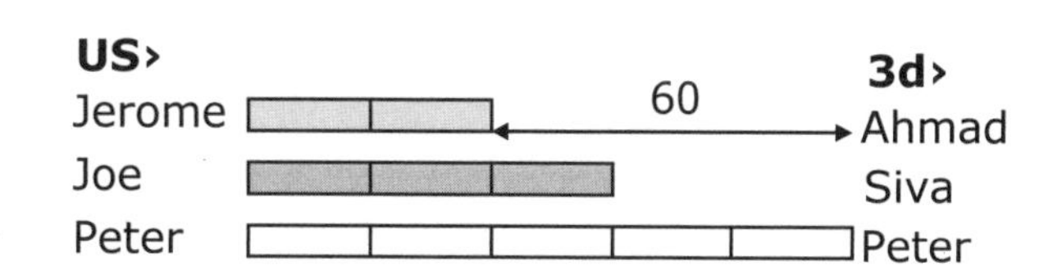

14. Time $= \frac{\text{Distance}}{\text{Speed}} = \frac{90 \text{ km}}{120 \text{ km/h}} = \frac{3}{4}$ h = **45 min**

15. Distance between Town X and Town Y = 50 km/h × 3 h = 150 km
Time for return journey = 3 – 1 = 2 h
Speed for return journey $= \frac{150 \text{ km}}{2 \text{ h}}$ = **75 km/h**

16. Perimeter = 2 × (3*a* + *a*) = 2 × 4*a* = ***8a* cm**

17. A quarter of the circumference of the circle $= \frac{1}{4} \times \frac{22}{7} \times 2 \times 14$ cm = 22 cm
Side of square = 14 cm + 7 cm = 21 cm
Perimeter = 2 × (7 cm + 21 cm) + 22 cm = **78 cm**

18. The shaded area is equivalent to the area of the square, since the shaded semicircle has the same area as the unshaded semicircle.
Area = 20 cm × 20 cm = **400 cm²**

19. Water level after stone is added $= \frac{2}{3} \times 36$ cm = 24 cm
Increase in water level = 24 cm – 14 cm = 10 cm
Volume of stone = 60 cm × 35 cm × 10 cm = **21,000 cm³**

20. ∠ABC = 40° (opp. ∠'s of //)
∠BAC = 90° – 40° = **50°** (right ΔABC)

21. (a) Student should draw a triangle withn AC = 6 cm, AB = 5 cm, ∠BAC = 60°
(b) **5.6 cm**

22. (a) $25\% \rightarrow \$500$
$100\% \rightarrow \$500 \times 4 = \$2{,}000$
Total expenses = **$2,000**

(b) Money spent on sightseeing = $2,000 – $500 – $300 – $800 = **$400**

(c) $\frac{800}{2000} = \frac{8}{20} = \mathbf{\frac{2}{5}}$

23. Cost of 3 guppies = cost of 1 goldfish
Cost of 6 guppies = cost of 2 goldfish
Cost of 3 goldfish + 6 guppies = cost of 3 goldfish + 2 goldfish = cost of 5 goldfish.
If he spent $\frac{3}{5}$ of his money, then he had $\frac{2}{5}$ of his money left.

$\frac{2}{5}$ of his money = $8

$\frac{1}{5}$ of his money = $8 ÷ 2 = $4

$\frac{3}{5}$ of his money = $4 × 3 = 12

5 goldfish cost $12
1 goldfish cost $12 ÷ 5 = **$2.40**

24. Samad had 4 units at first.
2 units = $30
1 unit = $\$\frac{30}{2} = \$15$
4 units = $15 × 4
= $60
He had **$60** at first.

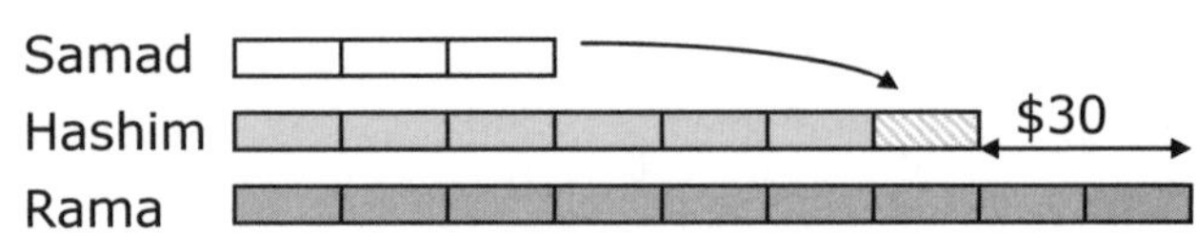

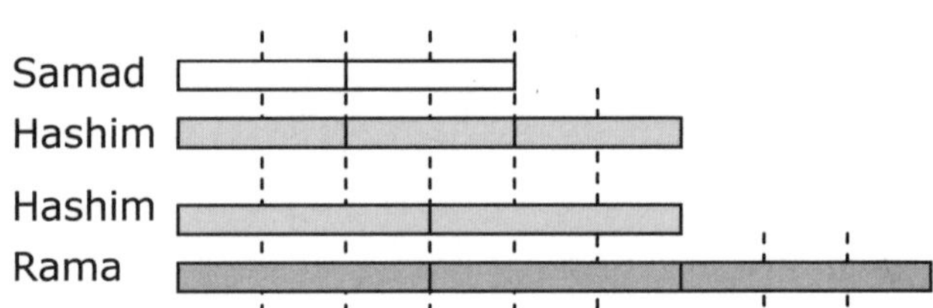

Review 6

1. Factors of 72 are 1, 2, 3, 6, 12, 8, 9, [24], 36, 72
Multiples of 8 are 8, 16, [24], 32, 40, ...
The number is **24**.

2. $3\frac{1}{2} = \frac{7}{2} = 7 \times \frac{1}{2}$ There are **7** halves.

3. $1\frac{3}{4}\text{ h} = 1\text{ h} + \frac{3}{4} \times 60\text{ min} = 1\text{ h} + 45\text{ min}$

$$\begin{aligned}10{:}20 - 1\text{ h }45\text{ min} &= 10\text{ h }20\text{ min} - 1\text{ h }45\text{ min}\\ &= 9\text{ h }80\text{ min} - 1\text{ h }45\text{ min}\\ &= 8\text{ h }35\text{ min} = \mathbf{8{:}35}\text{ a.m.}\end{aligned}$$

4. Average $= \frac{6.8 + 4.03 + 2.26}{3} = \frac{13.09}{3} \approx \mathbf{4.4}$

5. 8 apples $\longrightarrow$ \$3.60
4 apples $\longrightarrow \$3.60 \div 2 = \$1.80$
12 apples $\longrightarrow \$1.80 \times 3 = \mathbf{\$5.40}$

6. $25\% = \frac{1}{4}$

$\frac{1}{4}$ of a number $= 13$

$\frac{3}{4}$ of a number $= 13 \times 3 = \mathbf{39}$

7. 1 km = 1000 m

$\frac{1000\text{ m}}{4\text{ min}} = \mathbf{250\text{ m/min}}$

8. The remainder is $\frac{1}{3}$ of his money.

Amount of money left $= \frac{1}{4}$ of the remainder $= \frac{1}{4} \times \frac{1}{3} = \frac{1}{12}$

$\frac{1}{12}$ of his money $= \$50$

$\frac{12}{12}$ of his money $= \$50 \times 12 = \$600$

He had **\$600** at first.

9. Increase $= 35 - 25 = 10$

Percent increase $= \frac{10}{25} \times 100\% = \mathbf{40\%}$

10. Tax = 3% of \$240 $= \frac{3}{100} \times \$240 = \$7.20$

Amount paid $= \$240 + \$7.20 = \mathbf{\$247.20}$

11. The number of women is 100%. The number of men is 120%.
$120\% \longrightarrow 420$
$1\% \longrightarrow \frac{420}{120} = \frac{7}{2}$
$20\% \longrightarrow \frac{7}{2} \times 20 = 70$
There are **70** more men than women.

12. (**3d›** in. → cm)
Total units $= 2 + 3 + 4 = 9$
Shortest side $= 2$ units $= 4$ in.
1 unit $= 4$ in. $\div 2 = 2$ in.
Perimeter $=$ total units
9 units $= 2 \times 9 =$ **18 in.**

13. Total units when ratio is 1 : 2 : 6 $= 1 + 2 + 6 = 9$ units
9 units $= \$900$
1 unit $= \$900 \div 9 = \$100$
Amount of money Henry received $= 1$ unit $= \$100$
Total units when ratio is 2 : 3 : 5 $= 2 + 3 + 5 = 10$ units
10 units $= \$900$
1 unit $= \$900 \div 10 = \$90$
Amount of money Henry receives $= 2$ units $= 2 \times \$90 = \$180$
Amount more that Henry receives $= \$180 - \$100 =$ **$80**

14. 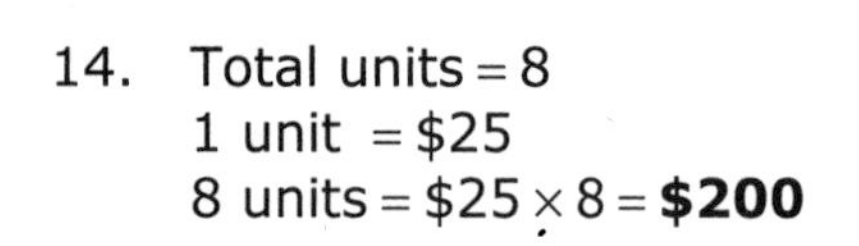
Total units $= 8$
1 unit $= \$25$
8 units $= \$25 \times 8 =$ **$200**

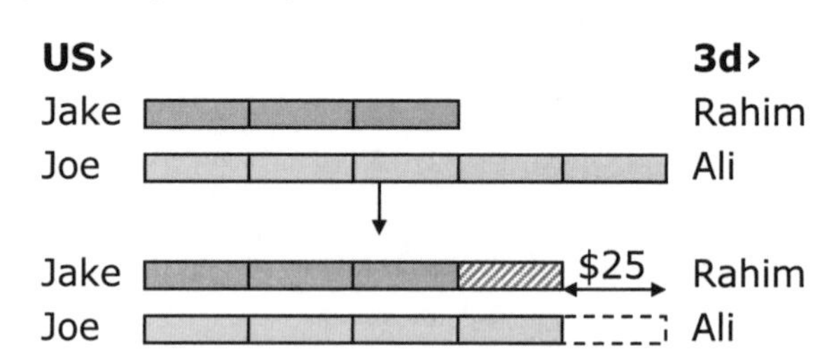

15. Time at 60 km/h $= \frac{150 \text{ km}}{60 \text{ km/h}} = \frac{5}{2} \text{ h} = 2\frac{1}{2} \text{ h}$
New speed $= 60 + 15 = 75$ km/h
New time $= \frac{150 \text{ km}}{75 \text{ km/h}} = 2$ h
Time saved $= 2\frac{1}{2} - 2 = \mathbf{\frac{1}{2}}$ **h = 30 min**

16. (**3d›** in. → cm)
Diameter of semicircle $= 5$ cm $+ 4$ cm $+ 5$ cm $= 14$ cm
Perimeter $= (2 \times 5 \text{ cm}) + (3 \times 4 \text{ cm}) + (\frac{1}{2} \times \frac{22}{7} \times 14 \text{ cm})$
$= 10 \text{ cm} + 12 \text{ cm} + 22 \text{ cm} = 44 \text{ cm}$
Perimeter $=$ **44 in.**

17. Shaded area = area of large circle – area of small circle
$= (\pi \times 3\text{ m} \times 3\text{ m}) - (\pi \times 1\text{ m} \times 1\text{ m}) = 9\pi\text{ m} - \pi\text{ m} = \mathbf{8\pi\ m^2}$

18. (**3d›** ft → cm)
The base of the top triangle is 5 ft, and its height is 12 ft – 5 ft = 7 ft
The base of the side triangle is 5 ft, and its height is 8 ft – 5 ft = 3 ft
Shaded area = area of square + area of the two triangles
$= (5\text{ ft} \times 5\text{ ft}) + (\frac{1}{2} \times 5\text{ ft} \times 7\text{ ft}) + (\frac{1}{2} \times 5\text{ ft} \times 3\text{ ft})$
$= 25\text{ ft}^2 + 17\frac{1}{2}\text{ ft}^2 + 7\frac{1}{2}\text{ ft}^2 = 50\text{ ft}^2$
Shaded area = **50 ft²**

19. Height of water $= \frac{3}{4} \times 40\text{ cm} = 30\text{ cm}$
Volume of water $= 64\text{ cm} \times 50\text{ cm} \times 30\text{ cm} = 96{,}000\text{ cm}^3 = 96\ \ell$
$12\ \ell \rightarrow 1$ min
$96\ \ell \rightarrow 1 \times 8 = 8$ min
It takes **8 min** to empty the tank.

20. $\angle TSR = (180° - 42°) \div 2 = 69°$ (iso. Δ)
$\angle PQR = \angle TSR = \mathbf{69°}$ (opp. ∠'s of //)

21. $\angle DBE = 60°$ (equ. ΔBED)
$\angle DBC = 60° - 30° = 30°$
$\angle BCD = 180° - (2 \times 30°) = 120°$ (iso. ΔBCD)
$\angle BAD = \mathbf{120°}$ (opp. ∠'s of //)

22. 6 : 8 = **3 : 4**

23. (a) **25%** (quarter circle)
(b) 25% ⟶ \$55
100% ⟶ \$55 × 4 = **\$220**
(c) 6D and 6B donated half, or \$110.
Money donated by 6B = \$110 – \$44 = **\$66**
(d) 55 : 44 = **5 : 4**

24. 1 unit = \$120 ÷ 2 = 60
Cost of toy = \$60 – \$45 = **\$15**

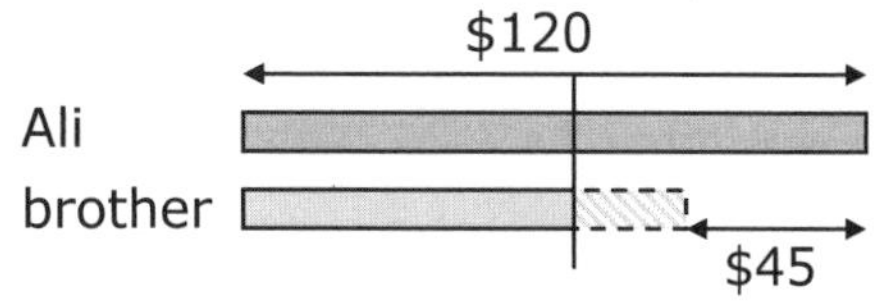

25. 2 units = 50
1 unit = 25
6 units = 25 × 6 = 150
There were **150** boys in the club.

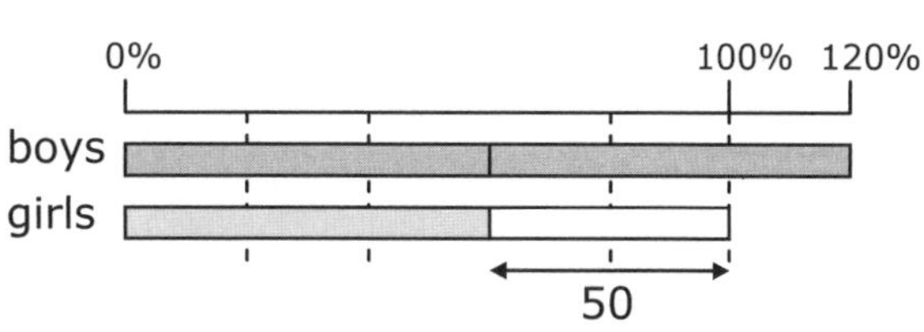

Review 7

1. **4.53**

2. $28 + \underline{15 \div 5} \times 3 = 28 + \underline{3 \times 3} = \underline{28 + 9} = \mathbf{37}$

3. $\frac{3}{8}$ of the number $= 27$

   $\frac{1}{8}$ of the number $= \frac{27}{3} = 9$

   $\frac{1}{2}$ of the number $= \frac{4}{8}$ of the number $= 9 \times 4 = \mathbf{36}$

4. **397.8**

US› 5. $\frac{5}{9} \div \frac{2}{3} = \frac{5}{9} \times \frac{3}{2} = \mathbf{\frac{5}{6}}$

3d› 5. $2\frac{1}{3}$ h $= (2 \times 60$ min$) + (\frac{1}{3} \times 60$ min$) = 120$ min $+ 20$ min $=$ **140 min**

6. 50 g $= 50 \times \frac{1}{1000}$ kg $= 0.05$ kg

   3 kg 50 g = **3.05 kg**

7. Each girl is 1 unit; each boy is 2 units. Total units = 7
   7 units = \$140
   1 unit = \$140 ÷ 7 = \$20
   2 units = \$20 × 2 = \$40
   Each boy received **\$40**.

8. (**3d›** Anne → Sulin, Morgan → Meihua)
   Anne's stickers $= \frac{3}{4}$ of Morgan's $= \frac{3}{4} \times 240 = 180$
   Total number of stickers = 180 + 240 = 420
   OR:
   Anne's stickers = 3 units and Morgan's stickers = 4 units
   Together they have 7 units.
   4 units = 240
   7 units $= \frac{240}{4} \times 7 = \mathbf{420}$

9. 1 unit = \$50
   3 units = 3 × \$50 = \$150
   Peter had **\$150** at first.

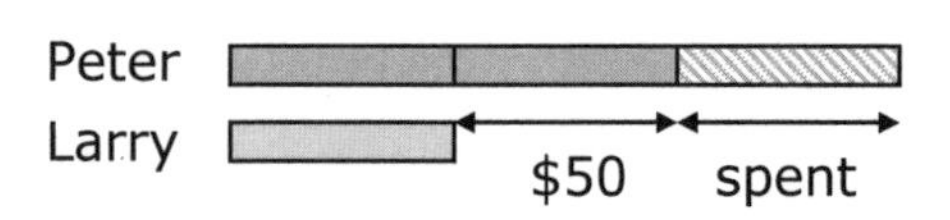

10. 5 units = 25
1 unit = 25 ÷ 5 = 5
2 units = 5 × 2 = 10

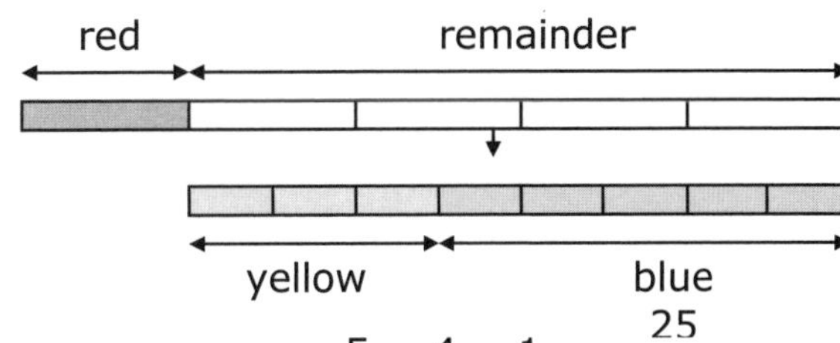

Or:

Number of blue balloons = $\frac{5}{8}$ of the remainder = $\frac{5}{8} \times \frac{4}{5} = \frac{1}{2}$

$\frac{1}{2}$ of the balloons = 25

All of the balloons = 25 × 2 = 50

Number of red balloons = $\frac{1}{5} \times 50 = 10$

There were **10** red balloons.

11. Total units = 4 + 3 + 2 = 9 John received 4 units.

Fraction of money John received = $\mathbf{\frac{4}{9}}$

12. Units of red beads = 4
Units of blue and yellow = 6 + 3 = 9
Ratio = **4 : 9**

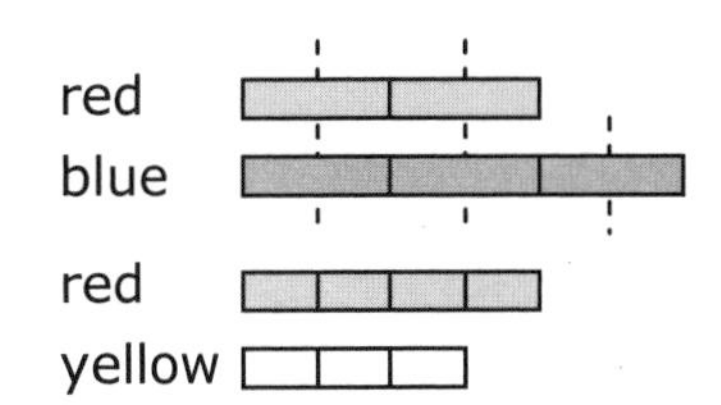

13. Percentage adults = 55% + 25% = 80%
Percentage children = 100% − 80% = 20%
Percentage more adults than children = 80% − 20% = 60%

60% of 400 = $\frac{60}{100} \times 400 = 240$

There are **240** more adults than children.

14.

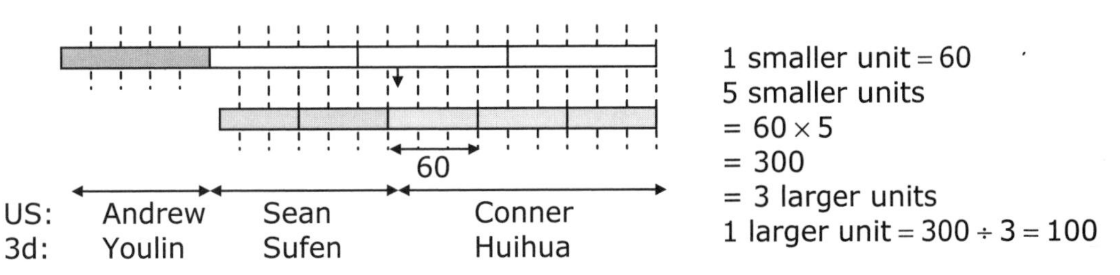

1 smaller unit = 60
5 smaller units
= 60 × 5
= 300
= 3 larger units
1 larger unit = 300 ÷ 3 = 100

OR:
3 larger units = 5 smaller units. Lowest common multiple of 3 and 5 is 15. Divide each larger unit into 5 and each smaller unit into 3 to get equal sized units. Andrew (Youlin) has 5 units.
3 units = 60

5 units = $\frac{60}{3} \times 5 = 100$

Andrew (Youlin) received **100** stamps.

15. 20 min $= \frac{1}{3}$ h

    Distance = Speed × Time = 66 km/h × $\frac{1}{3}$ h = **22 km**

16.

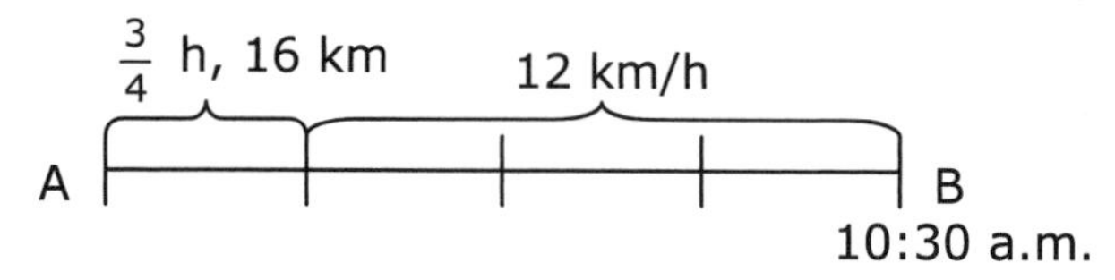

    Distance for first part = 16 km/h × $\frac{3}{4}$ h = 12 km
    Distance for second part = 12 × 3 = 36 km
    Time for second part = $\frac{36 \text{ km}}{12 \text{ km/h}}$ = 3 h
    Total time = 3 h + $\frac{3}{4}$ h = 3 h 45 min
    3 h 45 min before 10:30 a.m. is 6:45 a.m.
    He left at **6:45 a.m.**

17. $3 - \frac{a}{3} = 3 - \frac{4}{3} = 3 - 1\frac{1}{3} = 2 - \frac{1}{3} = \mathbf{1\frac{2}{3}}$

18. **$(6x + 18)**

19. Length of wire = half the circumference of circle of diameter 7 cm + half the circumference of circle of diameter 14 cm
    $= (\frac{1}{2} \times \frac{22}{7} \times 7) + (\frac{1}{2} \times \frac{22}{7} \times 14) = 11 + 22 =$ **33 cm**

20. Water height from stone's volume = $\frac{2400}{30 \times 20}$ = 4 cm
    Height of water = 8 + 4 = 12 cm
    $\frac{2}{3}$ of height of tank = 12 cm
    $\frac{1}{3}$ of height of tank = 12 ÷ 2 = 6 cm
    Height of tank = 6 × 3 = **18 cm**

21. $\angle BAD = 180° - \angle ABC$ (inside ∠'s)
    $= 180° - 68° = 112°$
    $\angle CAD = \angle BAD - \angle BAC$
    $= 112° - 62° = 50°$
    $\angle EAD = 180° - \angle CAD$ (∠s on a st. line)
    $= 180° - 50° = 130°$
    $\angle ADE = (180° - \angle EAD) \div 2$
    $= (180° - 130°) \div 2 =$ **25°** (iso. Δ)

22. $\angle TRS = 60^\circ$ (equ. ΔTRS)
$\angle QRS = \angle QRT + \angle TRS$
$= 90^\circ + 60^\circ = 150^\circ$
$\angle SQR = (180^\circ - \angle QRS) \div 2$ (iso. Δ)
$= (180^\circ - 150^\circ) \div 2 =$ **15°**

23.

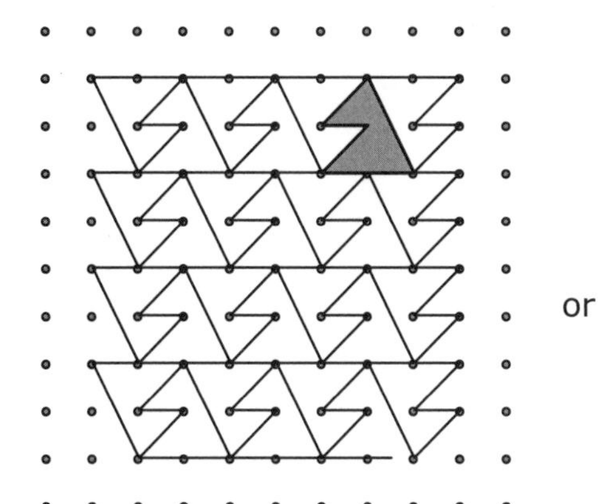

or

24. (a) It is full when the volume of water no longer increases, at **125 ℓ**.
(b) **10 min**

25.

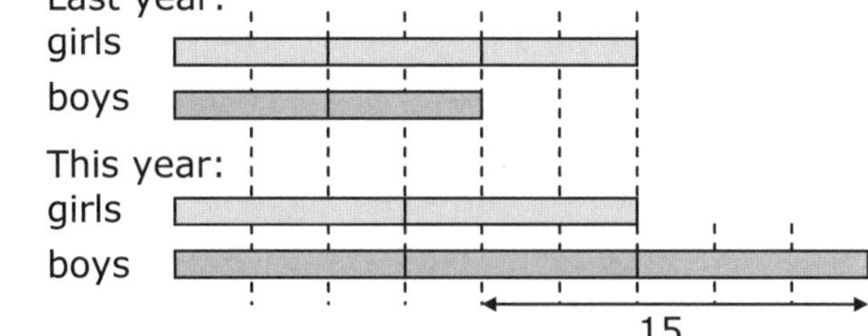

The number of girls does not change. The bar for the girls for last year has 3 units and the bar for the girls for this year has 2 units. The bars can be subdivided so that the girls have 6 equal units both years.
5 units $= 15$
15 units $= 15 \times 3 = 45$
There are **45** children in the club this year.

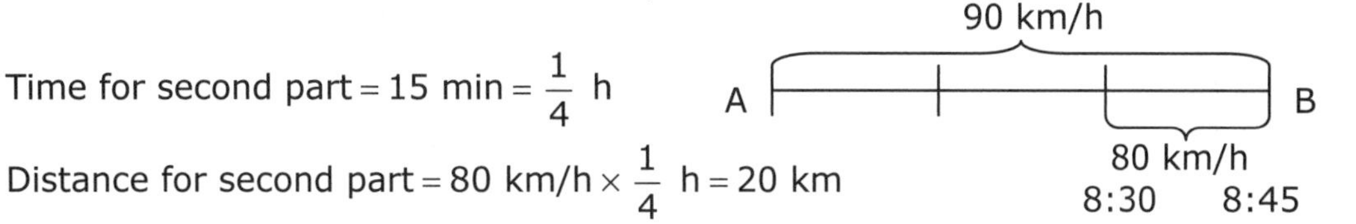

26. Time for second part $= 15$ min $= \frac{1}{4}$ h

Distance for second part $= 80$ km/h $\times \frac{1}{4}$ h $= 20$ km

Total distance $= 20$ km $\times 3 = 60$ km

Total time $= \frac{60 \text{ km}}{90 \text{ km/h}} = \frac{2}{3}$ h $= 40$ min

40 min before 8:45 a.m. = 8:05 a.m.
He left Town A at **8:05 a.m.**

US›

27. Amount each child got $= \frac{2}{5} \div 4 = \frac{2}{5} \times \frac{1}{4} = \frac{1}{10}$

28. $\frac{1}{6} \approx 0.1667$
(b) 0.116 has the smallest value

29. 3 gal 2 c = 50 c; $\frac{6}{50} = \frac{3}{25}$
Ratio is **3 : 25**

30. 6.5 gal = 6.5 × 8 pt = 52 pt
52 pint bottles can be filled.

24-Part Circle

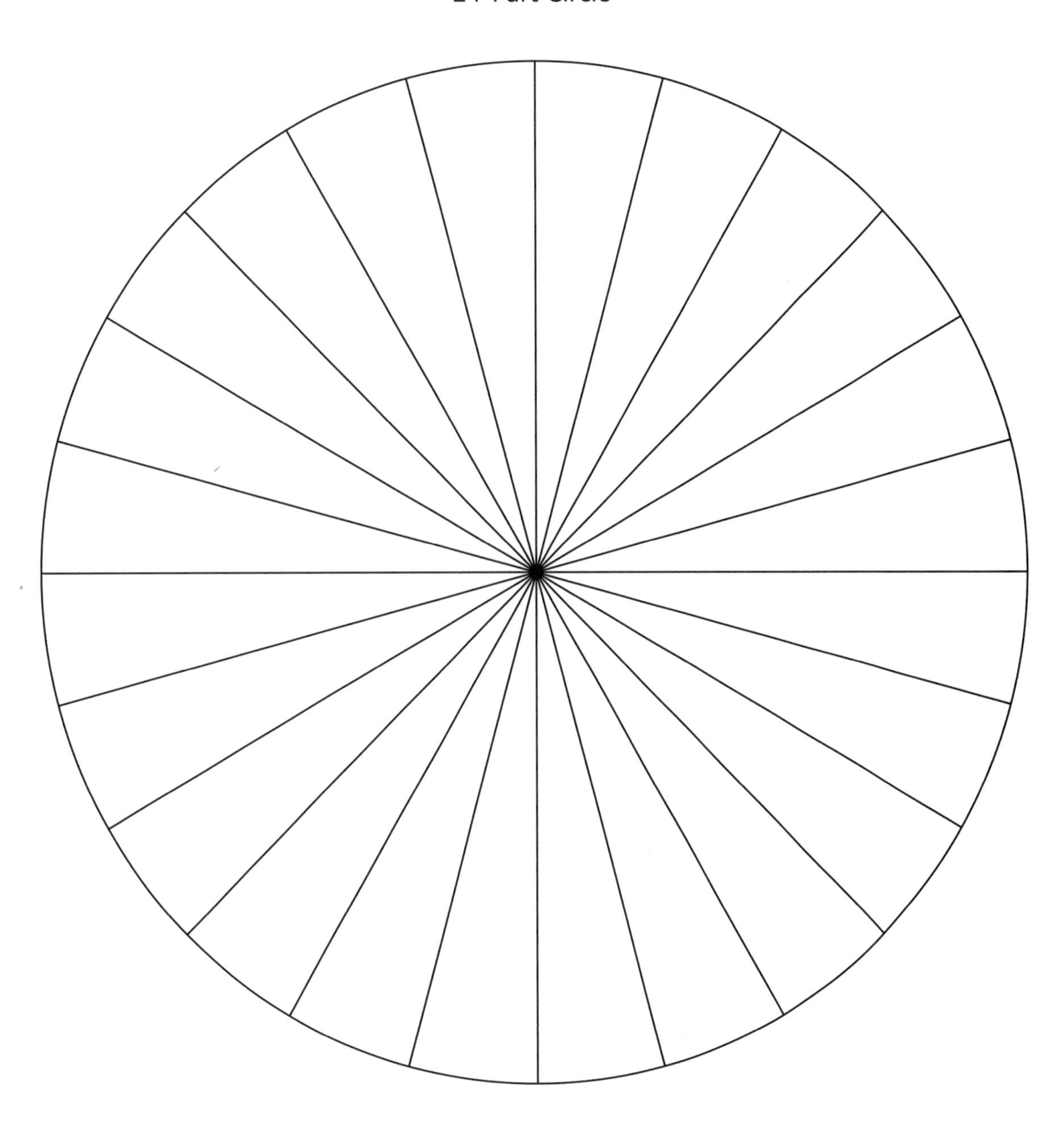

Fraction Circle Chart

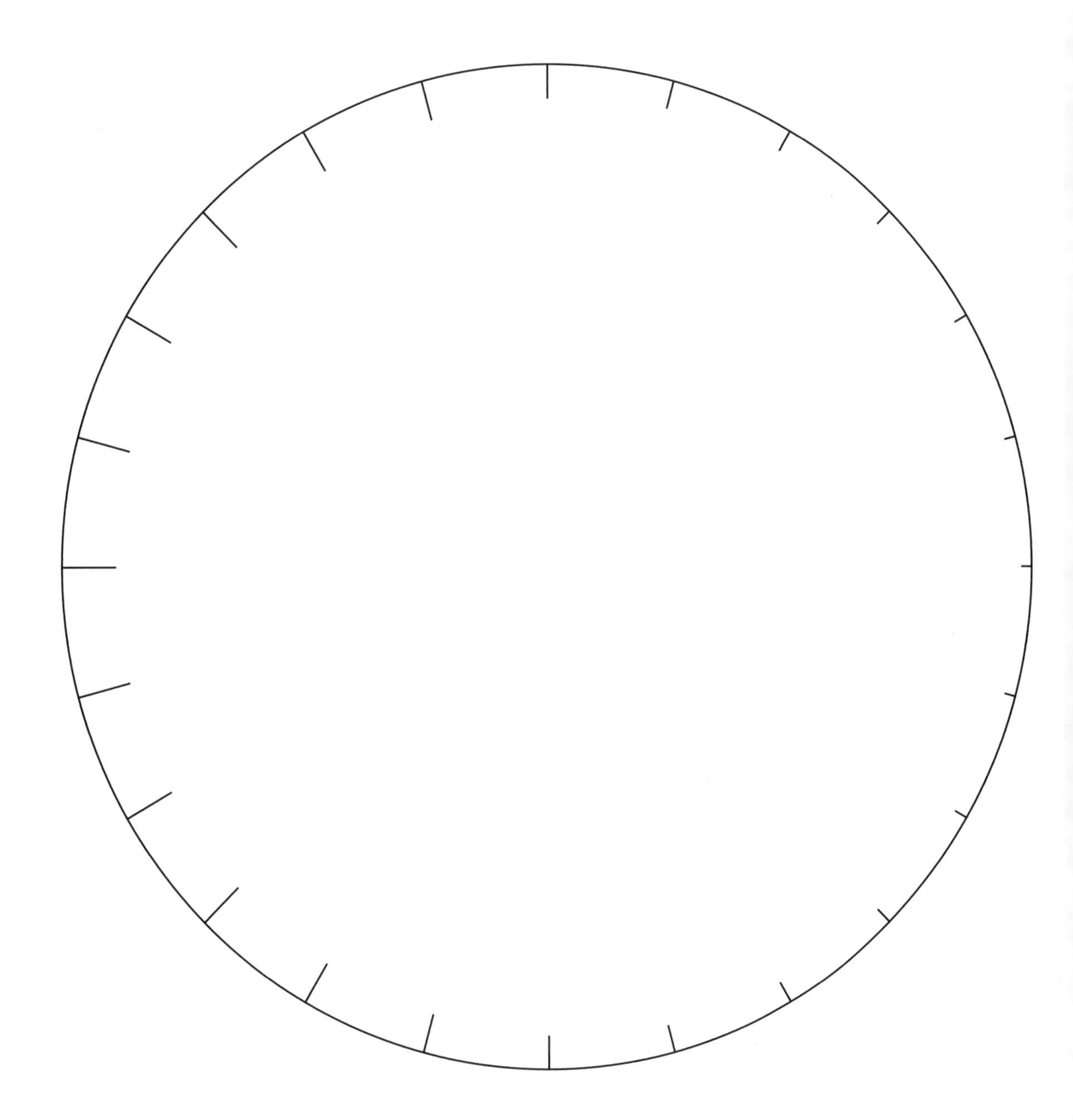

Percentage Circle Chart

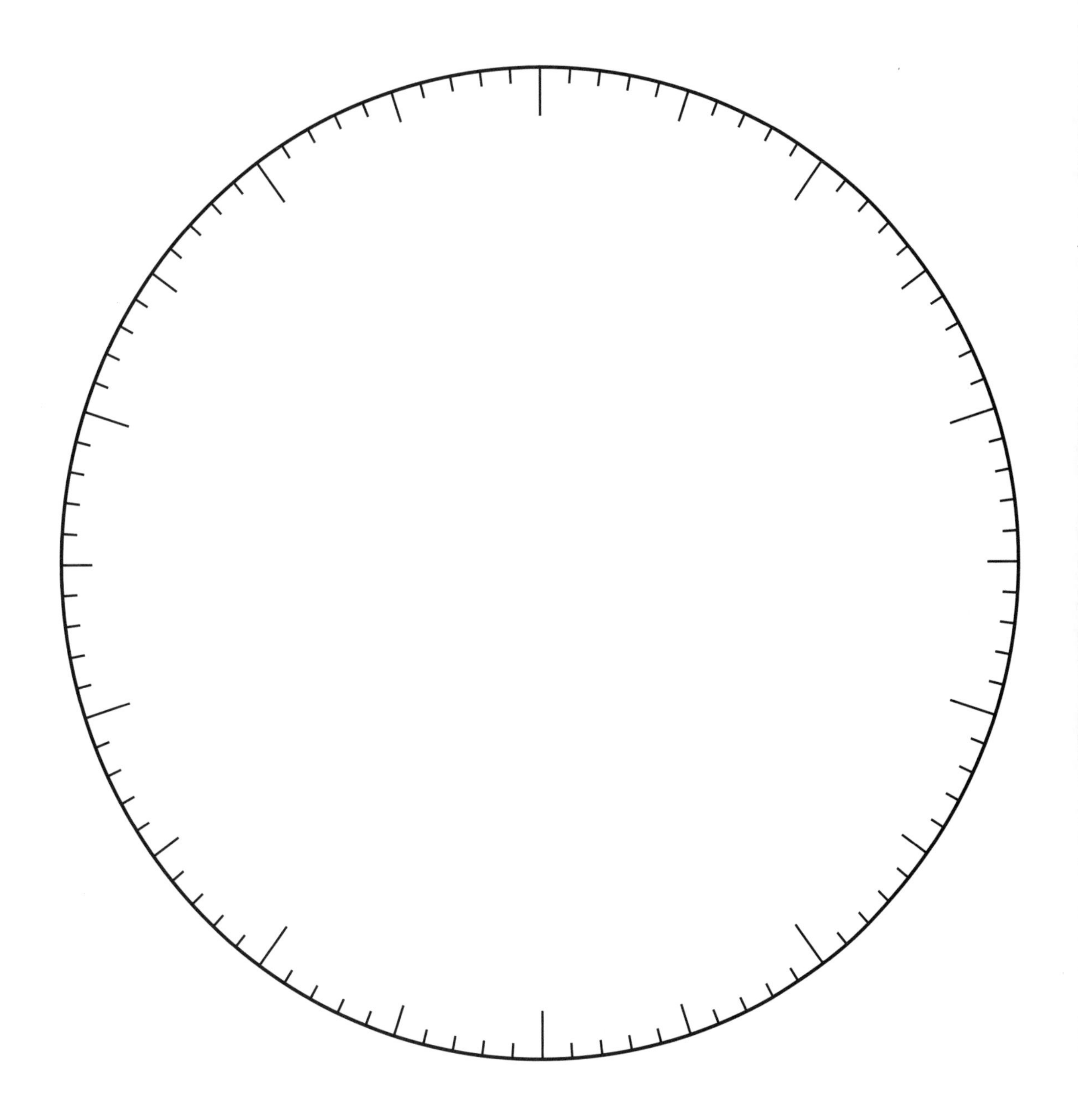